AN INTRODUCTION TO

Psychotherapy

Sidney Tarachow, M.D.

INTERNATIONAL UNIVERSITIES PRESS, INC.
NEW YORK

Library of Congress Catalog Card Number: 63-13476

Manufactured in the United States of America

For Sophia, Janet and Julie

Contents

Acknowledgments *vii*

PART I

General Problems of Treatment

1 A Point of View 3
2 The Theory of the Therapeutic Relationship 8
3 Some Practical Implications of the Theory 23
4 Types of Psychotherapy 39
5 The Theory of Hospital Treatment 57
6 A Clinical View of the Goals of Treatment 81
7 Gratification and Deprivation 87
8 Object Relations 102
9 Problems Relating to Administration 108
10 The Structure of the Treatment Relationship 118
11 Education and Reality 134
12 Values in Psychotherapy 144

PART II

Special Clinical Problems

13 The Initial Interview 153

14 A History Conference 187

15 Obsessive-Compulsive Defenses 205

16 Acting Out and Psychopathy 236

17 Depression and Suicidal Risks 264

18 Masochism and Paranoia 277

19 Paranoia and Homicide 291

PART III

Supervisors' Conferences

20 Supervision Outline 303

21 Teacher or Critic? 308

22 The Transference 316

Bibliography 333

Bibliographical Note 341

Author Index 343

Subject Index 345

Acknowledgments

I am deeply grateful to:

the successive groups of residents who attended these conferences and whose interest and curiosity were a delight to me as a teacher;

the group of supervisors at Hillside Hospital who contributed so much of value to the supervision conferences, especially Dr. Robert R. Luttrell, who so ably led off for the supervisors;

Drs. Joseph S. A. Miller and Lewis L. Robbins, the former and present Medical Directors of Hillside Hospital respectively, for permission to use the material of the conferences;

Dr. I. Charles Kaufman, Chairman of the Department of Psychiatry at Kings County Hospital for permission to use the material of a group of conferences with first-year residents on the initial interview;

Dr. Edward M. Weinshel, Chairman of the Program Committee of the course Everyday Psychiatry given by the staff of Mt. Zion Hospital, The San Francisco Psychoanalytic Institute and Medical Extension, University of California, Jan. 9-12, 1958, for permission to use my part of the several conferences and discussions in which I participated and for his helpful cooperation in supplying me with the tape recordings of the proceedings:

Dr. Angel N. Miranda for permission to use the material of a lecture on Acting Out delivered before the Psychiatric Section of the Puerto Rican Medical Association on April 22, 1957, and for his cooperation in sending me the tape recording of the proceedings;

The Journal of the Hillside Hospital, for permission to reprint several papers, with slight amendments;

Dr. Herbert J. Urbach for permission to cite an example from his case material;

Drs. Renato J. Almansi, Leon L. Altman, Frank Berchenko, Abram Blau, John Frosch, Mark Kanzer, Louis Kaywin, Sandor Lorand, Andrew Peto, Norman Reider, Richard Sterba, Max Schur, Max M. Stern, Walter Stewart, Martin Wangh, and Leonard A. Weinroth, who, in formal or informal discussions or via correspondence, made criticisms, suggestions, asked questions, all of which helped clarify my ideas, and from whom I borrowed liberally;

Several classes of candidates in the Division of Psychoanalytic Education at Downstate Medical Center with whom I enjoyed stimulating discussions of the theory of modifications of psychoanalytic technique, especially the problems of acting out, psychopathy, and masochism;

Drs. Maurice R. Friend, Sylvan Keiser, Richard Newman, Milton R. Sapirstein, and Aaron Stein, for being kind enough to read various sections of the book and who raised questions, expressed cautions, corrected errors, and suggested ideas. I did not follow all the suggestions, to the detriment of this book;

Peter Stein, for the preparation of the index;

Dr. A. S. Kagan, the publisher, for his unfailing courtesy and encouragement;

Mrs. Lottie M. Newman, who was much more than an editor, and upon whose wisdom I relied heavily.

The shortcomings of this book are my own.

February 10, 1962 SIDNEY TARACHOW

Part I

General Problems of Treatment

Chapter 1

A Point of View

This book is directed to psychiatric residents and their supervisors. It is based primarily on psychotherapy conferences with residents at Hillside Hospital conducted over a ten-year period. Further material is based on conferences with Hillside supervisors over a four-month period in 1960-1961 and on four conferences with first-year residents at Kings County Hospital. Other sources of material are indicated where appropriate.

The difficulties of teaching psychoanalytic psychotherapy to residents are great. Benjamin (1947) has made some appropriate comments about this. Various systematic or idiosyncratic approaches to this special teaching problem have been suggested (Ekstein and Wallerstein, 1958; Fleming and Hamburg, 1958; Grotjahn, 1953). I have found residents, and certainly first-year residents, to be not a homogeneous group. They are fresh to the field, often differ widely in age, have very different personalities, and occasionally come from other medical specialties or other professional backgrounds. There is no single pattern in regard to their exposure to psychoanalysis. A number of them have been in psychotherapy, some in psychoanalysis, and most in neither. There are great variations in what psychiatric reading they have done and in what their general reading and cultural interests are. It is difficult for the teacher to find the level at which to pitch a discussion to such a heterogeneous group, while at the same time offering an orderly and progressive discussion of theory and data in psychoanalytic terms.

In spite of all these adverse factors the teaching must be done: a knowledge of *elementary* psychoanalytic theory must be presupposed or, at least, immediately taught. This is not to deny the basic importance of teaching clinical psychiatry. The residents must have a grasp of the concepts of the unconscious, repression, unconscious conflict, infantile mental life, the transference and resistance.

Certain theoretical and technical aspects of *psychoanalytic* treatment require discussion with residents both for exposition of theory as well as for necessary comparisons between psychoanalysis and psychotherapy simply as techniques. Such exposition and comparison offer much to the beginning therapist. The therapist must learn basic principles of mental functioning. He must understand in psychoanalytic terms the problems and tasks of the therapeutic relationship. Classical psychoanalytical technique is a theoretical base line of thinking and a springboard to the understanding of psychotherapy as a theory and technique. The technique of psychotherapy is not the technique of psychoanalysis, but the theory of both involves an understanding of the same factors in therapists and patients, and in terms of the same concepts. This must be taught in a way the resident (generally not in analysis) can understand.

Psychoanalysis is by no means the optimal therapy for all psychiatric problems. There *are* positive indications for psychotherapy (other than a lean pocketbook) as the treatment of choice as against psychoanalysis. The therapist who introduces variations in technique to meet various clinical contingencies is under no burden of preserving the classical psychoanalytic relationship. The training of psychoanalytic candidates is the only situation in which this relationship must be preserved, and even then there are serious and perhaps even insurmountable difficulties (A. Freud, 1950). Analysis may have to be modified or abandoned in one or another clinical situation.

Occasionally there is even the rather delicate question of deciding whether analysis *has* been modified or abandoned (Eissler, 1953; A. Freud, 1954a). But the rationale for technical variations or for the abandonment of analysis must have a specific psychoanalytic base and consistency in psychoanalytic terms. The specific posture assumed by the psychotherapist must be rational and explicable. The therapist, be he analyst or psychotherapist must know what he is doing and why. The psychoanalytic situation (Stone, 1961) should not be modified or abandoned too readily; this might indicate unsolved problems in the analyst (Allen, 1956).

Although the reader will find ego factors dealt with in these conferences, the most recent developments in ego psychology are not explicitly stated or expressed. For this presentation they are unnecessary and too complicated. This area of theory has in general become quite complicated, and the complications are in danger of becoming ends in themselves. Nunberg (1953) commented at a Panel discussion on identification that the ideas in one of the papers were valid but unnecessarily complicated; this is a criticism that can be applied to other areas of current theoretical developments.

The approach presented in these conferences may, in some instances, be idiosyncratic, but this *is* an attempt to discuss psychotherapy from a psychoanalytic point of view. The conferences were designed to give the resident a grasp of the posture of both the therapist and patient in the therapeutic relationship. This is not a psychiatric textbook; this is not a psychoanalytic textbook. These conferences do not cover all of special psychopathology, nor do they give a systematic review of the opening, middle, and closing phases of psychotherapy. These problems have not been entirely overlooked. For a lucid presentation of the opening, middle, and closing phases of psychotherapy and for a discussion of confrontation and varying degrees of interpretation I strongly recommend Colby's (1951) excellent *Primer*. For a detailed discussion of and instruction in psychotherapy in all its many phases and situations I recommend Wolberg's (1954) monumental work. For a review of basic psychoanalytic concepts underlying psychotherapy one has a choice of many contributions. One might consult Knight (1952), Stone (1951), Bibring (1954), Gill (1954), Rangell (1954), and V. H. Rosen (1958). Glover (1960) would be especially useful for his recent critique of current psychotherapies. Several Panels of The American Psychoanalytic Association have been devoted to problems of psychotherapy (1953, 1954, 1955). Alexander (1953, 1954) and Fromm-Reichmann (1954, 1950) raise important theoretical issues, principally the idea that psychoanalysis and psychotherapy are essentially the same and are only a continuum of one another. The position taken in this book is that there is a clear theoretical and clinical difference between psychotherapy and psychoanalysis and that this difference can be conceptualized even for a beginner in psychotherapy.

Since I disavow so much of a systematic nature in this book, what then do I propose to do in these conferences? I propose to discuss the theory of psychotherapy and to distinguish and define both psychoanalysis and psychotherapy. I propose to discuss the relationship between the patient and therapist in detail and under the impact of various pressures which arise in a wide variety of treatment situations. These conferences attempt to fill out details of the treatment relationship and to help the supervisor in his dealing with the resident's task of learning this many-faceted relationship. These conferences attempt to reduce the intellectual task of coping with this problem to a few elementary principles. The resident will find little here of direct command but a good deal, I hope, in the way of notions designed to produce simplicity and order.

This book is entitled *An Introduction*. No book on psychotherapy can be more. The therapist must plunge into the fray and find his way in a new "as if" world. This is a world of voluntary ego splitting on his part and enforced ego splitting on the part of the patient. It is a world in which the most basic desires of both patient and therapist, i.e., to have real contact with objects, must be set aside in varying degrees. This situation of mutual frustration may become either a maturational or disappointing experience for both participants. This book is an attempt to deal with the theory, the exigencies, and the pitfalls of this difficult path to maturity.

Chapter 2

The Theory of the Therapeutic Relationship

The concept of the therapeutic alliance is an old and honored one. I should like to discuss the therapeutic relationship in terms of a converse idea, not of the therapeutic alliance, but of the therapeutic barrier. I am offering my own idiosyncratic approach. I shall devote a good deal of attention to psychoanalysis. This is necessary since we are discussing theoretical models of the treatment relationship. Psychoanalysis represents a basic model, and is the theoretical base line for various psychotherapeutic departures.

The propositions I am offering are as follows: both therapist and patient face a basic problem, the problem of object need. In my terms this basic object need is equivalent to Leo Stone's (1961) "primal transference." I am referring to an underlying and basic need for objects independent of any specific neurotic structure and having no specific relationship to any particular infantile projections. For purposes of the discussion to follow it is not necessary to specify whether it is a biological or psychological primary need (Balint, 1952). In earliest life it is impossible to separate biological from psychological needs. There is a need and a wish for a real object.

Every patient regards his therapist as real, regards all the manifestations of the treatment situation as real, and strives to regard the therapist as a real object. The therapist, vis-à-vis the patient, strives to do exactly the same. He, too, wants to regard the patient as real and respond to the patient as a real object. Thus, both patient and therapist have a basic urge to mutual acting out.

How is a therapeutic situation created out of this real relationship between the two parties involved? It is created by an act of the therapist. The therapist imposes a barrier to reality. We shall here term it the *therapeutic barrier*. The imposition of this barrier creates a therapeutic task for both therapist and patient. The *real* situation is transformed into an *as if* situation demanding attention and comprehension. The act which brings about this transformation is interpretation.

In a psychoanalysis the same task is to the same degree imposed on both patient and therapist. Nothing in the interaction is permitted to be regarded as real, and everything is subjected to the scrutiny of both parties. Since the initiative for the therapeutic barrier and therapeutic task comes from the therapist, we might grant that a greater degree of deprivation is imposed on the therapist than on the patient. The degrees of severity of the task for both parties may vary sharply. In some cases the therapist may permit the patient a high degree of reality in the latter's relationship to the therapist. For the therapist this might still only be a matter of technique, and he will still retain the *as if* character of the patient. The reference here to *as if* is not to be confused with the "as if" personality classically described by Helene Deutsch (1934). Her reference is to pathological identification without object relationship. In the context of this discussion the expression refers to a model interpretation, "You react *as if* I were, etc., etc."

The degree of the barrier and task imposed on the patient may vary from patient to patient and from time to time, depending on the clinical needs of the moment and on the long-term goals of the treatment effort. At one end of the scale is the rigorous psychoanalytic technique which puts the greatest demands on both. At the other end of the scale the entire relationship may be accepted as real, and the therapist may designedly enter all the phenomenology of the patient as a real object. This may be permitted to occur in some aspects of the treatment of psychoses, notably schizophrenia, and in the treatment of the young and certain acting-out psychopaths.

The need, in this sense, to take another person as object is neither transference nor countertransference. In our sense, object need must first be *overcome* to establish the conditions for transference, or transference neurosis, to be more precise. *An uninterpreted relationship to the therapist is real, as real as any other relationship.* The interposition of the *as if* problem creates a state of tension and deprivation which is the kernel of the therapeutic task. The degree to which this task is imposed will depend on the therapist's evaluation of the patient's capabilities.

Interpretation interferes with reality and with the acting out of the unconscious fantasy. This increases the pressure of the unconscious fantasy and brings it forward into free association, or at least into progressive conflict with defensive forces which can be analyzed. Through this interference with acting out, the real relationship is converted into a transference neurosis. The therapist has a choice: he may either join the patient in mutual acting out of the latter's unconscious fantasy, or he may act in such a way that the patient develops a transference neurosis. One might usefully differentiate between transference and transference neurosis. In a transference neurosis there is a distinct loss of reality sense; the patient is rigidly bound in his behavior by his projections onto the analyst; there is a strong preoccupation with the elements of the transference. In a sense the transference neurosis *apparently* directs the patient to reality, i.e., to an interest in the analyst, but in another sense it is a highly narcissistic preoccupation. The patient is fixed to the unconscious fantasy which is being played out about the person of the analyst. The analyst's refusal to become a real object to the patient thrusts the patient back to his inner fantasy—it makes him relatively more narcissistic—but it also makes the fantasy material more available for scrutiny. This fantasy might be first available only in the form of acting out, but it is available to the discerning analyst. The analyst is sufficiently confident of his own uninvolvement in the patient's fantasy that he is able to take a neutral interpretive position to the phenomena. Under such conditions analysis can take place.

The state of "transference" which exists in psychotherapy cannot be differentiated from an ordinary real relationship. The patient is permitted to act out his basic object needs as well as his infantile projections with the collusion of the therapist, to whatever degree the therapist deems necessary for purposes of treatment. When the patient has accepted the therapist as an object and when the therapist has assumed some importance to the patient, we generally regard that as the establishment of transference. When the relationship assumes rigidly irrational characteristics and is determined by fantasy and not by the real interplay between the two, we may speak of a *transference neurosis*.

The primary object need is present under all circumstances, although it might be obscured under the conditions of certain negative transference and transference neurotic phenomena. These two should be regarded separately in the mind of the analyst, i.e., object need proper and special transference phenomena.

The psychoanalyst must be capable of withstanding all degrees of the necessary deprivation, tension, and task, which especially require tolerance for loneliness. Winnicott (1958) makes some pertinent remarks concerning capacity to be alone, which he characterizes as one of the most important signs of maturity. In essence he states that the ability to tolerate loneliness depends on previous childhood experience with an ego-supportive mother who has been introjected, thus making real reference to the actual mother unnecessary. It would follow that the analyst can tolerate *not* using the patient as object if his introjections and projections are based on affectionate and supportive relationships rather than on hostile ones. Put in still another way, if the therapist is able basically to like and trust people, he is also capable of the necessary detachment to treat them. The transference neurosis can be established only if the therapist can tolerate the isolation of not taking the patient as object. Lonesomeness is not to be regarded in a naïve sense. A casual remark about the weather breaks the loneliness and establishes real object relationship.

Object relations arose at that unhappy moment when the symbiotic bond with mother was disrupted. I would suggest that there are two primary techniques aimed at restoration of the symbiotic, pretraumatic bliss: one is identification and the other is object relationship. One is repair from the inside and the other repair from the outside, and both forced upon us as unwelcome necessities. At an early point in development there is not even much difference between the two processes, as Freud (1923) reminds us in *The Ego and the Id.* The search for objects and the absolute necessity for objects remain with us for life.

Ferenczi's second paper on the development of the sense of reality has a most interesting title, "The Problem of the Acceptance of Unpleasant Ideas" (1926). Every new advance into reality is met by resistance and the effort to re-create the past as it had been before. All these well-known observations are repeated here simply to underscore the generic problem of the constant temptation to move close to objects, to have object relationships, to abandon mature ego differentiation for narcissistic and anaclitic object relationships, the temptation to identification, and finally and basically for fusion. The therapist as well as the patient have a constant struggle against this array of temptations to come closer together. Margolin's (1953) comment on the blurred ego boundaries between patient and psychotherapist refers precisely to this point.

The therapeutic task for the therapist is with his own struggle with his need for objects and with the self-imposed therapeutic barrier. The problem of spontaneous and unplanned acts of the analyst arises from this consideration. The temptation to breach the barrier will assail the therapist at all times. If the patient pleads for help, the therapist wants to extend himself; if the patient is hostile, the therapist wants to fight; if the patient is unhappy, the therapist wants to console him; if the patient is in need, the therapist wants to give. The therapist's task is to restrain himself from regarding these phenomena as real and thus destroying the transference *as if* potential. This restraint separates him from the patient as object and imposes upon the analyst the task of tolerating loneliness.

To complicate matters, certain aspects of the treatment relationship *are* real, particularly certain of the masochistic aspects of the treatment situation as discussed by Menaker (1942). There are also certain real deprivations in the analytic process. To begin with, every interpretation is a deprivation. This is more so in certain types of patients than others, especially for those who act out. Nevertheless every interpretation is designed to rob the patient of something—his fantasies, his defenses, his gratifications. Analysis and, to varying extents, psychotherapy involve real disappointment.

An important deprivation is that the patient's assaults do not reach the therapist. The patient may express most intensely his love or his hatred, and what does the therapist do? He analyzes it. It doesn't reach the analyst and he doesn't care (so the patient thinks). This is a real defeat and reduction to childish impotence which we expect our patients to tolerate lightly.

We assist our patients to develop access to their real feelings, especially to the therapist, and then we refuse to treat these feelings as real. The patient is urged to treat his love for us as real, and we snub him for his pains. The very basis for an analysis involves *really* disappointing the patient. In psychotherapy we do not so globally disappoint the patient. This makes the therapist's role more bearable in psychotherapy than in analysis.

We might summarize the course of an analysis by saying that at the very outset the analyst denies himself the patient as a real object. The patient, on the other hand, *begins* therapy with the therapist as a real object and must slowly learn to deny himself that gratification and so establish the necessary preconditions for the transference *as if*. Mourning is a necessary part of treatment, not only as a termination problem, but from the very outset of treatment, from the very first interpretation. Just as the origins of thinking depend on the disruption of the symbiotic tie to mother and are connected with the first unpleasant idea (the first thought is an unpleasant one), so is there an analogous process in therapy. The therapeutic task can be imposed only by means of a disappointment and by transformation of a real into an *as if* relationship. We force thinking in place of reality: the uninterpreted relationship is reality.

There are certain types of relationships in which we are especially tempted to take the patient as a real object. Glover (1928, 1955) has some sage advice indeed. He wisely cautions the psychoanalyst to observe himself for the slightest alteration in his own behavior with any one or another of his patients. As soon as he notices any alteration he should look to himself. Under such circumstances the therapist has joined in collusion with the patient in taking some aspect of the patient's behavior as real and has responded to it in some real, nontherapeutic way. Our spontaneous and unplanned remarks should be especially scrutinized, both the analyst's and the psychotherapist's. *The principal temptation is to play the role of mother.* It might suddenly begin to rain and your patient needs an umbrella. The rain is real, the patient's need is real, and you and your available umbrella are real. After you give the patient the umbrella he is under no tension and you have relieved him of his therapeutic task. His relationship to you is real and he has been gratified. The act of giving the umbrella has diminished both barrier and task for both patient and therapist. It has rendered an analytic cure somewhat more distant, though it might make a psychotherapeutic "cure" more stable. Such a loan of an umbrella may provoke a whole series of reactions, generally of a masochistic and homosexual nature (in men), problems which can be analyzed. However, these problems are of a different order than those with which we are concerned in this discussion, though they do not invalidate the conception that the act of reality assistance lessens the patient's therapeutic task. The relief from the *as if* problem lends approval to the acceptance of the relationship to the therapist as real. In analysis this would be unwelcome; in psychotherapy it might be most helpful.

Another sensitive area for illustration of our point is the area of speech. The patient's speech might be vulgar or pedantic, for whatever reason. Do we use the patient's speech as our own? If we use the patient's speech, we enter into collusion with the patient's neurosis and accept his defenses as real. We give the patient no therapeutic task. If we use our own speech, we do a number of things: we emphasize the symptomatic nature of the patient's speech; we set up a transference distance; we sharpen ego boundaries; we erect a barrier between the two of us; we avoid using the same defenses as the patient does. The sum of all this is that we give the patient a therapeutic task. The relief from this task deprives the patient's relationship to the therapist of its *as if* character and lends approval to its reality. In analysis the *as if* character must be analyzed and resolved; in psychotherapy it may be helpful to accept the reality of the relationship.

If the therapist treats his patient as real, he is using the patient to overcome his own sense of loneliness and sense of abandonment by his original symbiotic object. One's ego boundaries are the mark of one's disappointment and loneliness. We have a constant temptation and fear to break down these ego boundaries. This is the important anxiety which confronts the patient when he is required to associate freely. The most basic temptation between two individuals is the urge to regress in the character of object relations and to dissolve boundaries and fuse. Normal sexual intercourse offers just such an opportunity. Identification and object relations are not too far removed from symbiotic feelings and are an attempt to restore the symbiotic feeling.

It is a paradox that object relations, which we take as a mark of reality adjustment, are really designed to circumvent the painful recognition of reality. The need for definite ego boundaries in normal object relations has been vastly overestimated. Healthy object relations permit and even demand periodic regressions and fusions, for example, carnivals, vacations, religious belief, love-making. Schizophrenics show the most brittle and rigid ego boundaries of all. Schmideberg (1953) discusses this interesting point.

Another paradox. In the intimate successful therapeutic venture there is a real and close working together of two minds. How can we reconcile this with the therapeutic barrier and therapeutic task? The special problem of the therapeutic situation is that we need real joint thinking to go on, but at the same time prevent the union of the two individuals. How is this accomplished? We want to keep the barrier and still want the two to think *together*, not separately.

There are other paradoxical aspects to object relationships between individuals. For example, an ordinary conversation between two people does not at all facilitate contact between the two. In fact, conversation generally sharpens ego boundaries, and the two individuals are separated more at the end of a conversation than they were at the beginning. Most conversations are bilateral monologues, an observation French psychiatrists made long ago. A real conversation, which brings two people closer together, is rare. Such a conversation would represent a mingling of the thoughts of one with the thoughts of the other. The better the conversation and the relationship, the more are the ego boundaries between the two *broken down,* at least temporarily.

The answer to the apparent paradox of the therapeutic situation is the specific act of the therapist. He demands the *as if* even at the moment of relaxed ego controls, or moment of regression, if you will. To meet this demand *both patient and therapist* must be capable of controlled ego splitting in the service of therapy. My impression is that the emphasis in the past has been on the necessity for the patient to be capable of ego splitting; I would add that the therapist, too, must have this capacity. Gill (1954) also makes this point. Psychoanalytic working through is analogous to mastery through play—though play indulged in by only part of the ego. Kardos and Peto (1956) discuss this issue in a similar way; and so does Sterba (1934) in another context. The problems are relived in an *as if* manner until understood, integrated, and no longer pathogenic. Sterba (1934) discussed these problems in almost identical terms, as did Greenacre (1959) more recently. Sterba posited the need for a therapeutic dissociation of the patient's ego, in which one part would form a therapeutic alliance with the analyst, and the other part, the instincts and defenses, would be set off at a distance to be understood and analyzed. Sterba regards the analysis as a constant struggle to maintain this ego dissociation by means of interpretation. The object hunger of the patient is satisfied by the therapeutic alliance. Sterba regards this latter satisfaction as an important function of transference.

In spite of the remarkable similarity of the ideas of Sterba and those we are discussing today I choose to regard the object hunger in a somewhat different light, and emphasize that this object hunger is as much a problem of the therapist's as it is the patient's. This hunger must be set aside by both to establish the conditions for transference neurosis and analytic work. In my view the uninterpreted relationship is real; the interpretation creates deprivation and transference. The pain of the neurosis is generally accepted as the motivation the patient brings with him to the analysis. The analyst introduces another motivation—the pain of the transference. This latter motivation will be subjected to further qualification shortly.

In effective therapy there must be a capability of withdrawal from real object relations to guard the therapeutic task. A corollary of this would be that a real object relationship would involve a fusion of the two individuals to some degree. In therapy the withdrawal and fusion are both partial, hence ego splitting. In a therapeutic relationship both partners must be capable of the moment of loneliness. At least some part of the ego must be split off to perform the task of thinking and of tolerating loneliness, to play with the experience and not live it, to think and not live it. This is a difficult and time-consuming task; we may have patients who regard not only the therapist as a currently real object but who, to make things more difficult, regard the past as currently real.

I have presented a rather rigorous conception of the ideal therapeutic relationship. This concept, i.e., the concept of the conditions of analytic work, must be grasped firmly, but none of this can be experienced as sharply as I put it here. For example, in addition to the strictly controlled *as if* relationship, there is also the real relationship. The patient gets to learn real things about his therapist both in and out of the office, and the therapist behaves in a real, human way toward the patient (Glover, 1955). In fact, the reality of the therapist is a factor which keeps the treatment going. The real relationship leads to identification which also supplies motivation for the analytic work, for the ego splitting.

The oscillation between the real and the *as if* relationship can actually facilitate analysis and, if considered in terms of oscillation between gratification and deprivation, can serve as a useful model for identification processes. Seeing the therapist as he really is also assists the patient in correcting his transference distortions. In fact, it would probably be impossible to find any analyst who could rigorously maintain the detachment necessary not to use the patient as object at all. He would be bound to be real and treat the patient as real. Paradoxical as it may seem, the very human imperfections of the analyst make analysis possible in reality. Furthermore, it is the analyst's function to introduce reality to correct the patient's fantasies and distortions. The real relationship supplies the motivation to face the pain of the transference deprivations. In effect, there are two concurrent relationships, the real and the *as if*. The very act of interpretation may have a double significance. What I have emphasized has been the function of interpretation in separating the patient and therapist. But in another sense the interpretation brings the two together.

Garner (1961) has recently asked some interesting and important theoretical questions about psychoanalysis and psychotherapy. He wonders whether there may be something basic in the treatment itself as distinct from the various and differing psychoanalytic theories. The principal observation he makes is that the passivity of the analyst is a fiction, and he goes on to indicate the aggressiveness and activity of the analyst. Garner points to the invitation to the patient to lie on the couch; the analyst's silence is regarded as an aggression; failure to gratify the patient is regarded as an aggression. Garner concludes that the common nonspecific elements of different types of treatment far outweigh the theoretical differences. One important element which Garner neglects to emphasize is the analyst's *demand* for free associations, a demand that the patient surrender his hard-won defenses against painful ideas and affects. In psychotherapy there is of course no doubt of the activity of the psychotherapist. In terms of the conception of the object relationship between patient and therapist, Garner is really saying that the common denominator of all therapies of whatever theoretical persuasion is the establishment of an object relationship, a sadomasochistic one. This object relationship has certain consequences. Even in the most classical analysis the object relationship cannot be avoided. Garner maintains, then, that the establishment of an object relationship is more important than what specifically takes place in that object relationship. I accept Garner's emphasis, but would note that he does not carry his own conclusion far enough. All psychotherapists create real object relations with their patients; they establish a psychotherapeutic situation which can have clinically helpful results. The theoretical bias of the therapist *is* important, because this bias determines his attitude to the object relationship and to the changes in the patient as response. The relationship is a sadomasochistic one. Further implications of this type of relationship in the treatment process will be developed later, especially with regard to reassurance and neurotic worry.

I would like to turn to an immediate clinical implication of the problem of object relationship. What is the principal consequence of an interpretation? The principal consequence is object loss. A correct interpretation is followed by a mild depression. This is so whether the interpretation deals with the transference or any other material. I had occasion to indicate to a patient that he wished I were his father. He agreed readily, but the interpretation left him tense and depressed. This was a patient with tenuous object relations and whose symptomatology involved a great deal of acting out. What he could not tolerate in my interpretation was the object loss involved. My interpretation demanded (implicitly) of him that he give me up as father. His continuing tension and depression required additional interpretation. The first interpretation now required a second interpretation concerning the object loss I was asking him to tolerate. So I said, "By my last remark I have refused to be your father." This made sense to him. The tension and depression vanished and was now replaced by unhappiness. He still wanted me to be his father. However, I had shown understanding of the sacrifice I was asking him to make and was taking the blame upon myself. This also helped the patient reverse the direction of aggression within himself; his depression lifted. What remained was real disappointment of real wishes.

The point illustrated by this example is that an interpretation may require a second interpretation to deal with the loss of the object involved. Oddly enough the interpretation of the object loss might also be regarded as offering the patient something, in effect offering him a real object (the sympathetic analyst) in this way in order to help him tolerate the loss of an object in another area. There is still another way of putting it. We require the patient to abandon his infantile objects, and offer adult objects in exchange. *Without this incentive perhaps no treatment of any kind would be possible.* This could be a principle in education, too. After all, education is basically tolerance of pain and abandonment of pleasure. We cannot offer renunciation alone—we must also offer an object, generally the teacher.

I would like to make a further comment about the ego splitting necessary for the establishment of transference. In his classic paper on transference and reality, Nunberg (1951) describes an interesting situation which he characterized as *readiness* for transference. He described a girl patient who wanted the analyst to change into a figure like her father's. She did not *see* him as her father (which would have been a transference phenomenon); she badgered him to *change* into her father. Nunberg called this readiness for transference. I would regard this in a different way, i.e., as *resistance* to transference. This patient's treatment ended in failure. She was unable to tolerate the ego splitting necessary for the contemplation of the transference neurosis. She was unable to "play" the transference "game." There are degrees of reality appreciation. In a true transference neurosis, the patient misapprehends the analyst and regards certain phenomena as real and has certain wishes; when pressed the patient will detach himself and contemplate himself. Nunberg's patient had psychotic wishes and wanted no questioning of them.

Resistance to transference should not be confused with *transference as a resistance*. Transference as a resistance can be worked with analytically; in true transference there is a limited kind of turning to the analyst and a certain object relationship with the analyst. In the fully developed transference neurosis there are projections of the infantile object representations. There is also sufficient ego flexibility to tolerate a working ego split to contemplate this phenomenon. Nunberg's patient, although she seemed to demand that the analyst be her real object, had not really turned to the analyst. She was actually fixated to the original and real father, did not abandon that, and did not project her infantile fantasy onto the analyst. Instead she demanded that the analyst step into her system and conform to her infantile object representations. The impediment to treatment was that the analyst could not be interpreted to her *as* father, if he *is* father. She could not be persuaded to renounce her original attachment in exchange for another, which is what is done in analysis. She insisted on the original attachment at all costs. The cost was failure of the treatment.

Chapter 3

Some Practical Implications of the Theory

We have seen how at one end of the scale there is a type of treatment in which the therapist does *not* permit the relationship to become real for himself, nor does he permit the relationship to have reality for the patient either. That end of the spectrum would encompass the classical psychoanalytic technique. At the other extreme would be the treatment of the regressed psychotic and the hospitalized patients to whom everything is real, including the therapist. This patient is unwilling or unable to accept any kind of *as if*.

These patients have their wishes granted. The therapist becomes mother, becomes father. A type of therapy has been developed in which both patient and therapist accept the situation as entirely real. Whose type of treatment approach would this be?

RESIDENT: John Rosen's?

DR. TARACHOW: Yes (Rosen, 1947). If the patient needed mother, he would in effect say, "I am your mother." He would reward and punish.

RESIDENT: You are saying this is a real situation. Isn't this unreal? Acting as though you are the patient's mother does not make you his mother.

DR. TARACHOW: It is unreal if you subject him to the interpretive situation. If you do not subject the relationship to interpretation, the patient regards you as mother and you act as mother. You become his mother.

RESIDENT: Is it possible to define the circumstances under which it may be necessary to act in that way?

DR. TARACHOW: That is really the entire problem of technique. We are not going to be too specific as to which patient calls for which technique. But I do want to develop a set of propositions, a set of constructions which you will have as a frame of reference in thinking about the doctor-patient relationship. We are not discussing the difference between obsessional neurosis and hysteria. We are talking about the patient's need to convert you into a real object, and the doctor's need to turn the patient into a real object. The psychotherapist has the responsibility of setting the limits of reality for himself and for the patient; he will set these various limits depending upon what he judges to be the strengths and weaknesses of the patient.

If you are an analyst and the patient comes to you without any severe ego defect and with sufficient motivation, you may decide upon the technique at the extreme end of the scale. You do not actually say this to the patient, but you decide to adopt the technique in which all the patient's attempts to transform the therapist into a real person are going to be frustrated. He will have to regard the therapist entirely as an *as if* character: *as if* I'm the mother, *as if* I'm the father, *as if* I'm the brother, etc.

You give the patient a stringent barrier and a very important therapeutic task. I like to think in terms of the assignment of a therapeutic task to the patient. I hope this is not too abstract; it is really a very concrete issue. It is a useful way of looking at the relationship between you and the patient. There are a number of barriers necessary in civilized life. Various degrees of barriers are necessary, and various kinds and degrees of barriers are necessary in different situations. In a family, there is may give the patient the fifteen cents and by so doing not impose any therapeutic task on yourself either. You can refuse and then must tolerate the self-criticism that would follow.

The patient has to face a problem; and you have to face a problem. Every time you force a patient to understand something about himself, you are forcing yourself to a limited degree to tolerate a certain problem. A patient is very unhappy; you might develop moist eyes in sympathetic unhappiness with your patient. You have then joined in the situation with the patient and are treating the situation as real. But the unhappiness which this patient created might be a most sadistic symptom.

You are not entitled to weep; you are required to help him see that he is a sadist. The patient might be depressed because he really wants to kill someone. When the patient comes in depressed and *you* feel miserable, you have imposed no task either upon yourself or your patient. He has to face the task of understanding what's going on, you have to face the task of conscious and unconscious reactions of sympathy. You must resist the usual *ordinary* impulses to helpfulness. You must help only as a psychotherapist or as a psychoanalyst.

Resident: But even when you lighten the patient's therapeutic task shouldn't your task always be in terms of understanding and insight?

Dr. Tarachow: Ideally, you should function with an absolute barrier, and you should understand everything—the entire *as if*. But no one is that perfect.

Resident: Even if you give the patient the fifteen cents, should your task be lightened by so doing?

Dr. Tarachow: It may vary. Under some conditions it is lightened; under some conditions it is not. If you give in because you are unable to resist the simple human impulse, you have abandoned and really neglected your task to the same degree that you have lightened the patient's. But if you give in because you know that this is a person with a particular psy-

the incest barrier. In social relations there are other b
These barriers make relationships possible. If we did n
these barriers, there would be chaos and no thinking.

In a therapeutic situation barriers are essential to es
technique. The degree of barrier imposes a certain tasl
yourself and upon your patient. One can impose varyi
grees of tension or task upon the patient or upon yours

The greatest problem, of course, the therapist imposes
himself. He will impose a sliding scale of deprivation
patient, but a much more stringent deprivation on hims

RESIDENT: Could you clarify the sliding scale a litt
more?

DR. TARACHOW: Let us say the patient comes in and g
you with a very glum good morning, or walks in and do
say hello. What are you going to do? The patient is figh
Are you going to fight?

RESIDENT: No, you ask him what's troubling him.

DR. TARACHOW: That's right, the patient walks in
doesn't say good morning, but you do. The patient is figh
with you, but you do not enter the fight. You do not bec
part of the patient's neurotic or psychotic reality.

RESIDENT: I see. I didn't know exactly what you were get
at.

DR. TARACHOW: The patient comes and has forgotten
have any money with him and needs fifteen cents to get ho
You can be a nice person and give it to him, or you can be
stringent technique and not. It is a task you impose upon
patient; it is a task you impose upon yourself. The task impos
on the patient, if you give him the fifteen cents, is zero. T
patient blackmails (you as) his mother and the blackmail
successful. Or the patient is not given the fifteen cents and
forced to consider why he permitted this situation to arise. T
patient is trying to make you feel, "What a dirty dog I am if
don't give him the fifteen cents."

Such are the tasks you can give or not give the patient. Yo

chopathological problem, that it would be more helpful to his progress to have this benevolent picture of you at this time rather than some other picture of you, that the burden of deprivation and hatred against objects is too great for him to tolerate at this particular time, and that if you impose too much of a therapeutic task on him he will not be able to meet it, then your technique is sound. You are reserving the task of greater dimension for a later time. You indulge the patient, but reserve the right to bring it up for future discussion. If you are behaving properly, you have not lightened the therapeutic task on yourself. If you are behaving improperly, you will lighten it for yourself to the same degree that you lighten it for your patient.

RESIDENT: An example of this came up with a new patient today. She was hospitalized with scratch marks all over her face; she mutilates herself in this fashion. She came to the session today and asked me if I would prescribe skimmed milk for her, even though no other patient in the Adolescent Pavilion gets skimmed milk. Without my consciously making any response, she nodded her head and said, "You'll give it to me, you're a sweet guy." I asked her why she wanted it. The discussion didn't get anywhere, so I told her I would consider it and we would talk about it again.

DR. TARACHOW: You still have the therapeutic task. She is blackmailing you by predicting or coercing in one way or another, but you still have the task of deciding. You might nevertheless find it advisable to give her the skimmed milk. Patients will try to box you in. They will box you in so that you may develop a desire not to do the very things you feel you ought to. When that happens, you are treating the patient as a real object. A patient comes to you with neurotically prepared attitudes; and if you take them at face value and treat them as real, you are of no therapeutic use whatever to any of your patients.

RESIDENT: One could be reacting by refusing to give her the milk.

DR. TARACHOW: Yes. You have to impose a barrier on yourself in terms of the realities of the situation. You have to regard everything as *as if*. Under the proper circumstances you will certainly give things and be the generous person to patients with severe anxieties, to decompensated patients, to psychotic patients.

RESIDENT: But this means: to all our patients in this hospital.

DR. TARACHOW: Well, yes. These patients are not being analyzed. They are sick, decompensated people. To a greater or lesser degree, you are a reality to them and you have to recognize that. We are discussing this not because I'm suggesting that you impose a complete barrier against your reality in the patient's eyes. Not at all. You are a real person, and they need you as a reality; on clinical grounds you may decide that their need to turn you into a real object must be satisfied. There is a regression in the hospital situation which is not only permitted but is inevitable and necessary. And it is a reality from which we do not want to run; we simply want to understand it.

RESIDENT: It was my impression that it was desirable to be real to hospitalized patients.

DR. TARACHOW: Of course. Realistic to the point where you administer discipline—where you insist on discipline, where you set up rules, where you set up deprivation. You have to. I am developing this discussion not because I am suggesting we deprive and frustrate all our patients, but to understand the rationale of what is going on.

Now let us review some other examples of instances in which patients convert you into a real object. Can you think of any further ones?

RESIDENT: I'm thinking of something not too far from what you said. You were talking about the patients who make you cry when they tell their sad stories. I was thinking that when they tell you of things, of things over which they really have no control, things that are in themselves very sad, it may bring forth a response in you that is appropriate to what they're saying. For example, I had a patient whose wife and three children were killed in a concentration camp—a very sad event which he did not bring about himself.

DR. TARACHOW: Well, you've brought up a most useful, pedagogic example. This was something Hitler did, and not the patient. Will someone give us one method of handling it in which it is treated as only real and another method of handling it in which it is treated as not only real? In one you give the patient no task; in the other you give the patient an important therapeutic task.

RESIDENT: Offering sympathy and dropping it at that would be to deal with it as real and not give the patient any therapeutic task. The way to create a therapeutic task would be to try to get at his feelings about what happened, and see how it affects his current life, and find out what it means to him.

DR. TARACHOW: That's correct, or, even more to the point, "Why did this come up now?" In other words, do not only sympathize with the patient; put his nose to the grindstone of psychotherapy. Restrain your natural sympathy. The therapeutic task is in both directions. His painful story is not to be treated as real, but as an association. It is treated as material for the treatment. So something as real as that can be handled as material for therapy. You must decide, when something of such a nature comes up, how much of a therapeutic task to give the patient. Under certain special conditions, the only thing to do would be to accept an event as real. For example, someone is in treatment with you and his father dies. He comes back the following week—he has missed a session or two—it's perfectly appropriate, necessary, and human to give your condolences. Why? Why would the reality here be acceptable to the therapist?

RESIDENT: The patient probably can't do anything in therapy with it at the moment.

DR. TARACHOW: Regardless of what his neurosis is, what task does this patient have?

RESIDENT: Mourning.

DR. TARACHOW: Yes. He has a normal process of mourning to go through, and you must not interfere by interpreting it. In fact, if he didn't mourn, that would be a problem. The patient should be allowed to mourn. Mourning and grief are normal; everyone is entitled to it. In such a case you do not impose any therapeutic task, you simply allow him to mourn. In a sense you are exercising restraint; you hold back your therapeutic endeavors in order to let the patient do something by himself.

RESIDENT: Why say anything? Why not just go on from where you left off?

DR. TARACHOW: No matter how much of a therapeutic barrier and task we set up, there is still room for human reactions. I think it is perfectly proper under any kind of circumstances. There are very few situations in which reality should interfere, so to speak, and tamper with or hold back the therapeutic effort. But I think a death or a birth or a marriage are such real events.

RESIDENT: I had a stark example of this. I had to tell a patient in the hospital of the death of a member of the family. Ironically enough, this was also the delusion of the patient, a delusion which apparently had come true. She had the delusion that her husband was out to kill her and her children. About two months after admission one of her children died at home, when the husband was there. The family called the hospital and indicated that the child was found dead. I had to inform her of this.

DR. TARACHOW: There was no one else to inform her?

RESIDENT: There was.

DR. TARACHOW: This raises a very interesting question. I want to bring up a parallel situation for discussion. You are not quite finished with your story, but hold it for a moment. One day I received a telephone call from the wife of a patient. The husband, who was my patient, was due in my office one hour later. The wife called and said, "I just got a telephone call; my husband's father has just died. Please have him call me as soon as he gets in." The patient came in. I could have said one of two things to him: I could have said, "I'm sorry to tell you, and sorry to have heard that your father has just died; I think you should call your wife. She wants you to call; she just called." Or, I could have said, "Your wife called very urgently and wants you to call at once." What would be the rationale for dealing with my patient in one direction or the other? Would you have told him to call his wife, or would you have told him in advance? While he was calling, you knew his father was dead and he didn't. Which would you have done?

RESIDENT: I think I'd prefer the second course, to have his wife tell him. It is not my business to be a messenger boy. It is not therapeutic, it is not going to help him. My telling him might put me in a different light, though I don't quite understand why.

DR. TARACHOW: You should let the wife tell her husband. You would have entered into the real life of the patient by telling him of his father's death. There is another important reason why you should let the wife tell him.

RESIDENT: I would consider the wife in this too—in her relationship to the patient; it might be very meaningful for her.

DR. TARACHOW: You're undoubtedly right, but at this moment we are concerned only with therapy and with what belongs in or out of therapy.

RESIDENT: What did she ask? Did she ask you to tell him, or did she ask to have him call?

DR. TARACHOW: She asked to have him call, though she told me what the call was about. By telling me she sort of left it open. She didn't say, "Don't tell him, I want to tell him." The remark about staying out of the relationship between the patient and his wife is important. The patient is entitled to get this information from someone in his family. It's kinder. He should get it from his wife.

RESIDENT: What if he brings up subsequently that: "You knew. Why didn't you tell me then?" How would you explain then?

DR. TARACHOW: Oh, he was quite satisfied later that I did not tell him.

RESIDENT: Was this a patient in analysis?

DR. TARACHOW: This was a patient in analysis. I think this would hold, though, for anyone, in analysis or not.

RESIDENT: We have a similar situation in the hospital. We have a female patient whose relationship to me was very bad; her main hatred was of her mother. Her mother died while she was in the hospital. I was told to tell the patient.

DR. TARACHOW: A very sick patient?

RESIDENT: Yes, at the time she was very sick.

DR. TARACHOW: Well, I suppose you know every rule is made for exceptions.

RESIDENT: Who else should tell her while she is in the hospital?

DR. TARACHOW: Well, you could invite a relative to come to the hospital. This is an interesting issue. You might take this up with the Medical Director at some time.

RESIDENT: This is important too because that week there were three deaths in the family. Of course, we expected quite a violent reaction, which she did have. Isn't the task one for the family under all conditions?

DR. TARACHOW: Well, that's a delicate question. In one sense, it is always the family's responsibility.

RESIDENT: It is family business.

DR. TARACHOW: Yes, it is a family matter. And, no matter how real you permit yourself to become to the patient, you can never be the absolute reality. The patient may try as much as possible to turn you into a real mother, but in the absolute sense you're still only a surrogate. In a certain sense, this is always family responsibility.

RESIDENT: I also have a case in point in the hospital. We had a long discussion today at the Adolescent Pavilion. A girl, a new admission, broke the rules last night; she has been breaking them regularly. There are precedents, sometimes deprivations, punishments for certain kinds of infractions. The girl had an appointment with her therapist, at 10 o'clock. The supervisor who acts as ward manager posted punishment for this girl at 9 o'clock. She made a violent scene with her therapist and attacked him. Our discussion centered on whether her doctor should have been the one to tell her of the punishment or whether the staff administrative section should be. The issue is still not settled.

DR. TARACHOW: Well, that's an old issue in hospital treatment: should administration and punishment be vested in you as therapist or separated from you in the administration? If it is vested in you, you are much more real. If it is vested in the administration, the whole situation becomes more of an *as if* situation. There are then different demands made on both the patient and on you. In some way it's easier, in some ways not. It seems to me that in the Adolescent Pavilion the therapist should carry the entire burden. The patient will deal with him in that fashion anyway.

RESIDENT: Can you come to a conclusion as a result of the patient's action as to which method would have been more appropriate?

DR. TARACHOW: I shall give you a proposition upon which you can base the answer. If the patients are less sick, you'll come to one conclusion; if the patients are sicker, you'll come to another conclusion.

RESIDENT: I think what might be said is that the sicker the patient, the more real the doctor should be.

DR. TARACHOW: In terms of what I've been constructing for you, that would certainly be the conclusion, though I am not absolutely certain that that is the best way to do it. When you assume the administrative authority you automatically assume other hospital aspects. With certain patients this might not be the best thing to do. If the patient is very sick and you let someone else be the bad one, your work will be limited to the friendlier feelings to you. This sharply limits the kind of therapy that you will be able to do. But if the patient cannot tolerate ambivalence to you, you might be driven to such a limitation in the goals of your therapy.

RESIDENT: In fact, the patient's therapist wanted to tell the patient of her punishment. The ward manager wanted to isolate the hostile feelings. We could not agree which was best.

DR. TARACHOW: Well, someone has to take the clinical responsibility and decide. Can the patient tolerate his ambivalent feelings to the therapist, or can the patient not tolerate such ambivalent feelings to the therapist? Is the patient so troubled and so guilty about the ambivalence and hostility that it would be more disastrous to the patient to hate her own therapist? Is the patient so fragile that the libidinal or affectionate feelings attached to the therapist must be protected very carefully? Does the patient generally tend to see people as either all good or all bad and therefore make a similar split between hospital routines and therapy, thereby carefully keeping all hostile feelings out of treatment? At Chestnut Lodge, I believe, there is complete separation of the authority and discipline aspect from the treatment aspect. The man or woman who is treating the patient has nothing to do with discipline. He is the pure therapist. This problem can be rationalized either way, depending on the various circumstances of treatment and the individual case.

RESIDENT: In the case you mentioned of the telephone call, if that patient then asked to be excused from the session because of his father's death, would your assent amount to entering into a real situation?

DR. TARACHOW: Certainly. I regarded that as a real family matter. After getting his telephone message he said, "I have to leave." And I said, "Of course." It was quite proper. I was not going to subject him to any kind of relationship which had even the smallest degree of an *as if* problem for him, in view of his just having been told his father died.

RESIDENT: Did he tell you?

DR. TARACHOW: Yes, and he then left at once. I treated it as a real family matter not requiring any treatment attitudes.

RESIDENT: Would you visit a patient?

DR. TARACHOW: Under some circumstances, yes. I will even call up a patient on the telephone. For example, with reference to a woman coming out of a depression, whom I had treated over a number of years and who had great difficulty tolerating the real separation of my summer vacation, I did the following: I let her know exactly at what telephone number I would be the entire summer, and told her not to hesitate to call me. In addition, I called her several times during the summer to ask her if she wanted to see me. The fact that I called her seemed to make a visit to me unnecessary. I was regarding myself as real for her, and her need for me as real.

If a patient is in treatment with you and has some serious physical illness which requires hospitalization for a long time, I do not think there is anything wrong with dropping in once or twice during the hospital stay to see him. The theoretical ideal of treatment is to have the patient work out all his conflicts, problems, and symptoms to their ultimate meaning, but at the same time you are two human beings, and you are a physician with a physician's responsibility.

RESIDENT: If a patient makes a suicide attempt, would you visit the patient in the hospital?

DR. TARACHOW: Yes, I would. Depending on the seriousness of both the physical and psychological possibilities, I might even visit often or regularly.

Some time back I called your attention to the need for a certain kind of self-observation, to watch oneself for any variation in one's own behavior with one patient or another, on the theory that this indicates you are responding in a real way, that you are taking something of the patient's as real. If the patient is likable, you are liking him; if the patient is unlikable, you are not liking him—you are treating the relationship as real, and imposing no therapeutic task upon yourself. The entire background idea of this discussion is the problem of imposing a therapeutic task upon yourself and upon the patient. The underlying notion is the drive to be real, to treat things as reality.

For example, a patient has all sorts of critical ideas about you: you don't tie your tie right, you don't shine your shoes, you're too young, you're too old, you're not experienced enough, you look unhappy, etc. The patient wants to criticize you. You are aware that the patient has these criticisms and has trouble expressing them. You might be tempted to say, "It's all right to express these criticisms of me." What are the complications of saying that?

RESIDENT: You tell him you accept it as criticism. As a matter of fact, if you feel that he criticized you, it means that you're reacting to him.

DR. TARACHOW: The problem I am posing is that you are telling him that it is all right to express this criticism of you.

RESIDENT: You are lessening his task in terms of understanding his criticizing you. You're telling him to go ahead and do it, don't bother understanding, just do it.

DR. TARACHOW: That's right, you're not giving him any task at all. You're certainly lessening his task. Go ahead.

RESIDENT: You're lessening the guilt or fear of punishment. You're giving him the judgment he is anxious about.

DR. TARACHOW: You lessen his task. What about your own task?

RESIDENT: You're certainly lessening your own also.

DR. TARACHOW: Yes. And so, when you do that, what have you actually done? It's not therapy. It's helping him along. If you do this, with what angry complaint is the patient going to return to you later on?

RESIDENT: You are insincere.

DR. TARACHOW: No, it has nothing to do with insincerity. The final complaint against you will be: "You're treating me like a baby".

RESIDENT: He may complain that you didn't let him say what he wanted to say.

DR. TARACHOW: Either that or that you're treating him like a baby. You had become sympathetic instead of therapeutic. You really become the mother helping the child over a hurdle. The neurotic problem has been converted by you into a real problem. Instead of focusing on his difficulty, you say, "Well, I'll take care of the difficulty; you just go right ahead." You have played out a real role by reassuring him. You have played out a real role and not a therapeutic one. You have lightened the task for yourself; you have lightened the task for the patient. But as a result, much less gets done in a therapeutic or maturational sense, and the patient eventually will resent it.

RESIDENT: Is it possible to do this with regressed patients who have difficulty expressing themselves?

DR. TARACHOW: Yes, but I'm not giving you a rule that holds for everybody. As I said, you may have instances in which the reality of the relationship to your patient has to be very great, and where you cannot impose much of a task on the patient. There you step in and play a real role, and you actually have to tell him, "Yes, you seem to have something you want to tell me about me, it's critical; please say it."

I have a paranoid schizophrenic man, whom I literally beg to tell me his thoughts about me. I say, "Please tell me; I want to hear it." I know in advance it will be either some paranoid accusation or some homosexual idea. It's either a reproach or a homosexual wish. I make a point of regarding his difficulties as real. I don't ask him to confront the difficulties at all. I just ask him to tell me—for the simple purpose of helping him avoid brooding obsessively about it later.

RESIDENT: I have a paranoid patient who presented a similar problem, difficulty in expressing criticism of me. I indicated that she could express these thoughts. She did, but she then came up with a reproach, "You told me to go ahead and tell you these things. Obviously, I don't mean a damn thing to you, because you listened to them and didn't get angry. They don't mean anything to you, or you wouldn't have listened."

DR. TARACHOW: This is most interesting; she wanted it to be real to you. She wanted it to be even more real than you were permitting it to be. You were treating her difficulties as real and not as neurotic, and helping her over that. And she wants an even greater degree of reality than you gave her. She is quite right. If you treated the content as real, you would get angry and would not want to hear it at all. You treated it as real, but not quite real enough. If you had actually taken it for reality, you would have abandoned your neutrality and have become angry. But apparently the patient wants something in addition to reality. Even a schizophrenic wants equality of roles. The moment you are reassuring or encouraging you destroy the equality in the doctor-patient relationship and consign the patient to the position of the helpless child. Even though the patients seek this and often seduce you into this, the moment you oblige they will resent the deterioration of their position vis-à-vis you.

Chapter 4

Types of Psychotherapy

In a previous seminar I emphasized the problem of reality and the therapeutic task. The point I stressed was the need of *both* therapist and patient. In order for analysis to take place the need of one for the other as real object must be set aside. Another way of putting it would be to say that in the unanalyzed transference the patient takes the therapist as real, and no analysis takes place. *The task of setting aside the other as a real object I regard as the central problem in the theory of the treatment process.*

Today I wish to enlarge the theme and also place this conception within a larger framework which might serve as an over-all conceptualization of all psychotherapeutic techniques including psychoanalysis. I shall open with two introductory dimensions of the problem: first, an elementary review of the task and goal of treatment; second, definitions of psychoanalysis and psychotherapy. After this brief review we will then go on to the formulations of the types of psychotherapy.

Let us begin by saying that the patient has erected a barrier to the disorderly expression of his infantile and archaic wishes and drives. The barrier is his neurosis as well as his total personality, particularly his ego structure. We might also say that the total personality is a conglomeration of drive and defense. To speak in local, clinical terms, we might say that the obsessional neurosis is a barrier to and often a disguised gratification of archaic anality or anal sadism; depression is a barrier to and, in fantasy, the gratification of cannibalistic love-murder; hysteria is the barrier to and also the symbolic gratification of incestuous sexual wishes. The normal ego structure is the barrier to impatience and disorderliness. Both the normally functioning ego as well as the neurotic symptoms serve as barriers; the tyro therapist should regard *both* as equally necessary for the patient, especially at the outset of treatment. Glover (1931) carefully cautions about this. We tend to underestimate the task we assign the patient, to set aside his hard-won ego defenses.

We must add that the neurotic barriers become impediments to functioning, to happiness, and are often the sources of great mental pain. Even this must be qualified, since in some individuals the symptoms and compromises have so thoroughly found ego approval or superego approval that they have become inextricable and ego-syntonic elements of the total personality. Treatment of such individuals is often hopeless from the start.

The purposes of treatment are, *first of all,* to give the patient relief from suffering, and *then,* to equip him better to live in peace, affection, and stable equilibrium with himself, his immediate objects, and the world as a whole.

What design or plan do we follow?

We must assess the possibilities of intrapsychic change, the reality possibilities, the stability or precariousness of the balance of defenses confronting us, the degree of change necessary or desirable, the minimum and maximum areas of intervention or susceptibility to interpretation or even confrontation, the magnitude and regressed quality of the defenses, the danger of eruption of powerful archaic feelings, an estimate of the tolerance to insight, the risk of psychotic anxieties, the strength of the ego, its ability to form either new defenses or new ego structures if insight or certain dislocations are attained. To arrive at this estimate, the therapist must also contemplate the patient's age, sex, marital, financial, and occupational status, current success in life, talents, possibilities of sexual gratification, and last but not least, favorable or adverse family constellations.

We are now poised with the assessment and the therapeutic intention. We now add the doctor-patient relationship, the transference and transference neurosis to our discussion. We may decide that the patient can tolerate analysis or we may decide he can tolerate psychotherapy in various areas and to varying degrees. This decision leads directly to what the therapist will *permit* or *prevent* in the treatment relationship.

How can we state our treatment choice in terms we can define? We may have more than one definition. Suppose we define psychoanalysis and psychotherapy. Even the simplest definition demands consideration of the idea of the transference. Psychoanalysis would be that treatment in which the transference, repression, other ego defenses, and resistances are all freely subjected to analysis and resolved as far as may be required by the task of dealing with the infantile intrapsychic conflicts and the derivative symptoms. Rangell (1954) has offered an excellent, comprehensive definition of psychoanalysis, but it seems preferable to have a definition which is briefer and more concise. I could make my own definition even simpler: psychoanalysis is that treatment which takes into account the transference and the transference as a resistance. Of course, one has to know what the transference is. Some remarks on transference and transference neurosis will be made later.

Psychotherapy, on the other hand, is a selective, limited treatment in which a rearrangement rather than a resolution of these elements is aimed at. The transference, repression, and resistances are dealt with in such a way that their stability is preserved, while trying at the same time to effect whatever of the therapeutic goals are desirable or possible.

We must search for psychoanalytic conceptions which will encompass all varieties of psychotherapy; we should be able to conceptualize even bad or unintended or spontaneous psychotherapy. The maneuvers of psychotherapy are endless, but the conceptions underlying them should be simple and few.

Psychotherapies have been variously classified as (1) supportive or (2) supportive with varying degrees of exploration and insight searching. Knight (1952) and Alexander (1954) have both offered similar divisions—supportive versus exploratory. We will not here discuss the controversy over Alexander's idea that psychotherapy is a continuum and not different from analysis.

Various principles of treatment are suggested for psychotherapy. In exploratory psychotherapy, transference, resistance, and unconscious content are dealt with. However, emphasis is placed on setting limited goals (Stone, 1951; Knight, 1952). In turning to more specific technical measures we might note that Coleman (1949) advises avoidance of intense dependency reactions, attention to current material, more active and more superficial interpretations, and limiting the duration of treatment. Stone (1954) emphasizes dealing with the realities of the patient's life, his daily events; the patient should be dealt with in his own idiom and attention should be centered on a few selected dynamic issues. My point of view about the instruction to pay attention to the reality issues of the psychotherapeutic patient would be to say that such instruction misses the central point. One pays attention to reality in analysis as well as in psychotherapy. The difference is that in psychotherapy the real events are treated as *a reality*. In analysis these same events are, in addition, treated as expressions of the patient's fantasies and as determined by the inevitable needs of the patient's solutions of his unconscious conflicts. This is a most important distinction; if the psychotherapist bears this in mind, such specific instruction becomes unnecessary. Both Gill (1954) and Bibring (1954) give extensive instructions about what a psychotherapist should do and classifications of what he does. The critical concern is the status and function of the relationship between therapist and patient. If it is taken as real, then the symptoms and life events are also taken as real, and both therapist and patient turn their backs on the unconscious fantasies and anxieties. If the real relationship is set aside, then both therapist and patient turn toward an understanding and working through of the unconscious fantasies.

I shall suggest three overriding principles of psychotherapy. Within these three principles any and all psychotherapeutic techniques should be comprehensible. The following are the three measures:

1. Supply the infantile object in reality, i.e., the unanalyzed transference.
2. Supply displacements, i.e., new symptoms and/or resistances.
3. Supply stability, i.e., ego or superego building, or education, or reality events.

Any given technique may have the qualities of one or all of these three measures. We will begin with the first, that of supplying an object in reality. My remarks in this area have been published (1962a) and we have already discussed this in some detail. The differences between psychoanalysis and psychotherapy were stated in terms of object relationship and loneliness. In analysis the analyst rejects the patient as object and (via analysis) teaches the patient to reject the analyst as object. Under such conditions problems are resolved by interpretation. In psychotherapy the therapist and patient retain each other as object, and varying degrees of the patient's life remain uninterpreted, unanalyzed. The two have entered each other's lives as real, serving as infantile objects to each other.

Nunberg (1951) distinguishes between psychoanalysis and psychotherapy in almost identical terms. "The psychoanalyst and the non-psychoanalyst differ in their treatment of this phenomenon (transference) in that the former treats the transference symptoms as illusions while the latter takes them at face value, i.e. as realities."

In psychotherapy the therapist actually intrudes into the life and personality of the patient and *stays there*. He offers himself for the creation of a new symptom. In an analysis the emphasis of the therapeutic process is the analysis of the transference (this new symptom) as a resistance. In psychotherapy we regard the transference manifestations and their substructure as a vehicle for the cure, in the sense of being necessary building blocks for the patient's continued psychic functioning. The therapist uses himself as a building block in the ofttimes jerry-built structure of defenses the patient has erected. In analysis this is (hopefully) resolved; in psychotherapy this is welcomed. What is resistance in analysis is a necessary permanent factor introduced into the patient's mental economy.

Glover (1960) has an identical exposition of this idea. "The fact that the success of psycho-analytical techniques depends ultimately on the reduction of resistances tends to give rise to the mistaken impression that these defences are as pathological as the symptoms they are intended to conserve. On the contrary, the stability of normal ego-formations is promoted to a considerable extent by psychic resistances to change. What is a stumbling block to psycho-analytical technique is usually a pointer to the technique of non-analytical therapy. In this sense the difference between psycho-analysis and general psychotherapy is the difference between a mainly dynamic approach and a mainly structural approach, in the one case reducing pathogenic charges and in the other reinforcing the ego-defences against pathogenic charges."

Since the area of object relations has already been dealt with in an earlier seminar, we may turn to the second area of the outline: supplying a displacement. For the theory of this measure I turn to Glover (1931) for his conception of "inexact interpretation." Glover distinguishes between an incomplete and an inexact interpretation. The incomplete interpretation is simply a step in correct analytic technique, in which the analyst gets the patient to move closer by degrees to the unconscious and infantile truth about himself. An inexact interpretation has a different purpose, even though at a given moment it might seem to be the same as the other. An inexact interpretation is offered as the definitive meaning of a certain arrangement of material, a meaning which, in the opinion of the analyst, actually falls short of the unconscious or infantile truth. The analyst has judged that the complete truth would be dangerous or intolerable to the patient. The patient seizes the inexact meaning eagerly because it helps him continue to repress the truth; he can turn his back on the truth, and with the newly offered belief, in effect, form a new symptom. In a sense the patient has been offered a benevolent phobia and he grasps it eagerly. The real focus of the problem remains repressed and is displaced onto the given interpretation. This new symptom, the displacement, is the psychotherapeutic "cure." Glover correctly emphasizes that psychotherapy is on the side of defense.

Glover classifies nonanalytic techniques as follows: (1) ignore the truth altogether; turn away from the problem; "take a vacation"; (2) hypnosis or suggestion, which he characterizes as transferred obsessional symptoms; and (3) partial truth and suggestion.

In terms of my own outline the area of displacements can be broken down into four headings: (1) displacement onto the transference: it is incompletely interpreted or not at all; (2) displacement in the benign phobic sense, in the sense of Glover; (3) projection: we might join the patient and blame the environment or specific people in the environment and neglect the intrapsychic conflicts that grew out of these outside factors, in effect establish a benign psychotherapeutic paranoia; (4) introjection: we blame something within the body. The patient is treated medically. We help the patient blame or attack his introjected objects, and along with the patient take these somatic symptoms as real, and not as derivatives of his unconscious intrapsychic conflicts. In the third and fourth directions we offer a delusion as a substitute for the presenting symptomatology. The *cost* is the sacrifice of knowledge of the truth: the *reward* is a functioning stability.

The concept of supplying displacements includes an entire array of maneuvers in which the therapist selects the more ego-syntonic aspects of a problem and interprets only these, leaving undisturbed the more troublesome factors. In pathological ménages the heterosexual aspects might be dealt with. In pathological dependency relationships the libidinal aspects might be tolerable but not the hatred or murderous feelings. In working with dreams, the manifest content or the immediate reality-problem-solving aspects might be utilized. In passive aggressive characters the aggressions might be worked with, but the passivity might be gratified in the unanalyzed transference relationship.

The third and last area in my outline is that of supplying stability. This might be done in a variety of ways. We might note in general that this also is in support of the defensive structures. Stability may be supplied by ego support or superego support. Id support would not be in the direction of stability; it would lead to difficulties. A patient scolded me for smiling at her in greeting. She accused me of insincerity and of stimulating her without promising her gratification. Ego support can be given by reality discussions of real events and by participation in decisions. A most important means of ego support is education and information. This enlarges the powers of the ego and so strengthens it. Education strengthens the ego but blocks the expression of fantasy. It contributes to stability, but interferes with access to the unconscious. Education strengthens resistances and defenses. Education is restrictive in terms of the unconscious and is similar to inexact interpretation in terms of access to the unconscious. Any weakening of the ego might lead to a relapse into fresh symptomatology. Superego support is given by commands, prohibitions, and expressions of morals and moral values. Values are transmitted in a variety of ways, principally by the therapist's selection of which symptomatology he pursues and which he neglects. Changes in the environment might also contribute to stability.

One can turn to many authors in the literature and note how various techniques can all be understood in terms of the three general measures suggested: (1) supply an object; (2) supply displacements; and (3) supply stability.

Reider (1955) describes a fairly large number of cases who were either treated psychotherapeutically or who experienced spontaneous cures. Perhaps we can indicate the principle in each. He described a case helped by a hobby serving as an auxiliary defense. This patient had been supplied with a new symptom. Another patient gave up alcohol at the time when she developed a new symptom which clearly represented a vicarious gratification of femininity. Again a new symptom. Another patient was helped by an ego-strengthening event to give up certain obsessions. Stability was supplied. These are cases of spontaneous cures. The dynamics are to be understood according to the same principles as in planned psychotherapy. Among cases of planned psychotherapy Reider describes the replacement of one symptom by another, the playing of a real role, the offering of controls to a patient, helping the patient stabilize a set of projections in the form of blaming the parents, and strengthening the defenses. These can all be understood in terms of our diagram.

Repeatedly writers on psychotherapy emphasize, "Do not disturb the patient's defenses, assist repression." This would certainly fall under the general heading of supplying stability. This can be done in many ways. Berliner (1941), in discussing various of his cases of brief psychotherapy, indicates by a case example that psychotherapy should give the patient narcissistic satisfaction; in another case the therapist plays a mild superego function. These measures contribute to the stability of the mental apparatus by assisting the ego or superego. We might add that in some cases a weak ego might be assisted in its struggle with the power of the superego or the id. A certain degree of role playing might be necessary to effect this: a statement of values, morals, or judgments might even be necessary at times. Stability is thus supplied by ego building in one instance, superego strengthening in another, and mediation between superego and id in yet another.

Reassurance is frequently suggested as a psychotherapeutic measure. One should be aware of its complications and dangers. Reassurance is the assumption by the therapist of a real role in the patient's life. In one sense it fulfills the measure of supplying an object. However, this measure can be understood more completely. Reassurance sets up a new sadomasochistic relationship between the patient and therapist. It offers the patient a new and, on occasion, dangerous set of symptoms. The dangers are the risk of depression, masochistic fantasies, homosexual fantasies, or even paranoid ideas.

The sadomasochistic complications tempt me to make a tangential reference to neurotic worry. Worry is a comfortable, defensive masochistic flight from extreme sadistic preoccupations. Worry is a masochistic defense against a sadistic object relationship. What does the therapist do when he reassures the worrying patient? He offers the patient a *new* sadomasochistic object relationship, but one in which the *patient* is now in the position of the helpless object. He has given the patient a new symptom from which he gains a degree of comfort and relief. Instead of the patient being troubled by his own drives to attack and by his superego tensions, he has now been made the object of the therapist's attack; he is momentarily free of guilt and superego tension over his own sadistic drives. We relieve the patient by turning him into a victim. This, of course, brings its own complications.

Kindness should also be mentioned as an assault along with reassurance. A suggestion, too, would also be an assault. In fact, even an interpretation is an assault. Patients who have especially sensitive problems of passivity or latent homosexuality will become restless and angry or will even refuse to listen to an interpretation. How complete should an interpretation be? An interpretation should rarely go as far as possible. It should, by preference, fall short even of its immediate intended goal. This gives the patient an opportunity to extend your interpretation, gives him a greater share in the proceedings, and will mitigate to some extent the trauma of being the victim of your help, your approaches via interpretation.

The conception of "support" in psychotherapy deserves at least passing comment. Explicit verbal support has its dangers, as was discussed in connection with reassurance and kindness. The most effective support is permitting oneself to be real to the patient in some implied or indirect way. A comment about the weather is sufficient to notify the patient that you are in his world and have not withdrawn into the remote distances of the transference *as if*. The patient then feels he is not alone. Such indirect joining in the realities of the patient has the fewest dangers.

The character of terminating the treatment which the therapist accepts may also serve psychotherapeutic ends. A severely spiteful patient cannot acknowledge gratitude or obligation to anyone. He has been in treatment for a long time and has made many gains. He is faced by the difficulty of acknowledging that the therapist has helped him. He finds an excuse to become violently angry at the therapist and breaks off treatment. Under certain conditions this is an acceptable termination. The therapist makes no effort to acquaint the patient with his difficulties in loving the therapist. Another way of saying this is that the patient is permitted to end the treatment with the transference resistance at its height. This is precisely the reverse of the psychoanalytic goal. The therapist makes no effort to get the patient to confront his libidinal feelings. Contempt for the therapist becomes integrated into the feelings of independence. The therapist's narcissism must be sacrificed in the interests of the psychotherapeutic "cure." I certainly do *not* agree with Szurek (1958) that psychotherapy properly done *must become* psychoanalysis. This is a wholly unrealistic approach. Szurek underestimates the ego deformities, the weaknesses, the brittle defenses, and the id resistances, which so often make change impossible.

Let us take another example of working with only a part of the patient's problem. Assume you have a patient with a powerful, insoluble latent homosexual problem. This patient wants to get married, wants to be potent, and wants to be a man; perhaps he finds a girl and does get married. The attitude the therapist takes to this in psychotherapy is entirely different from that he would take in analysis. He will accept this patient's ambitions at face value, even though his heterosexual adjustment is a thin, precarious crust. The latent problem would remain untouched. This means, of course, not tampering with any of the transference attitudes derived from the latent homosexuality.

RESIDENT: What do you actually do?

DR. TARACHOW: For example, all the problems which arise between the patient and his wife, or with any women with whom he might be having a relationship, would be taken at face value, as heterosexual problems. Interpretations would be offered in a heterosexual context. Relationships to men would be dealt with not in terms of the homosexual implications, but preferably in terms of the aggressive and rivalrous facets. Assume your patient is involved in a relationship to a girl in a situation which involves another man. We might reasonably assume that this suggests an important latent homosexual problem. Consciously, however, this patient is involved in a heterosexual problem. We would deliberately stay within that frame of reference. The patient would be assisted to deal with the problems in terms of the heterosexual issues. This is what I mean by taking defenses at face value.

A similar type of problem might be worked out with the defensive positions remaining relatively undisturbed. You may be confronted by a situation in which your patient is one of two partners; the two men do not get along together very well. They have had a relationship of many years' duration, but they have had many clashes. Here too, one could limit one's interpretations to the rivalries between the men; one could seek out from the patient's past only the aggressive and rivalrous facets. One could seek out the old rivalries with father, brother. One could choose to neglect the latent passive homosexual relationship which might be a large ingredient of the tie between the two men. Since it is uncomfortable to deal with the homosexual fantasy involved, you offer the patient a fantasy which is more ego-syntonic. He does, of course, have conflicts in the heterosexual sphere, but it is only half of the story.

Another type of situation in which one might deal with only half the story is that involving problems of pathological dependency. Your patient might be extremely dependent on some other person. In psychotherapy it might be possible and quite useful to work out the vicissitudes of this relationship to an extensive degree and still overlook the murderous impulses, the hatred, the destructive side of the relationship. Such halfway measures may contribute to stability and to repression. These are further examples of inexact interpretation, of offering displacements.

The use of dreams might be selectively limited. A patient might dream that his mother died. Interpretations might be confined to the attachment, to the need, to the fear of losing mother. The therapist might stop short of pointing out the murderous wishes to mother. Interpretive work might be limited to the manifest content, to the current problem-solving aspects of the dreams, to the relationship of the dream to current, consciously known events.

The most important aspect is to *know* that one has taken a limited approach. This may be done for a variety of reasons. The patient might not be able to tolerate his infantile or even his preconscious thoughts and feelings. Or the patient might be seeing you only once a week, and the less stirred up the better. Or the therapist might not have been analyzed and might (properly) be unready or unwilling to deal with a great deal of archaic material.

One special aspect of the manifest content of dreams may be extremely useful to the therapist. The therapist should learn the common symbols for the treatment situation. This will often give him ready insight into current transference attitudes. The treatment situation is often dreamed of as a busy public place such as Grand Central Station (reversal of the privacy), a public toilet, a laundry, a torture chamber, a police inquisition, a class in some foreign language, a class in archaeology or history, a visit to a museum, a surgical operation, a bus ride or taxi ride (this is very common; the driver is the therapist). These dream symbols repeat themselves so frequently that the therapist should be familiar with them. I shall add another one: the dinner table or banquet table. The amount of food the patient permits himself to get at this table gives you some ready information about his unconscious orality and the current transference attitude.

RESIDENT: A patient of mine dreamed of me taking her on a guided tour through her apartment.

DR. TARACHOW: The apartment is her body, of course. It is interesting to note whether the patient lets you into the apartment through the front or rear entrances. Anatomy is everywhere in dreams and symbols. Basements, downstairs, upstairs, attics, front porches, all have anatomical implications. It might be interesting to note in passing that many therapists are quite willing and able to work through many of their patients' problems in terms of dependency and orality, but the anality is neglected. Anality is too dirty, too closely connected with archaic aggressions.

It *is* correct psychotherapeutic technique to limit the scope of one's interpretations. The therapist should be aware that he is bypassing troublesome areas of difficulty which might lead to symptoms or relapse later on. Sometimes they do not. The psychotherapist takes a calculated risk. In psychotherapy an active attempt might be made to encourage the patient's attachment to the therapist. It might be quite common to interpret a patient's aggressive wishes, but to gratify his passive wishes in the uninterpreted transference relationship. In doing so the therapist offers himself as an object and offers a displacement, too. He will, under such conditions, permit the patient to give him a Christmas gift. The attachment to the therapist is cemented in this fashion. The patient may want an occasional visit after treatment is finished. This is a fairly typical kind of working equilibrium established with patients in psychotherapy.

There is another typical psychotherapeutic situation I would like to mention. The therapist is treating a young man with a good deal of passivity in his make-up. The patient presents himself with a struggle against domination by a woman and offers many complaints about her cruelty. The naïve therapist enters the fray with great gusto. He is eager to help his submissive patient deal with the unhappy situation. Both he and the patient will be thoroughly occupied with the passivity of the man and the aggressiveness of the woman. What the tyro therapist might be overlooking is the possibility that this predicament is the patient's ideal defense against his own sexual aggressions against the woman. Being victimized by the woman helps him overlook his sadistic conception of the sexual act and the masochistic aspects of the woman's sexual role. In more precise psychoanalytic terms, the patient is living through a relationship with a phallic woman to avoid his castration anxiety. The naïve or nonanalytic psychotherapist might regard the man's passivity as the central problem. The psychoanalytic psychotherapist will regard the passivity as a defense and construe the man's aggressions and castration anxieties as the central problem. If the naïve psychotherapist pushes the patient too hard in the direction of aggressiveness and is blind to the patient's more basic problem, he will only push the patient into greater difficulties. The psychoanalytic psychotherapist will be guided by how great the patient's need is for the continuation of the phallic woman as a defense and will help the patient toward only as much amelioration of his defensive passivity as is safe under the circumstances of the total psychological situation. As we can see, psychotherapy requires even greater sensitivity and empathy than psychoanalysis does. I know psychoanalysts who can practice analysis, but are lost in psychotherapy. The psychoanalytic psychotherapist is selective. He will disturb defenses only as much as necessary or even not at all. He will strive to buttress ego-syntonic feelings even though they may be defenses against infantile wishes or conflicts. In dealing with a man who has difficulties in dealing with his father, the therapist may choose not to probe into the patient's identification with mother and his feminine identification.

RESIDENT: I was wondering how one knows which of these dangerous areas to avoid. Why would it be safer to deal with the passivity to mother rather than the passivity to the therapist?

DR. TARACHOW: Passivity to mother is still, in the mind of the patient, a heterosexual relationship; passivity to the therapist suggests homosexuality. With a woman patient the homosexual side can be pursued a bit further than it can with men. A certain degree of female homosexuality is socially condoned. Girls can walk in the street hand in hand. A woman is expected to be attached to her mother, but a son should not be too attached to his father. There are certain characteristics which suggest paranoid traces in men: a man who changes jobs frequently, who has administrative difficulties, who seems litigious and unduly irritable should be suspected of being paranoid and struggling with a difficult homosexual problem.

RESIDENT: The important point seems to be the social acceptability. Passive drives or aggressive drives might both be equally pathological, but it seems that the social acceptability determines the gravity of the pathology.

DR. TARACHOW: The social acceptability has grown out of

the underlying problem and not vice versa. The underlying dynamics are important; the social acceptability is a lesser factor. A man with a large homosexual problem has not solved the castration problem. The castration anxiety is critical.

RESIDENT: But a man with very aggressive impulses also has a problem.

DR. TARACHOW: Of course, but each problem should be pursued on its own merits. The anxieties about passivity involve body-ego fears (including castration and penetration). This is more difficult to tolerate than the problem of attacking or destroying someone else's body ego. The social factor permits more homosexuality to women than to men in most cultures. However, in France men kiss each other publicly: one would think that Frenchmen would be less disturbed by problems of homosexuality or paranoid psychoses. It might be interesting to study comparative statistics.

RESIDENT: What about a passive dependent individual who has certain insights into his homosexual strivings and is seen in psychotherapy only once a week? He might even bring up his homosexual wishes openly.

DR. TARACHOW: If the patient is able to bring them up that openly, the danger of paranoid reactions would be less, though not eliminated. Overt homosexuals may develop paranoid psychoses. The issue would be pursued only to the degree to which the patient insists. Patients often insist on the homosexual nature of their problem. In psychotherapy the first tack to pursue would be the heterosexual implications of the homosexual fantasy. Even some of the pregenital implications might be less frightening than the homosexual ones.

For example, a patient has a fantasy of sucking on something having the qualities of both a penis and a breast. If the patient is anxious about the homosexual implications I would pursue the breast implications first. I would search for some situation in the current life of the patient which indicated lonesomeness or suggested some need for a derivative fantasy of return to mother. It might as well be said that there is a large element of unconscious fantasies of mother concealed in the homosexual partner. Fellatio fantasies are often derived from fantasies of sucking on the breast. The pregenital aspects of homosexuality are enormously important. This may be reassuring to the homosexual, since the relationship to mother at least seems to bear the quality of heterosexuality. All patients are by no means alike: patients have anxiously reproached me for identifying mother as the person lurking behind the fantasied homosexual partner. The abhorrence of women was too great for them to be so reassured.

Patients will insist on one fantasy to avoid another. Some patients will insist on homosexuality to avoid facing the tie to mother. Still, in a patient with precarious stability it is safer to deal with heterosexual issues before the homosexual ones.

RESIDENT: Have you ever known of an instance in which a psychosis was precipitated by a therapist's interpretation along the lines of homosexual material?

DR. TARACHOW: I take it you mean a psychosis that had not been present before. I think this can be done. It is possible to precipitate recurrences of paranoid psychosis by being too hasty. I have done so. Sometimes one can sense provoking paranoid reactions in one's patient. On occasion a patient whom one does not suspect of being in precarious balance may blow up in a florid psychosis in the first week of treatment, even before any interpretations are made. The patient simply cannot tolerate the uninterpreted burgeoning transference relationship.

Chapter 5

The Theory of Hospital Treatment

Hospitalization is a means of offering a patient an opportunity to act out his psychodynamic patterns under controlled and observed conditions. The observed behavior, particularly its regressive aspects, is used in a manner analogous to the use of the associational process in individual interview therapy. Based on these formulations an active therapeutic effort can be planned and executed.

The treatment process may be outlined in the following way: (1) removal of the patient from external problems; (2) reconstruction by the patient of the problem within the hospital; and (3) application of the observed data for treatment purposes. This last, the treatment effort, may be regarded as having several parts: (a) tolerance of the regression, (b) the insight aspect, and (c) the ego-building aspect.

The most useful point at which to begin our discussion is with the problem of a therapeutically useful attitude toward the understanding, acceptance, and use of regression in the management of the hospitalized patient. One way in which the regression can be described is to say that the patient takes everything in a literal and real way. He sees his resident therapist most realistically. He does in fact require a most real relationship for his affective needs, his needs for supervision, his needs for discipline, for control.

Though the situation for the hospitalized patient is real, it is nevertheless a necessary relief from his reality on the outside, from the reality of his previous embroilments. In the hospital he gets a new reality which he will soon enough transform into a repetition of his old. Although we will discuss the necessary regression in the hospital, we might note, in passing, that the hospital environment might be less regression provoking than some homes from which the patients come.

The patient accepts all the circumstances of hospitalization in a real way. The therapist must be willing and able to lend himself to this. In many ways accepting the role of therapist to a hospitalized patient is more demanding on the therapist than an office situation is. The psychotherapist of clinic or private patients is sheltered from much of the patient's regression. If a psychiatrist gets away from hospital realities for a time, he may actually experience hesitation and perhaps even a certain amount of anxiety about going back to it.

Does any one want to comment or raise any question or issue about the general concept of the reality of the hospital situation to the patient? It occurred to me that perhaps one of you could draw a distinction between the outpatient and the inpatient.

RESIDENT: Yes, in the outpatient clinic, I think most of our therapeutic attempts are toward *overcoming* regression. Though regression is pathological, it is reversible and we struggle against it in most of the outpatients. There might be a different situation among the inpatients who are thoroughly overwhelmed and so largely regressed. It may be that the situation in the hospital is quite different from that in the outpatient department.

DR. TARACHOW: Tolerating regression is no simple matter. We may safely assume that immersion in the regressed hospital atmosphere is bound to be anxiety provoking to the beginning resident. The new resident has anxiety and not enough insight. He has not an easy task in turning to his new duties. The principal direction of our discussion should be in terms of learning to tolerate the intense and often exasperating demands the patients make upon us. Beginner residents may have difficulty in seeing the reality of the patient's needs. The concept of decompensation is also something the resident has to understand. Perhaps we could turn for a moment to the task of defining decompensation. We talk about a decompensated obsessive, or a decompensated neurotic—but can we clearly put into words what we mean?

RESIDENT: I would think a fairly good synonym would be regression, by which I would mean the patient moves from more healthy defenses into more primitive defenses, acts in a way more typical of early psychosexual development.

DR. TARACHOW: Primitivization of defense is an excellent conception of certain kinds of decompensation.

RESIDENT: I think you get very close to some body-image difficulty as decompensation occurs, and along with that fuzziness, one might even observe some difficulty in distinguishing between one's own thoughts and feelings and perceptions from the outside world.

DR. TARACHOW: Well, let's not get into clinical symptoms too much. The one notion given is quite useful, a regression of defenses, primitivization of defenses. That's an example of decompensation. One might also term it primitivization of ego structures.

Let us take the concepts of ego, id, and superego, and apply the conception that something has gotten out of hand, is running away with the situation. Either the id is out of hand or the superego is out of hand, or there are certain ego disturbances. The ego may have suffered distortion or weakness through organic or psychological causes, or the ego defenses may have either collapsed or gotten out of hand and become too florid. For example, a man might have gotten along for many years with washing his hands ten times a day; that might have been his defense against whatever his unconscious crime had been. Something happens and he starts washing 200 times a day. A man can be destroyed by his defenses. This happens often in schizophrenics in whom the terror of the inner problems may be so great that the defenses bloom and destroy the patient.

So the defenses might bloom and destroy the patient, the superego might bloom and the patient commit suicide, the id might bloom and the patient commit murder. Or the ego may become distorted, fragmented, weak—leading to various disorganizations. The primitivization of defenses would be a conception of an ego disturbance. The ego becomes regressed, which would involve functioning according to an earlier, more infantile, and more magical pattern. You may observe a clinical syndrome existing for years in a certain kind of neurotic, or even psychotic balance, and at a certain point, due to problems of age, or problems of instinctual pressure, or through burdening by external reality situations which push the patient in one direction or another, the balance of forces becomes disturbed.

This is not to say that this is the only way of conceiving of decompensation, but it is one useful way. The diagram is least accurate with reference to the id getting out of hand since it somehow suggests that psychopathy can be understood only in the simple terms of id exuberance. While this may be true in some cases and a substantial factor in others, it by no means tells the story of psychopathy. Many psychopathies are the result of intricate and complicated defensive maneuvers involving rather busy defensive ego functioning. However, the suggested simple diagram can nevertheless serve a useful working function. I present it as a simple diagrammatic conceptual statement, so that when you say the patient is decompensated, you are saying, at least to yourself, a little bit more than just that things were getting along and then they suddenly started going bad. It should not be overlooked that the decompensation can take place on the basis of organic brain change. In fact, this is the basis for an important differential diagnostic issue which arises in middle age.

I recall a man who had gotten along for many years as a moderately severe obsessional neurotic. At about the age of forty-five the obsessional neurosis began to bloom. He went into psychotherapy. But it turned out he had Alzheimer's disease.

The therapist has to learn to accept the decompensation and regression of any hospitalized patient and the reality which this possesses for the patient. He must be prepared to offer a degree of reality in order to be a real object to the patient.

In the office the therapist is the *as if* object, but in the hospital he is a real object.

There are instances in the outpatient department when a rather sick patient will give a therapist a present. If you have decided previously that you are going to do primarily supportive treatment and are going to try to be a real object, it would be out of keeping to do what some young therapists do. They set the present aside and say, "Now, tell me why you brought this," instead of saying, "Thank you." In their zeal to imitate analysts and not realizing the need to be a real object to the patient, they make this kind of mistake.

This is perhaps the most common mistake a beginning resident makes, to behave like an analyst, even to neglect history taking and to brush aside and not recognize the real needs of the patient.

It is literally the reality of the therapist's interest that keeps some patients alive. I remember treating, on an ambulatory basis, a schizophrenic girl whom I kept going for ten years until I grew tired of the situation and arranged to transfer her to a younger colleague. Within a week she was at a state hospital. I was all of reality to her; the whole world had been mediated through this contact with me for the ten years. She had not a perfect existence, not a normal existence, but she had had a personal and social existence and a social identity for ten years, until I grew tired of my role.

I would like to comment on the matter of being supportive and being a real object to the patient. If you accept the role of a real object (i.e., accepting and not interpreting a gift), that *is* support. You are then in the patient's real world, you have treated his feelings as real, you have not stepped back into the shadows and (for the therapist) the anonymity of simply being something to be interpreted. You have *not* abandoned the patient. *This is support.* A common misconception of supportive treatment is the assumption that it involves encouragement, reassurance, hopeful prognostic remarks, etc. Nothing is further from the truth. The degree to which the therapist departs from the interpretive position is the critical element which indicates the degree of support. Overt verbal reassurance is another matter, since it so often represents in the unconscious of the patient the institution of a new sadomasochistic relationship between therapist and patient. It often represents attack more than support.

RESIDENT: An important point demanding clarification is that a patient can be focally regressed in an area of transference relationship, but function elsewhere at a much higher level; regression need not be synonymous with *total* decompensation.

DR. TARACHOW: Regression can be synonymous with decompensation, but the useful point you are making is that there can be regression in sectors. There are many varieties of ego splits, some involving different degrees of pathology, and others of a relatively normal nature. For example, can any of you think of some splits in normal life in which there may be one or more areas of ego functioning which are quite regressed, and others relatively not? I am using the term ego splitting, though this might be somewhat inaccurate. We are discussing focal areas of regression.

RESIDENT: Love-making.

DR. TARACHOW: Exactly. Love-making is a perfect example of normal regression in a sector. There are others. These vary from normal to minor pathological.

RESIDENT: Various play.

DR. TARACHOW: Yes.

RESIDENT: Sleep?

DR. TARACHOW: That's one, *par excellence,* but there are others which occur in the waking state. Sleep is not an ego split, though. Sleep is an almost total regression. Almost the entire ego abandons itself to the regression. What about waking life?

RESIDENT: Daydreams.

DR. TARACHOW: Yes. Games, play, love-making, dreaming, varieties of religious feeling. I think religious feeling is an excellent example of ego splitting in which healthy persons accept an unreal set of conceptions as real, though they would not conceive of accepting the same unreal conceptions in other areas of their lives. Certain aspects of patriotism might be the same.

Perversions and fetishism illustrate ego splits in which one part of the ego knows what sexual anatomy is and another part is confused. There are various pathological denials. Certain of children's lies illustrate ego splits.

The conception of focal areas of regression applies in hospitalization, too, where you become accustomed to seeing patients who function beautifully in many respects, but who are utter infants in their dealings with the therapist. It is easy to underestimate the regressive power of the transference, and certainly in your novice days you are bound to. Furthermore, you might be terrified by it.

Several years ago a resident started a research problem of studying initial dreams upon hospitalization. We thought that what would come through in the dreams would be the patient's conception of the hospital and the infantile importance of the hospital. We did not work through the data thoroughly, but our first impression of the material clearly indicated that in the initial dream the patient set up his relationship to his therapist and not to the hospital. These patients were adults. I do not know what it would have been on the adolescent side. This is still a useful project that some resident could do. The moment he assumes his therapeutic role to the patient he is important, both realistically and transference-wise.

I have seen residents become impatient with a regressed patient, especially with those who are on an oral level and quite demanding. The patient says, "Give me advice. Why can't you tell me what to do? I've been coming here week after week and you don't do anything. You just sit there." The therapist in these situations might freeze up, become grim, and have intense hostile outbursts. Or he may simply not comprehend the desperate plight of the patient, the whole nature of the regression in which the patient finds himself.

The pulls in the children's department are unique and different. The young therapist might have trouble with the adult, regressed patient who has sexual or aggressive problems. But with children he might be much more willing to handle the situation. The danger is of overidentifying with the children in the age group from five to twelve. He may be completely identified with the child, making unreal plans, being overindulgent and overly permissive. There are different degrees of stress put on the therapist in the outpatient department as against the hospital. But let us stay a moment more with the comparative difficulties of treating adults versus children. With patients under the age of twelve the therapists identify, accept them, defend them, and readily forgive them. But with an adult who makes regressive demands, either of a greedy-dependent or spiteful kind, the therapist becomes furious or loses interest.

RESIDENT: It is less threatening to identify with a child. The child does not have the apparatus with which to carry out the kind of aggressive or sexual acts which an adult has. It is a little too close for comfort if one identifies with an adult patient. It is too close to acting out one's own impulses. It is safer to identify with a child acting out. One gets the vicarious satisfaction, yet remains reasonably guilt free.

DR. TARACHOW: Yes. A child is allowed regressive action, but an adult is not. You may permit your own regressive identifications to be processed through a child who is permitted it. But an adult is not permitted the greediness, the selfishness, the destructiveness, which the small patient is. You may become furious because the adult is doing what you want to do. Your superego does not get to work on the child, but it does very much so with an adult. Róheim said somewhere that the child wants to do what the adult does, and the adult wants to do what the child does.

RESIDENT: We expect less from a child.

DR. TARACHOW: That, I think, is too conscious to be much of a factor. I think the factor is not so much the level of expectation as the permissibility.

RESIDENT: Perhaps the revulsion in the therapist is not so great when a child shows regression as when an adult does, because the distance the child regresses is not so great.

DR. TARACHOW: It certainly looks sicker and is sicker in an adult.

RESIDENT: Yes, If a five-year-old wants to be hugged, we hardly give it a second thought.

DR. TARACHOW: Yes, that is an excellent, and simple observation. Perhaps some further remarks might be added to what has been said about residents and child patients. Although the resident may become permissive to his child patient, it need not be on the basis of accepting the regression of the child. It might be the opposite. Your therapist is farther from his child patients than he is from his adult patients. The inexperienced therapist might not know how to get to the child, so, in desperation, he resorts to permissiveness. In this fashion the therapist can bring about excessive regressions in his child patient and the therapeutic situation will go from bad to worse.

There is also another factor favoring the unhappy therapeutic situation. In the case of therapists who have not solved their own problems of rebellion against their parents, they will for that reason join in the regression of the child. The therapeutic situation then becomes quite hopeless.

RESIDENT: I do not know whether this is a contaminant, but I think in some ways that which is tolerated at certain levels of society or classes might not be tolerated in another class. Not only is there a matter of expectation, but there is also the tolerance of the environment. Certain behavior is expected of a child in a certain class.

DR. TARACHOW: I suppose to some extent that is a factor. Different groups have different values. The psychiatrist himself has values which he introduces into the therapeutic situation. Certainly the differences between men and women in social relationships are quite marked. Illnesses vary and perhaps even psychiatric recommendations vary according to the class of the patient or the social class of the therapist. A recent paper by Sterba (1960) discusses the global aspects of this problem. He discusses the problem of the changing reality of the entire world, a reality which in general militates against emotional expression or individuality. In the "playground" area of analytic working through or psychotherapy, the patient is encouraged to be himself and to express his own feelings. This might have disastrous consequences in reality.

Also there are differences between dealing with healthy children and psychotic children, and also differences between relating to an adult psychotic and a child, either psychotic or not. For instance, if a psychotic smears, it is more difficult to tolerate than if a five-year-old smears.

Let us put this in terms of the psychological vicissitudes of the therapist. If an adult psychotic patient smears, *it is more difficult for the therapist to tolerate.* It is more difficult for him to accept it than to accept the smearing of a child. Our discussion of regression is in terms of learning to tolerate the regressions of one's patients, because the regression will last for quite awhile throughout the patient's hospitalization.

I would like to express a word of caution about taking regression in too narrow a sense. Regression is more than slipping back from a phallic or genital level to either anal or oral levels of personality organization. In regression the ego abandons its supremacy over the mental apparatus. What obtains is difficulty with the sense of reality, increased magical and primary-process thinking, an increased burden of aggression and ambivalence, and, most importantly, interference with object relations. This gives the therapist of the hospitalized patient an added duty, that of fostering the object relations of his patients and also of fostering orderly, realistic thinking, i.e., reality testing.

RESIDENT: Do we relate ourselves to regression as a phenomenon which is characteristic of the problem with which we deal or do we relate ourselves to regression as having some reparative function? Do we exploit it for treatment? Is it a necessary part of insight or a precursor of insight into the psychogenetics of the particular patient?

DR. TARACHOW: What we have been discussing today has simply been the task of learning to tolerate the patient's regression at all, and also of learning that the patients who come into the hospital are regressed to begin with, that their regressions take certain forms, whether they be demanding or aggressive or parasitic, and that the therapist has to learn or be steeled to face this and live with it and accept this as a necessary part of the hospitalization. This is the beginning. At this beginning point the resident is real, the patient is real, and the situation is real, especially the regressive aspects of it. This acceptance by the resident establishes the base line for hospital psychotherapy.

The ultimate weapon in hospital psychotherapy, in terms of the therapeutic barrier or in terms of the regression or in any other terms is going to be the power of the transference.

This does not mean that the therapist should interpret everything or even anything at all. He simply has to recognize the power of the transference. He has to recognize the relationship the patient is forming with him, that it is a relationship, and he should then use this relationship, in progressive steps, to thrust as much confrontation or insight as is safe or feasible upon the patient.

It is worth reviewing some of the progressive steps in the hospital treatment of patients.

1. The first is removal of the patient from a difficult situation, from the outside interacting process. The patient is now in the hospital. We are past that. The therapist knows that this has been done for the patient.

2. The next step is the reconstitution of the problem in all the areas of the hospital and the splitting or dilution of the transference. This is what we have been discussing today; the reconstitution of the problem in our terms would be the establishment by the patient of his own characteristic typical style, his own symptomatic and regressive pattern. He sets up his psychosis or neurosis all over again in the hospital. This develops in relationship to everybody he deals with and, most typically, with the therapist himself. This step requires no effort on your part. The patient will do this on his own. The therapist must learn to recognize this and tolerate what the patient has done. The patient is spared all reaction and interaction with the outside and now reconstructs this pattern again with you and the other hospital personnel. The therapist must learn to understand and tolerate this.

Perhaps it might be useful at this point to interpolate a few remarks about the hospital as a generic symbol. It is quite easy to see the hospital as an id symbol; it represents mother who feeds and comforts and relieves one of all responsibility. However, it may be a symbol from the superego side as well. It acts as a control of behavior. You may at times have some difficulty with this specific aspect of your functioning vis-à-vis the patient. The hospital may also offer tasks and explicit or implicit incentives to get well. In this sense the hospital is an ego symbol. We will get to the ego-building aspects of treatment later.

Up to this point the therapist has not yet taken any therapeutic steps, but what we have done is set up the basis for the possibility of therapeutic steps. The therapist is now willing to tolerate the regressed patient and to view the patient's real and transference attachment to him as it exists in the present. He is largely a neutral observer.

3. The third step is the application of the increased observational data in the hospital to treatment purposes. The therapist is now in a position to control, to confront, to educate, and to interpret at appropriate times and levels. At this point we are engaged in the active *personal therapeutic process.* The total therapeutic process can be observed in all areas of the hospital. Let us assume that the therapist collects data of the patient's performance in social groups, occupational therapy, ordinary ward activities, and also the office behavior with the therapist himself. He also collects data indicating that the patient's trust and confidence in him are growing.

We might pause for a moment to observe that the patient is struggling not only with his transference and transference-splitting problem but also with the pain and anguish of the pathologic process itself, his clinical symptomatology.

Let us return to the therapeutic process in more concrete terms. The therapist collects the various data about the patient, his behavior in the various areas of the hospital as well as in the private office situation.

The first step is for the therapist to get a tolerant as well as a dynamic conception of what is going on in the patient. Up to that point everything and everybody is real. Then the resident, in conjunction with his supervisor, should decide at what point the patient must confront his own behavior and to what extent and how far the style and the nature and the character of the patient's behavior has to be thrown back to the patient, even if only for confrontation. The patient may have a pattern of teasing and antagonizing every authority figure. The patient may have a pattern of being utterly dependent on authority. The patient may have a pattern of an unpleasant kind of greediness, a hostile greediness or a dependent greediness. The patient may have a pattern of attaching himself to old people or only to young people, or have a homosexual pattern, or have some other kind of pattern. For a fruitful therapeutic approach, one should pay attention to the life or behavior pattern and not to symptoms. This might be a surprise and an unexpected or even unpleasant task to the patient. This has its advantages. A neurotic illness is seldom overcome by frontal assault. When the therapist has decided that the patient likes him enough and trusts him enough, then he may begin to rob the patient of the real (to him) nature of all these expressed and acted patterns. This is done by adopting a confronting or a comparative or finally an interpretive attitude. Colby (1951) in his lucid book on psychotherapy, outlines very clearly graded types of interpretations and various ways of offering them, e.g., interpretations may serve purposes of clarification, comparison, or wish-defense interpretation. They may be offered as questions, suggestions, tentative assertions, or definite pronouncements.

We must view hospitalization as a means of offering a patient an opportunity to act out his own psychodynamic patterns under controlled and observed conditions. The active therapeutic effort then follows.

Any behavior of the patient contributes to therapy in so far as it provides something to be observed and, at some point, used for therapeutic purposes. Whether the patient is acting out or not is relevant only in an analytic situation where one's observation is limited to the auditory sphere. But in a hospital setting we may have many other modalities which become observable behavior.

Acting out in a hospitalized patient cannot be defined in

quite the same way as the acting out of an ambulatory patient. A patient assigned to occupational therapy might cling to the occupational therapist or might refuse to go to the occupational therapist. I do not know whether we should regard his behavior to the occupational therapist as acting out, but if he refuses to go to occupational therapy or if he elopes or if he persistently comes too late or too early to interviews with you, or absolutely refuses to take a bath or clean his room, we might conceivably refer to this as acting out. It is difficult to define acting out in a hospital setting because we are prepared to deal with the entire behavior from the very beginning.

It is up to you to be observant of the details of your patient's behavior. I might recall to you that several years ago a resident and a supervisor in this hospital did an unpublished study which is quite germane to this matter. They subjected either one or a very small number of patients to intensive study in that *all* the behavior of the patients over entire twenty-four-hour periods was recorded and reported to the therapist. The results were surprising in that the resident was able to have an astonishingly better and more useful picture of the patient than when he relied on the usual routine reports. The resident should learn to use nonverbal material, use everything as communication. The patient might think he is not communicating, but it is up to you to note the manner in which he is. It is an error to attempt to separate out acting out in a hospital setting. We have tried to in this discussion, but in a larger sense, there is no such thing. We simply learn the principle of utilizing total behavior.

RESIDENT: I thought that the point being made was that even behavior which is not conducive to the eventual resolution of the emotional problems can nevertheless be used in the hospital treatment situation, can be incorporated into treatment. One could express it most explicitly by saying one uses observed behavior in much the same way that one would use the associative process in interview therapy.

DR. TARACHOW: Yes. This point involves the very conceptualization of hospital treatment. We are discussing it now in terms of the first necessary piece of education of the resident therapist. If a resident neglects his patients' hospital behavior, he misses most of the possibilities of hospital treatment.

RESIDENT: Perhaps what we are looking for is a distinction between acting out and action, since acting out carries with it the analytic implication; by definition it pertains to the psychoanalytic relationship.

DR. TARACHOW: You can take your choice. Acting out may be defined in terms of resistance to psychoanalysis or it may be defined in terms of a plastic working out of one's inner conflicts, without reference to being in analysis. In terms of hospital treatment, we have no special use for the concept of acting out. Acting out is a dramatization of an intrapsychic problem. Action is an object-directed, reality-oriented phenomenon. We will discuss this in more detail when we discuss psychopathy (Chapter 16).

Suppose a therapist repeatedly permitted himself to be drawn into answering questions about himself. Without realizing what he was doing, he might answer, either because of his own needs to answer or because he simply does not yet know enough to separate out the dynamic implications of the patient's behavior. If the resident participates with the patient, he is not contributing to cure. The resident must make use of the patient's behavior, not become a party to it.

RESIDENT: This discussion of acting out is more important to those of us who work with adolescents who act out all the time.

DR. TARACHOW: Yes. In the Adolescent Pavilion acting out is taken for granted. On the adult side, in a sense you condemn it, and want to take it away from the adult patient. On the adolescent side the acting out might be all you have to work with.

The final *as if* step is to rob the patient of his right to do it at all. This is really the last step. The therapist might be too fascinated or too frightened by the symptoms to pay proper attention to the patient's total behavior. Treatment rarely proceeds through the symptoms, but will proceed through the total behavior.

Suppose we begin with a patient behaving very badly in the interview situation. It might be difficult for the resident, beclouded and confused by the patient's regressive transference reactions, to see that the patient might have undertaken certain positive activities leading to maturation or insight in some other area. The resident might see his patient hallucinated and incoherent. However, the patient might be functioning beautifully in school. Treatment opportunities may arise elsewhere in the hospital situation, *apart* from the one-to-one relationship to the therapist.

We are underlining the absolute necessity of having a grasp of the patient's total behavior, of the entire setting, the whole hospital operation. The resident who fixes on the office relationship requires further education.

There is an additional educational possibility in these "splitting" situations. If the patient's behavior with the therapist has certain characteristics and is quite different from the remainder of his functioning, this might indicate that the therapist is the patient's favorite. He might have become the principal object of the patient's regressive needs. The patient might be behaving in this regressive way to the therapist because he cannot tolerate other people or does not dare express his wishes or demands elsewhere.

A patient can split in various ways; he can split his objects, split his feelings, split the nature of his relationships to objects, especially in a hospital setting with all its ancillary services. A total picture is necessary. The resident has to collate all of the split fragments, collate all the various areas of focal regression.

The same problem arises in psychoanalysis. Many analyses go on for years because some simple observational datum which the wife (or husband) observes every day is unknown to the analyst. It never gets talked about. But in a hospital you have a decided advantage, not always made use of by the resident.

The hospital patient might not have enough ego structure to be able to relate and accept a highly structured situation such as the office interview. It requires a well-functioning composed ego to be able to relate in such an artificial situation. It is easy to overlook this factor.

The resident must learn to accept the fragmented and regressed egos with which he has to deal. He might become very much annoyed. The patient does not answer, or assumes you know the answer, or gives a surly answer. The more experienced of you are familiar with this.

RESIDENT: How much intolerance of regression can be attributed to envy or anger on the part of the therapist?

DR. TARACHOW: An excellent point. The regression may be seen as a self-indulgence. I believe we discussed this when we compared attitudes in working with children as opposed to working with adults.

RESIDENT: The mere fact of coming into a hospital and accepting a dependency role is a regression. But there can also be too much tolerance of regression. I think there has been a marked change in this hospital since we reorganized some of the wards. The change we made was to have patients go through their entire clinical course on one ward. A disturbed patient would be admitted to a ward which contained patients already much improved and with pretty good control over themselves.

DR. TARACHOW: That is a most interesting point. What you are saying is that if you put the very sick patients into a group in which there is a range of people who have relatively well-functioning ego structures, these sicker patients will pull out of their regressions faster.

RESIDENT: We expect more of them. It is one of our core ideas. The aim is to allow only the smallest degree of regression. This helps resist the process of ego deterioration.

Dr. Tarachow: One can say a glass is half full of water or half empty, and both would be correct. The "anti-regressionists" would say we should allow the patient only the smallest degrees of regression that are possible or necessary and thrust the therapeutic task upon the patient as speedily as possible. I would say: realize the existence of regression, tolerate it, and then thrust the therapeutic task upon the patient only slowly and at the rate he can tolerate.

I would like to extrapolate a principle out of this discussion of regression and the factors which foster or militate against regressive tendencies in the patients. The principle would be that the hospital serves an ego-building function, too. We serve an ego-building function more consciously than in office therapy, even though we play a formative role in office treatment, too (Sterba, 1944). It might well be that putting very sick patients in wards with improved patients has an ego-building incentive, in an implied way and in one that is not experienced as specific coercion either from the outside or directly from the therapist.

There are other related data. Many soldiers, when in combat with their familiar groups, held up well. After the combat period was over, when they were sent back, they folded up. Under the ego pressure of standing up among their fellows and not losing face and being as good as the next man, they tolerated all sorts of pressures.

Resident: They have taken that into account by moving, in the postwar era, men by units. They functioned better in groups.

Dr. Tarachow: That would be logical.

Resident: There are literally hundreds of these maneuvers which in a certain sense constitute a significant aspect of hospital treatment. We are constantly in one way or another utilizing just this kind of antiregressive factors. We need to have a concept of factors which resist regression too. Regression is reversible and responsive to various influences.

RESIDENT: There is one point about which this hospital feels strongly; we will stop any kind of regression that is seriously harmful to the patient, where the patient endangers himself, through whatever motivation. We will definitely say, "This we cannot tolerate. We will not let you destroy yourself."

DR. TARACHOW: Sometimes the patient has to be told he is destroying himself. There is a nice example of just this problem in the Symposium on "Problems of Technique in Adult Analysis" (A. Freud, 1954a). Douglas Bond described a young girl patient who was starving herself to death. He worked with her every day for several months and was getting nowhere. She was going downhill to certain death. Finally he told her, "If you keep this up, you will die." She began to eat.

In my own experience I have a dramatic example of a severe regression responding to a strong appeal to the ego. A young woman developed uncontrollable postpartum vomiting and diarrhea at the birth of her first child. Within less than a week she was in danger of dying. I was called to see her. Although an intelligent woman, she could not be reached in any sophisticated dynamic psychotherapeutic sense. I procured a small rotating hypnotizing wheel that centers vision, and simply sat at her bedside and droned into her ear that all she heard was my voice and she would do exactly as I said. I kept this up for hours, morning and evening, droning on to her that she would be able to eat. She started to eat, the diarrhea and vomiting stopped. She was released within less than a week and continued in office psychotherapy with me.

A year later she offered to tell me why she had started to eat. I expected some profound element of transference and symbiotic union with me, but she said, "You know, you were working so hard, I felt sorry for you." At any rate, I made a massive attempt to reach her and she did respond.

To review three areas which stand out about hospital treatment. First is the *regression* which you must recognize and accept up to a certain point and for a certain time. If you accept it forever, if you put no demands on a patient, that's another matter. Eventually you will have to put some demands on the patient.

Then there are two others. I do not know which to put first and which second. One would be the *ego-building aspect* and the other would be the *insight aspect*. The insight aspect has to come from you in graded doses. The ego-building aspect comes from such factors as have been mentioned about ward reorganization as well as many other factors implied in the hospital setup. This does not exclude incentives which might arise in the personal therapeutic relationship.

RESIDENT: We have mentioned the aspect of dilution of transference. I would like to call attention to the curious phenomenon of resistance to dilution of transference. I was wondering if we could not possibly define the resistance toward dilution of transference, perhaps also discuss the kind of regression sought by the patient, and our influence upon this. Can our therapeutic influence in some way be oriented toward accepting or not accepting certain maneuvers on the part of the patient?

DR. TARACHOW: I cannot answer your question, but I shall give you the thought that immediately arose as you began to ask the question. Your question leads to a refinement in the estimation of a patient. You have posed a wonderful problem for a clinical research study, i.e., a study to determine which patients tend to adhere only to the therapist and regard all other figures offered as relatively unimportant, and which patients will dilute or split their transferences and be even more attached elsewhere, to two, three, four, five figures, rather than to the therapist? This is an excellent research problem. The research problem could be stated as follows: what are the factors which influence the degree of response to the transference-splitting potentialities of the ancillary services? These factors might be within the patient or outside the patient.

It might have to do with the nature of the patient's object

relations prior to hospitalization. I would suspect it has to do with the degree of ambivalence patients can tolerate toward objects. This could be related to the patient's prior tendency to split object choice.

A patient might not have been able to tolerate any ambivalence. The patient might have had one friend whom he liked very much and whom he never criticized. He hated most other people. Such a patient cannot tolerate ambivalent feelings to any one person. Perhaps this is the type of patient who requires many transference objects, each one being the target of some unmixed feeling. He may not have the ego capacity to fuse his conflicting feelings.

It might be precisely the opposite. The patient might be able to tolerate ambivalent feelings to one person. He might fix only on the therapist or on some other staff member. He might permit himself to have this single most important relationship. This one person would become the target of both love and hate. There might be other aspects of object relations on the outside which are either repeated or not repeated in the hospital.

The history taking should be able to define this. I am a great believer in pointed history taking. If during the first week or two it comes to your attention that the patient has an attachment to one of the ancillary workers and only to him and nobody else and not to you, then make careful note of this. The history should be re-examined. What is there in the background that either disposes the patient to this or prevents him from doing something else?

RESIDENT: Your remark helps me to clarify again what I really wanted to say. Prognostically, an ambivalent relationship is a poor object relationship.

Our knowledge and our observation as to what extent the patient can dilute may perhaps also indicate what amount of regression we may have to tolerate. We inevitably have to take this into our calculation in deciding where we can attack the regression and not tolerate it. I am also thinking of the problem exemplified by a patient able to deny the entire hospital including the doctor and to act out his transference to some object on the *outside.*

DR. TARACHOW: You should even be able to predict historical material from the pattern of hospital behavior, if you have a good picture of the patient's hospital behavior and a genetic sense about psychopathology.

RESIDENT: One factor which was not touched on in our seminar, in addition to ego-building, is superego amelioration, especially important in certain conditions.

DR. TARACHOW: I wish you would all read the Anna Freud Symposium on "The Problems of Technique in Adult Analysis" (1954a) which I mentioned before. You will find a most interesting omission in the long discussion in which twelve or fifteen people took part. The superego is scarcely mentioned. The entire discussion is in terms of drive and defense; the superego was pretty much amalgamated into the ego as a defensive structure. The approach offered was to evaluate the dangers from the drive side, dangers from the side of defense. You alter the approach to the patient depending on the direction of the greatest danger to the patient. Is the defense going to destroy the patient or is the drive going to destroy the patient? This determines the conditions of treatment. You would all enjoy reading the Anna Freud discussion. Conceptions of treatment under varying conditions are discussed, although not specifically hospital conditions.

Before closing I want to give passing and grossly inadequate mention of the family. For one thing, the family might be more regression provoking than the hospital. The therapist should learn about the reaction of the family to the patient's absence and also about the family's capacity to change and to accept improvement and change in the patient.

This is about as far as we can go with the problem of the regression, the reality of the relationship, the acting out, and the problem of learning tolerance of the regression. We have outlined a theory of hospital treatment and the special burdens it places on the therapist.

Chapter 6

A Clinical View of the Goals of Treatment

Today we shall turn to the matter of goals of treatment or rather the limitation that one should realistically impose upon the goals. I should like to discuss a bit more specifically attitudes to specific types of problems. We will begin with the type of therapeutic ambition one might have with a psychotic patient. This would be different from and less ambitious than the goal one might have with a neurotic.

First of all, if you can help a patient over psychotic problems and leave him a psychoneurotic, that would be quite a major achievement. But there are other ways of thinking of the therapeutic ambitions one should have with a psychotic. For instance, one might pay relatively little attention to the symptomatology, but pay a great deal of attention to the patient's activities and general life development. This would hold for many neurotics, too. Don't be afraid of long-term treatment: it is no reflection on you. It is simply a clinical fact of life. I have one patient I am treating for about twenty years. His symptomatology is changed, though not too much, but it has changed. He is married, working and has a family. He is getting along, even though he has a cryptic paranoid relationship to certain sectors of reality and on occasion even with me. I consider it quite a satisfactory ongoing result. The duration of treatment is no reflection on its success. Treatment with patients like that might be intermittent. You may treat such a patient for as long as is necessary and then give the patient a conditional discharge. It need not be put that way to the patient, but he could be instructed to get along without you for as long as possible and to return if some difficulty arises.

I have had patients whom I have discharged and who see me perhaps once a year when some minor or major issue arises. I sometimes take them back into treatment, sometimes simply to clarify the outline of some current problem that is confusing to them. Sometimes they simply want to talk to me. They just want to hear my voice, and I might not hear from the patient again for several years.

This is quite a satisfactory therapeutic goal. One cannot always aim for a clear-cut finish to therapy. Sometimes you have to serve as a perpetual buttress to the ego structure of these patients. These people are at the mercy of their impulses or their enormous guilt mechanisms. This can lead them to be disastrously masochistic or suicidal; they tend to hurt themselves, ruin their jobs or their bodies. These are the people who will go on frantic bouts of absolute self-denial in one way or another. They will stop eating. They diet ruthlessly. They stop smoking. They are buffeted about by their impulses, either libidinal or sadistic, or by their excessively strict consciences. They need someone to help them corral these powerful forces within themselves which they themselves cannot control.

I have one schizophrenic woman patient whom I am keeping out of the hospital on the basis of seeing her for two minutes a week. A few years ago I made the mistake of trying to wean her; after seeing her for a year or two once a week, I successively reduced it to once in two weeks, once in three weeks, once in four weeks—I had her down to about once every six weeks when she fell apart. She landed in Rockland State Hospital. I don't repeat that mistake. Now I see her two minutes a week and she has been going like that for many years. She has a job and is keeping up a minimal social adjustment. So much for the therapeutic ambition that one might set for borderline or psychotic individuals or for someone with a very tenuous ego structure who needs your active assistance to stabilize his inner organization.

In the case of obsessional neurotics, if you can help an obsessional to become a hysteric, you are also doing quite well. I venture that this will not be accomplished too often.

There are problems of patients who act out. If you can help such an individual to develop sufficient conflict about his impulses so that he develops neurotic symptomatology, you may also rest quite content. In other words, if you can get a patient to move one notch up the ladder either in the level of his personality organization or in the level of handling reality, or in the character of his symptoms, you are doing something helpful for this patient. Conflict over the symptoms will develop in a psychopath only if he has formed a strong attachment to his therapist.

I now turn to the duration and frequency of treatment. I have already remarked that some patients have to be treated for life or for extremely long periods. In other instances, either by accident or design, one may plan on very short treatment. I once saw a man who had only three months available for treatment. He was impotent and was to be married. His potency was restored in time. Oddly enough, with certain patients, very brief therapy can be dramatically successful. The most dramatic results in my psychotherapeutic work have occurred with patients whom I treated very briefly, varying from only one or two sessions altogether to one or two sessions a week for a year or so.

But one needs luck and a bit of help in the type of problem with which one is working. You may get a case in which the forces that push the patient in the direction of health and the forces that push the patient in the direction of illness are almost equally balanced. The patient is not clear what the forces are. The forces might be hatred or rivalry paired against a powerful conscience. It is sometimes possible to clarify such a total situation for a patient in a session or two; the whole problem crystallizes quite dramatically, and the patient may abruptly take a turn in the direction of health. Not every patient needs analysis. Not every patient needs prolonged psychotherapy. Under favorable conditions a psychotherapist can be quite a magician.

But you do require a situation in which the balance within the patient is ready for you. Once in a while you and the patient are lucky enough to encounter that. Empirically, in my own experience, the problems of sexual impotence in men seem to be quite disposed to brief and dramatic cures. In several cases I can think of at this moment the chief problem was a compulsive and not hysterical one. The problem was a need for revenge against women. When the patient was able to see that this was his device for getting even, for his expression of hostility or rage, the impotence disappeared. The patient probably then took a different path for the expression of his hostility, or the forces found a balance in another way, and he developed other symptoms.

Once the potency returns, the patient will not return to you. He is afraid to come back for even a single further session. He fears that what he got from you you might take away. I received a follow-up note from the family physician of one such patient, a man whom I had seen for only a few weeks. He had since married, had several children and would not hear of me. He is terrified of even a follow-up visit.

RESIDENT: I was wondering if the setting of a fixed date for termination of treatment was the critical factor in the success of brief therapy.

DR. TARACHOW: I do not think so. Setting dates has both good and bad aspects.

RESIDENT: If you decide in the first interview on brief therapy as the treatment of choice, do you make interpretations immediately, in that session?

DR. TARACHOW: Possibly. You might start before the first session is over. You might do so if there is an acute emergency. However, you should be certain that the patient definitely wants you as his therapist. This is an important point. If you sense that the patient has not yet committed himself to treatment or to treatment by you, you should not rush in with interpretations.

Brief therapy may certainly be the method of choice in certain cases. A patient might have a personality which does not require or cannot tolerate major change or searching investigation. In some instances a single issue is disturbing the patient. The therapist does his best to crystallize that one issue for the patient. That might be all that is necessary. Every patient need not be made over: we must not play God.

RESIDENT: Does the patient's improvement depend on the accuracy of interpretation or does it stem from positive transference?

DR. TARACHOW: That varies. This question is taken up in detail in the seminar on types of psychotherapy (Chapter 4). There is such a thing as transference cure, of course; and sometimes patients who stay with you for many years are living off you on a transference basis. When I referred to crystallizing one specific issue for the patient, I was not thinking of transference cures. I was talking about offering the patient real insight into a specific troublesome sector of his life. If the patient can recrystallize certain factors within himself, he can then go ahead without too much difficulty. This can be achieved in brief therapy by brief interpretive work in which the interpretation must be quick, active, and aggressive, and to the specific point.

Oddly enough, it need not always be correct. It is better if it is correct, but occasionally you may give a patient a wrong interpretation and the patient will use it in a stabilizing, therapeutic way. Glover's (1931) ideas on inexact interpretation are relevant here.

There is another variety of patient who lives on interpretations, in a clinging way. Sometimes these patients, after treatment is over, will live in a spurious kind of health. "I've been treated by a psychiatrist. I know what's wrong with me." They are held together by clinging to a system of ideas about themselves. It is a precarious stability, but many incompletely treated people get along just that way.

In a psychoanalysis such an attitude is a resistance and should be attacked and resolved. But we are not now discussing analysis. We are discussing varieties of clinically practicable resolutions, varieties of treatment endings that might be accepted as satisfactory. We might elect such terminations or be forced to accept them.

RESIDENT: This comes back to the problem of working through. There is a sort of dichotomy here. We have heard that an interpretation by itself does not suffice. The patient has to be able to work it through. Could you give us some idea of what sort of things you *do not* have to work through? This would be an essential aspect of psychotherapy.

DR. TARACHOW: Of course. In our previous discussions of analysis versus psychotherapy we did discuss the matters we should avoid working through. The point is that in a brief, or a sectorlike interpretation, you offer only a limited issue to work through. The patients will work this through if you do not give them too much at one time and if you have stuck to the heart of the issue.

Chapter 7

Gratification and Deprivation

Today I should like to turn to a discussion of the issues of gratification versus deprivation. We are inclined to think of the treatment relationship as essentially a gratification. The beginner's first tendency is to assume that the patient views the hospital and the therapist as a source of gratification in somewhat of an oral, dependent way. Hospitalization gratifies the patient's needs for maternal care, dependency; he sheds his responsibilities; his food is made for him. He is surrounded by various mother and father figures. All this is a reassuring comfortable regression. A regression of a similar nature is offered in individual psychotherapy or analysis. Certainly in the free-association technique a regression is not only offered but insisted upon. The success of an analysis depends on the patient's ability to attain a regressed state within the bounds of an analysis, though not by acting out.

The interpretive part of the treatment is designed to help the patient understand the regression, to understand the symptoms and defenses and all the psychic developments that lie between his childish feelings and wishes and his functioning ego, i.e., the barriers, the compromises, the symptoms that have been interposed.

To be sure, the hospital does offer regressive gratifications. But the hospital also offers something else. I shall introduce that something by giving you a clinical example. I shall describe a patient and then ask you to make the proper ward assignment.

The patient is a twelve-year-old boy who was admitted with intense compulsive thoughts to hurt and to kill. The question arose regarding ward assignment. There was a choice between a children's ward, an adolescent ward, and an adult ward. The boy was so distressed and upset that the immediate consideration was to provide some relief from the tremendous pressure of these terrible compulsive thoughts. Where do you think the boy would be most comfortable—in which of the three wards?

RESIDENT: The adult ward.

DR. TARACHOW: Why? What's the reasoning?

RESIDENT: There, realistically, he would have the least opportunity to put his compulsive ideas into practice because of the fact that the people surrounding him would either be stronger or able to resist. He would not need to worry so much about his own resistance to these compulsions. He would be able to resist these impulses because the external world is much more able to resist them.

DR. TARACHOW: Precisely. The adult ward is correct. The administrative decision had to be based on an understanding of the boy's needs at the time. He did not require interpretation at that point. His superego had to be buttressed or strengthened. His superego was reinforced from the outside, by actually surrounding him with strong, aggressive men. The ward of disturbed aggressive men was most comfortable for him. He was surrounded by allies for his superego. This is one of the sources of comfort which certain patients with problems of aggression derive from hospitalization. The specific symptomatology would be immaterial, whether phobias, projections, introjections, depression. The patient needs external help in controls. Do not overlook the helpfulness of a closed ward to a disturbed patient. I understand that a technique has been worked out here in the Adolescent Pavilion in which the patients ask to be put in seclusion when they feel their controls are too shaky (Glynn, 1957).

I was also going to add that patients, no matter how psychotic they are, do respond to reality. The most violent psychotic or the most withdrawn psychotic both see reality and react to it.

I recall a most violently paranoid patient who was kept in a padded cell. No single attendant dared go near him. One day six male attendants walked into his room at once. He had to be moved. He saw the six men and his psychosis gave way. He was as meek as a lamb. He said: "Well, what do you want me to do, boys?" and he did whatever was asked of him.

RESIDENT: We had the same sort of experience in a receiving ward. There were six policemen present, but they never had to exert themselves.

DR. TARACHOW: We'll come back to that question again later. I want to continue with the thread of the original idea, namely, the fact that the patient absorbs the authority about him and responds to it. The patient uses the person about him to control his own impulses and his own behavior.

A colleague told me of an experience he had had with a patient. He was interviewing a psychotic man in a small interviewing room off a ward, when the patient suddenly got up and threatened to beat him up. The doctor, responding by intuition, stood up and, in most vicious language, told the patient to sit down. The patient sat down. This illustrates a useful way of controlling an emergency situation which could be dangerous or fatal. The theory of this involves the concept of a primitive superego still ready to incorporate new additions, i.e., a regression of the superego, if you will. There is then little difference between the external command and the inner prohibition. This young and, at the time, inexperienced psychiatrist appealed to the patient with the most archaic kind of relationship, simple brute authority. This should be considered a regressive type of gratification for the patient. This is, of course, not recommended as a daily psychotherapeutic measure, but in an emergency it has its rationale. You have to understand the patient's need stemming from his most regressed and only primitive ability to have relationships. You reinstate not only the loving relationship but also the disciplinary one. Both the love and hate are internalized by the patient and, under certain conditions, help the patient in exercising self-control.

RESIDENT: What interests me in particular are some of the milder forms of hostility, negativism. If you give a negativistic patient a firm command, the negativism often clears up.

DR. TARACHOW: Don't depend on that too much. I think it is relevant here to notice that in the institutional treatment of disturbed children quite a change is taking place from the theoretical and practical approach advocated by Aichhorn (1935), whose book *Wayward Youth* all of you should read. The permissive and loving approach is there recommended as a technique for handling aggressive acting out: you finally prove to the child that you love him no matter what. You are acceptable as a superego figure: his aggression then burns out. But recent workers with children find that children must have discipline. It helps them overcome the fear of their own aggression and to regain control of their own aggression. They welcome the commands. It is helpful to them. Melitta Sperling's (1951) and Geisel's (1951) works are relevant to this subject.

I will give another example of a patient seeking a superego alliance. A patient came to treatment because he began to have desires to make love to girls. He considered this—he was a man of about thirty-seven or thirty-eight—an illness and he came to have me help him in his struggle against these wishes. He wanted help, not to *carry out* these wishes but to *suppress* them. He was quite actively seeking a superego ally.

I shall now turn to a number of aspects of the treatment situation which offer both gratifications or deprivations and discuss some of the complications of such things as reassurance, advice, or commands.

I shall begin with the following. Supposing you have a patient who asks you question after question, in a barrage. "Doctor, when am I going to get well? What's the cause of mental illness? Is a neurosis as bad as a psychosis? How long am I going to be sick? Am I your worst patient?" He has an endless supply of such questions. What are the various things that this could mean? What could the patient be after?

RESIDENT: These questions would be to test you.

DR. TARACHOW: Yes, that's correct. That's one aspect.

RESIDENT: An attempt to run the therapeutic session according to his own will—the way he wants it to go.

DR. TARACHOW: Yes, it could be aggressive. . . .

RESIDENT: He could be asking for reassurance in a disguised way. His other questions may be disguised.

DR. TARACHOW: Yes. Any other suggestions?

RESIDENT: Well, it could be a manipulatory way of defending against your asking any questions, and it could also be a way of trying to set up a dependent situation in which he wants gratification in the answers.

DR. TARACHOW: Yes, go ahead.

RESIDENT: It could be an attempt to provoke the therapist.

DR. TARACHOW: Yes. All these answers might be correct in various instances.

RESIDENT: It could be an instance of resistance.

DR. TARACHOW: Certainly in an analysis it would be regarded as a resistance: it is an avoidance of associations. However, what I was driving at was the gratification of hearing your voice. These patients ask questions simply to hear you talk. One must not be misled by content; one must grasp the pattern of the patient's behavior. Friedlander (1942) described a most illuminating incident which bears on the type of problem I have just described. She reported the instance of a teacher who was writing a children's book. In order to check on the appeal his book might have for children he read the manuscript, chapter by chapter as he wrote it, to his class. The pupils were entranced. After the book was published, it turned out to be a complete flop. What the teacher had overlooked was the child's love of being read to.

I will take a moment to make a tangential comment about

technique. The therapist should be able to surprise the patient by interpreting the unexpected. Avoid the obvious: do not tell the patient what he already knows. The most effective interpretations are those which catch a patient unawares as you approach a problem from an unexpected area. The management of a patient hurling a barrage of questions could profit by such an approach.

There are other elementary aspects of gratification and deprivation which should not be underestimated or overlooked. Entering the room and leaving the room are important. Entering is love; leaving is abandonment. A patient turned on me in rage because I closed the door after she left. This meant I was happy to get rid of her. I am not exaggerating the importance of these factors to patients. They are very real to patients and you should be alert to all these small matters. Related to the above material would be premature mention of cure or discharge. The patient will accuse you of simply wanting to get rid of him, and he might even be right.

Another source of gratification to a patient is his knowledge of you. The ideal, the theoretical ideal of the relationship in an analytic or interpretive treatment situation, would be one in which the patient knows nothing about you, so that all his reactions are dominated by his own inner needs and his own inner problems. In psychotherapy as well as analysis it is better that knowledge about you be kept to a minimum. But that very seldom happens in actual life; patients are bound to know something about you. That is really a gratification. They love to have the knowledge that you are brilliant or that you are successful or that you are very much in demand. It's an extension of: "My father is the strongest man in the block." Depending upon the basic therapeutic position you have taken to the patient, you will either leave that situation alone and let the patient live happily with this relationship to you as a strong and omnipotent person or you will interpret it as a childish need. But the more of a dependent relationship you think is necessary, the less will you interpret and thus rob him of his picture of you as an omnipotent person.

Sometimes accidental things happen in a treatment situation which enable the patient to trust you, enable the patient really to enter the treatment. Supposing you have a patient who is troubled by murderous and aggressive impulses. Such a patient has to have the feeling that his psychiatrist is a very strong man and is not afraid of the patient in any way, does not fear the patient's aggressions, and will be able both to forbid and prevent the patient from carrying out his feared aggressive impulses. This is often seen in phobic patients; they want you to be strong. A common figure for relief of phobic anxiety is a policeman. The policeman is not only a punitive figure; he is also a loving, protective figure. Treatment can go along for a long time on an extremely tentative and inconclusive basis if the patient does not have a firm sense of the therapist's courage and strength.

I had a young male patient with strong, compulsive impulses to murder his mother. He never knew whether he could trust me or not, until one day an accidental event took place. It so happens that the bathroom in my office at that time opened off the waiting room. The patient arrived unusually early one day. I was in the bathroom urinating with the bathroom door slightly ajar. Unbeknownst to me he heard me urinate. The first remark he made in the session was, "Well, now I can trust you." I didn't know where this bolt had come from. He continued, "I heard you urinating. You were urinating in the center of the bowl. You're not afraid. If you were timid you would have urinated on the side of the bowl, making it silent, but you urinated in the center." Treatment moved along very well after this incident. I do not recommend this as a planned technique for winning the confidence of your patients—but these things can happen. Sometimes our patients understand these accidental events more promptly and precisely than we do.

I recall a paper written many years ago describing the analysis of a very withdrawn patient who could not make contact with his analyst. The patient persisted in regarding the analyst as a remote, intellectual, and forbidding figure; this went on for a long time, with no real rapport developing between patient and analyst, and no progress. The patient could not ever regard the analyst as a real person until one day in the midst of the session, the analyst inadvertently and noisily passed flatus. This was the turning point of the treatment. The treatment from then on went along in a satisfactory direction. It proved to the patient that the analyst was a real person. It enabled this withdrawn patient to feel that his analyst was a human being.

RESIDENT: There's a humorous note to this. Why does a fart smell?

DR. TARACHOW: Go ahead.

RESIDENT: So that a deaf man can also get it.

DR. TARACHOW: There's a point to this joke. What is the point of the joke?

RESIDENT: It's an aggressive act.

DR. TARACHOW: Of course, but that's not the point.

RESIDENT: It's funny, but I don't know why.

DR. TARACHOW: The point of the joke is that there is an object relationship involved in the fart; it is directed to somebody, and the other person can appreciate it. If you cannot smell it, you will hear it. If you cannot hear it, you will smell it. It is an action directed at an object. That is the point of the joke; it has to reach the other person. Of course, it's most likely an aggression. But we were discussing the problem of the analyst or psychotherapist reaching the patient as a real person. That is why this joke occurred to you in the context of this discussion. The last subject of our discussion was not aggression, but the matter of reaching someone as a real object.

A patient gleefully announced how he was going to start his analysis. He was going to get down on the couch and fart the room up. The point of this story as well as of the joke is precisely the point I am making now, the establishment of a relationship between two people. If you cannot reach someone one way, you will reach him another way.

The transference relationship, incidentally, is regarded as real. I would say it is especially real in borderline patients, in psychotics, in severe neurotics. You have to be extremely careful of what you say and the way you say it. I will give a concrete example.

I am treating a severely depressed woman who feels tremendously alone. She cannot turn to anyone. She feels she is drifting. She is hopeless. There is nobody to turn to and nothing to hold on to. In a moment in which my love of humanity overcame technique, I said, "Well, you do have someone to hold on to. Hold on to me in the treatment." How do you think she reacted to my remark? She came back the next session with a very specific reaction to what I had said.

RESIDENT: She thought how long treatment would last. Sooner or later it would have to end too. It would be unsafe for her to do this. She wondered how long you would be interested in her.

DR. TARACHOW: That's close; go ahead.

RESIDENT: To enter some kind of sexual relationship.

DR. TARACHOW: You've almost got it.

RESIDENT: Well, perhaps anger, perhaps contempt for being willing to sell your love.

DR. TARACHOW: The answer falls somewhere between the two of you. The patient returned to the next session full of rage, bitterness, and disappointment. I had teased her. I had said, "Hold on to me," but I had not really meant it literally. The point was that she really did want to hold on to me, but had she taken my invitation at face value I would have rebuffed her. She wanted to make love to me. She said, "You misled me." I had issued an invitation which I was not going to honor. My attempt to make her feel better by offering this kind of reassurance simply infuriated her and enraged and depressed her even more. I am making a point of this because the transference is real to these patients. This patient would even reproach me for smiling at her in greeting. She regarded the smile as an insincere seduction which she was being asked to take at face value.

You are more real to your patient than you think. When you shake hands with a hysteric, it is a sexual overture. When you shake hands with an obsessional neurotic it is a challenge. With a paranoiac it is an assault. Every contact has its own reality. Glover (1928) discusses the importance of these matters.

Incidentally, if you discuss the first few years of practice with psychotherapists who have been practicing for many years they will tell you they did their best work in the first few years. Why should that be?

RESIDENT: They were more involved.

DR. TARACHOW: Yes. They were more enthused, more eager, more interested. They have not become fatigued or bored. There is also another aspect. As the years of practice go on, the therapist finds himself contending with the ingratitude, the spitefulness, the hostilities of patients. This could slowly take its toll and in subtle ways reduce the burning enthusiasm of the therapist. The patients know the degree of the therapist's interest and respond to this knowledge. Berman (1949) has discussed this subject in term of the dedication of the analyst.

Let us turn for a few moments to the problem of the complications of reassurance. This is a subject which might even be studied experimentally. We will consider giving reassurance regardless of the source of the patient's anxiety. You exercise your magical knowledge of the future and say to the patient, "Everything will be alright. Don't worry."

Such an entry into a patient's life has definite sequelae and definite dangers. The sequelae can be seen quite clearly and can be easily predicted. They fall into one or another variety of homosexual reaction. Reassurance provokes either homosexual dreams or anxieties or masochistic or paranoid reactions. These will be seen without fail. When you offer reassurance you are adopting an omnipotent, Godlike role with all the possible complications of such a role. You are implicitly asking the patient to submit himself to your will and knowledge. Careful attention to the immediately subsequent material will confirm this. This is a clinical sequence which could readily lend itself to experimental study. The moment you play an active, aggressive role in the patient's life you will provoke an unconscious homosexual reaction. In some cases this might be a welcome development. In instances of treatment organized in a supportive way the patient may be wed to you in an unconscious homosexual bond. The patient might welcome it. The therapist should be on the alert for the development of such material. In some cases the therapist may choose to neglect it; in some cases he may choose to interpret such material. The therapist must remember that the moment he starts tampering with a patient's future he is taking an aggressive homosexual position. This sequence should be borne in mind; let's call it a complication of reassurance.

RESIDENT: What would happen with a patient of the opposite sex?

DR. TARACHOW: It then becomes a sexual assault. It is treated as a sexual assault by either sex. But, putting a woman into a passive relationship is not quite as dangerous as doing this with a man. The woman's sexual direction is already accepted as passive. What will provoke a paranoid response in a man may provoke a hysterical response in a woman.

RESIDENT: Suppose the therapist takes an active role with a catatonic female patient who has great difficulty in forming object relationships. She may develop a romantic interest in her therapist. Is that a signal to stop?

DR. TARACHOW: If you know what's going on you need not necessarily stop. Assuming that you are not seduced by the patient's reactions and have a clear idea of the sequence of events you need not stop. The patient's imagined love relationship to you might be a force rescuing her from her inner reality and helping turn her interests in an outward direction. To be sure, this might all still be greatly under the pressure of inner fantasies. In a hospital you might permit a larger degree of such responses. The important thing is to know what you are doing and what the meaning of the patient's specific response is.

It is possible to regulate the degree of gratification that you are offering the patient. You might offer this to the patient for the sake of adhering to reality via the interest in you. The therapist might be the only route to reality.

Let me give you a crude example of dosage of transference gratification. A woman patient makes a trip to Paris and returns with ten new hats. She comes to her first session wearing a new hat. I make a comment to the patient. The patient returns with a new hat each subsequent session. What would you do?

RESIDENT: You shouldn't interpret if it is a psychotic woman. If anything, compliment her.

DR. TARACHOW: I did, but after a certain point I decided to put a halt to the intensifying romance. Only after I had complimented her on at least a half dozen hats did I offer an interpretation. I pointed out the extent to which she was seeking my interest and admiration. After this intervention she stopped appearing in new hats, but she was disappointed and unhappy. You will note I did not offer the interpretation at the appearance of the first hat. I first permitted the patient to get a good deal of pleasure out of the experience. I permitted her transference gratification up to a point. When I thought it was beginning to be more troublesome than helpful I put a stop to it. The interpretation was a deprivation; in fact, it was a command to begin to tolerate some deprivation.

Such a psychotherapeutic approach requires knowledge of what is going on and the ability of the therapist to resist the gratifications inherent in the romantic tensions of the situation. One of the tremendous gratifications of being a psychiatrist is the tendency of patients to fantasy about you. The therapist is in danger of luxuriating in the patient's fantasies about him. You will find you have every virtue under the sun until your obsessional patient goes to work on you.

RESIDENT: The danger of being seduced by a patient is often discussed. I don't really see any danger. Except for failure of interpretation I don't see how anything real could happen.

DR. TARACHOW: You're wrong. Just as transference is the source of danger, so is the countertransference. Psychiatrists have been seduced by female patients, and by male patients too, I suppose. On the patient's side there are many dangers. A patient may act out her transference love for a therapist by having an affair on the outside. I know of a therapist who became angry and perhaps jealous of his female patient for doing just that, and threw her out of treatment instead of interpreting the transference acting out. The therapist acted like a rejected lover. There may be another type of complication for the patient. If the patient has a therapist of the same sex, he may find it necessary to have a heterosexual affair to defend himself against the power of the unconscious homosexual transference love. There are many dangers. Take neither transference nor countertransference lightly.

I have had patients roll about on the floor, writhe, and hiss at me: patients do all sorts of things in a pathological transference situation. The therapist might even be afraid or unable to cut into the manifestations. You will recall this is what caused Breuer to stop working with Freud. Breuer could not tolerate the transference love. He took it at face value, and not as a further instrument of treatment.

There are other, subtler types of seductions into which a therapist might be trapped. Sadomasochistic relationships are especially enticing. The patient might lead the therapist into mounting reactions of anger, irritation, or moral indignation: the therapist might be drawn into hostile interventions, well rationalized. The therapist might label as interpretation what is really discipline or reproach or punishment or permission or even enticement. I offered an interpretation to a patient that a certain constellation of material indicated he wanted to divorce his wife. He promptly did so and broke off further treatment.

RESIDENT: I can recall a bad situation in which I participated. A tense schizophrenic patient told me how he had gotten angry at someone and then he quietly asked me if I thought he was homicidal. I replied, "No." The patient went into a rage. Looking back, I can see that this might have represented my homosexual attack on him, since I was reassuring him. I implicitly said, "Don't worry."

DR. TARACHOW: Yes, simply passing judgment on a patient is an aggression against him, but this could have been even more complicated than what you suggest. The patient might have been afraid you were *underestimating* the dangers with which he was struggling. He fears he is homicidal; and I would say that, latently, it is a justifiable fear. He was really afraid he could not control it. When you underestimated his danger he became terrified and angry since you were of no help. You did not even recognize his plight.

RESIDENT: He actually said that. But I wonder if there was a homosexual element, too.

DR. TARACHOW: Oh, yes. The moment you make a positive remark to a patient you put him in a passive position to you.

RESIDENT: How would you have handled that?

DR. TARACHOW: My response would be in the following vein, "Your fear that you are homicidal is a problem that we have to talk about some more so that we can understand it and help you with it." Such an approach is indirect reassurance since you are not treating too casually his fear of being homicidal. You accept it as a real problem but have not been too aggressive toward the patient. You must be careful not to be too aggressive to the patient. Reassurance is an aggression in the sense that it robs the patient of his free will. You rob the patient of his own judgment about himself, even if his judgment is a self-critical one.

It is best to be neutral, to offer help. All rules have exceptions. In certain problems it is quite necessary to step in and become part of the patient's functioning ego.

RESIDENT: Did the lady with the hats turn to someone else in her disappointment?

DR. TARACHOW: This patient was given to fluctuating paranoid reactions. I could keep her paranoid responses to a minimum by keeping her transference nearness to me at a minimum. If I let her get too close, her paranoia would be stimulated. It is quite a delicate matter of showing the patient you are interested, permitting the patient to get some gratification from you, but not permitting the relationship to become too intense or turbulent or troublesome.

There are all sorts of gratifications, such as giving a patient a cigarette or telling him the time. You may hear the most absurd questions, such as, "Where is the nearest bus stop?" You must decide how to deal with such questions in terms of the individual's pathology. One device patients resort to is the visual caress. Some patients will not leave after a session until their eyes have met yours. Patients also take your failure to speak as a rejection.

A last remark about interpretation as deprivation. Any interpretation is a deprivation, no matter what the direction of the attitude interpreted. The patient wants to keep all his infantile wishes. There is a perpetual battle between patient and therapist, the patient guarding his defenses and his infantile wishes and the therapist attempting to rob the patient. More often than not the patient is unwilling to make the effort of renunciation which you are demanding of him.

Chapter 8

Object Relations

An early estimate of the character of a patient's object relations is of crucial importance. I regard the capacity for good object relations as a critical prognostic sign; regardless of what the clinical psychiatric diagnosis might be.

There are schizoid or schizophrenic patients who give a history of behavior which creates the impression that they have adequate or extensive relationships with people. This should be scrutinized most carefully. They may be engaged in a busy but spurious kind of relationship. They delude themselves and others into assuming they have many friends and many activities. Withdrawn or schizophrenic individuals occasionally engage people in deep conversation. A busy conversation is often accepted as a substitute for a real relationship. It is often only an attempt at a relationship. One must differentiate between real and spurious relationships.

A male patient had the habit of addressing all men by the same given name and also women by the same given name. Although he was seemingly in contact with everyone, this was his defense against forming a real object relationship with any one specific person. He was adopting the general as a defense. When I began systematically to attack this defense he left treatment.

There is a similiar situation with manics. A conversation

between two manics is not really a conversation. It is two monologues going on at the same time. The two manics are both tormented by constant inner pressure and are responding not to inner content or real contact, but only to the most external and superficial stimulation. This is of course the manic defense against pain and depression. You will find that a real conversation is quite rare, even among "normal" people. Each participant in a conversation pursues his own train of thought.

RESIDENT: Could you give us some criteria for a good object relationship?

DR. TARACHOW: Yes. I would say strong interest in, affection for another person, a willingness to give up something for another person, a willingness to spend time with the other person, a willingness to assume responsibility for another person. It is quite an achievement to have real interest in someone else and be able to give up something for the other person. You will find in your neurotic patients that very few of them have really attained that level of maturity. In a good object relationship love has won out over hatred. One hears so much, in the description of patients, about difficulties in expressing aggression, and so little about difficulty in expressing love. This latter is really much more important, since the prospects of cure depend on the capacity for love and not on the capacity for aggression.

Sometimes a wife or a husband is only an intermediate object. The real object is someone else; for example, a man married a girl because she had a brother. He had been an only child and all his life had wanted a brother; at a certain point he married the first girl he found who had a brother. There was plenty of trouble, of course, later. To his dismay, the brother moved out of town.

It is easier to say what a bad object relationship is than to say what a good one is, but I have given you some elementary qualities. You may be surprised at the difficulties you will have in getting people to give up their claims on their objects. A relationship can be a relationship of claim and be mistaken for love. I treated a man whose mother had buttered his bread all his life. He had never buttered a piece of bread. He married and, of course, expected his wife to butter his bread; she wanted to be his wife and not his mother. They fought over that for years. For this man it was quite an accomplishment, though a reluctant one, when he finally buttered a slice of bread for himself.

As you see there can be many kinds of object relationships of an infantile kind.

RESIDENT: Would you list some more of the distinctions between people who apparently can make just one intense kind of object relationship, and others? For example, two people are married and love each other very much, but then build a wall around themselves. They apparently cannot make object relationships outside. This seems to be somewhat of a contradiction, though. If a person has a capacity to make object relations, then he makes it with all people with whom he comes in contact.

DR. TARACHOW: That is not so. Sometimes they have made it with one object and that one only with great difficulty. Such people often wind up with depressions because the one object represents the entire world, and if they lose that, they are in dire straits.

It is healthier to have more than one object. Why do children love to have big families; why do children love to have grandparents? It is a good thing for a child to have a big family, and to have many objects. It gives them a better base, more roots in object relations, and it makes them feel much more secure. It develops capacity for object relations. It gives them greater ground for the spread of ambivalent feelings: ambivalence is then less dangerous to the child.

RESIDENT: Somehow the big qualitative difference seems to be no object relations versus object relations. It seems to me if you can make one good object relationship—

Dr. Tarachow: The man or the woman who does that is still in a precarious spot.

Resident: I have such a patient who made her first object relationship at the age of twenty-one. It was an all-or-none proposition. A Jewish girl had become very much interested in a non-Jewish boy, contemplating marriage. Terrific conflicts arose because she was raised in a very religious atmosphere. This boy died: nine months later she was still suicidal. All her eggs were in one basket; she still mourns. She says, "I have nothing left in life."

Dr. Tarachow: One should question whether or not that was a good object relationship to begin with.

Resident: What about children who make up fantasies that they are orphans?

Dr. Tarachow: That's another matter. That has to do with transient feelings of being rejected by the parents. If you have a young man or a girl patient who goes off to college and can only make one friend, there is potential trouble.

A stamp collection can be an object. Humans can be collected in the way that stamps are collected, of course. One can collect friends that way. I treated an obsessional patient who did the following. He had a list of his friends. Not only did he have such an accurate, complete list, but he had them graded as to whether they were good friends or only intermediately good friends. This method of collecting objects is similar to collecting stamps, to hoarding and other anal preoccupations; it is an attempt to have object relations in a very anxious, infantile way. I have another patient who has lists of all his possessions. He has a list of all his money, his shirts, underwear, shoes, friends, etc. He has his friends categorized into sexes, age groups, etc. Another patient kept a written list of all the flattering and complimentary remarks people had made to her. These are examples of a highly compulsive, hoarding type of object relations. A patient treats his objects in the only way he can.

You have a wonderful technical device at hand—the transference, the patient's relationship to you. Depending on the pathology, you either use or create the relationship to you, and you interpret how the patient behaves to you. The patient may behave very spitefully to you. He may be very hostile or very meek, or he may be very loving or very affectionate. If the patient has no object relationship to you at all (we are talking here, of course, of schizophrenia), you must try to create one.

With certain psychotic patients I walk about the room. The patient sits in the chair and I walk around. I stand up. I will move all the time. I sit on my desk. I sit on my chair. I thus reassure the patient against all his paranoid anxieties, against all his anxieties about objects, by putting myself in a place where he can see me and hear me and almost touch me. I thrust myself upon him. The principal point in this technique is to thrust myself upon the patient as an object. This approach has its complications, too, but it is effective.

I made a house call a few years ago. It was to see a young boy of about twenty who had not left his bedroom in ten months. He had not had a haircut in all that time. Would some of you hazard a guess what his hobby was? This was a schizophrenic boy, of course.

RESIDENT: Exploring?

DR. TARACHOW: He had not left his bedroom for ten months. He was a radio ham; from the description of other radio hams that I got from this young man, it seems to be a hobby wonderfully suited to schizoid people.

The radio hams live out schizophrenic delusions of communication through the ether. They are constantly getting waves through the air and talking to people and getting messages. They materialize a delusional existence. He had close pals in Australia, in England, in South America, but none on his block. He had a powerful set, for receiving and sending: he would have busy conversations all night long with people in California, in Alaska, but he never spoke a word to a neighbor face to face.

These people are quite interesting and quite sick. At any rate, I made the effort to reach this boy. I visited him and as a result he came out of isolation and visited me for many years. Now he has a job; he repairs and services aeroplane radios. He is still communicating through the skies, but at least at a level that is much more socialized and realistic.

Chapter 9

Problems Relating to Administration

Today I would like to bring up the problem of the relationship of the resident to the patient as complicated by the problems of hospital administration, discipline, and related matters. This is best done by comparing the two principal contrasting configurations which might be established in a mental hospital. These two are:

1. The role of the resident is strictly confined to therapy, and all matters of discipline, administration, punishments, curtailment or granting of privileges are sharply reserved for administrative officers.

2. The resident is not only the therapist but also the source of administration, discipline, granting and withholding of privileges, etc.

We shall begin with the separation of functions, that is, the therapeutic from the administrative. Will some one tell me what the advantages of the separation of functions might be?

RESIDENT: It would help in the development of the positive transference. The patient would like his therapist more, and this would make working through and developing material much easier.

DR. TARACHOW: That is correct. Anything else?

RESIDENT: It would serve as a check against acting out on the part of the resident. Varying with his emotional reactions to the patient, he might be tempted to reward or discipline his patients too readily if he were also the source of discipline.

DR. TARACHOW: Very good. Anything else?

RESIDENT: The separation would tend to check the patient's tendency to confuse reality with fantasy about the therapist. If the therapist were also the administrator, it would facilitate the development of an omnipotent picture of the therapist.

RESIDENT: It seems to me that it would be better to keep the two functions separated. The therapist could still work through the hostile aspects of the transference by specifically doing things, gratifying or depriving the patient transference-wise so that the hostility would be elicited and then worked out.

DR. TARACHOW: I'm not sure I agree. We are discussing the theory of the effects of all the therapist's actions upon the patient. We are not out to equip you with a bag of tricks to use with the patient, but we do want you to have a thorough understanding of your impact upon the patient. Provocative or manipulative devices should be used only after you have had a great deal of experience, and I certainly do not recommend them now. Of course, certain accidental things do happen, and your knowledge should be sufficient to understand and even make use of such events.

RESIDENT: Another reason, it seems to me, why the two functions should be separated is that it is a better preparation for life. After all there are some people the patient will like, others he will hate; this is the configuration such a split hospital setup provides.

DR. TARACHOW: Such a split in object relations is not a better preparation for reality. Furthermore, the hospital framework in general does not correspond to reality. To begin with, split in object choice is more difficult to repair psychotherapeutically than ambivalence to a single object. A man might need two women, one whom he hates and one whom he loves; another man may need two women, one is treated as the desexualized mother and the other is used for sexual (regarded as debased) pleasures. In contrast to patients with such a split in object choice, there is the patient who has both these conflicting attitudes to the *same* woman. The patients in the first group are more difficult to cure. The ambivalence *had originally been* directed to one woman, and in treatment has to be *brought back* to one woman again for fusion or reconciliation of the mixed feelings. So is it also with our hospital cases. If we want to prepare our patients for better object relations on the outside, we at least have to give them some experience in reconciling all mixed feelings in the transference to the therapist. This is accomplished by directing all ambivalent feelings to the one person of the therapist. This is a better preparation for life than the administrative split. In the configuration of the administrative split, the hospital would offer a real decompensation, at least for a time. Of course, it brings up the entire issue of what type of patients should be treated in one way or the other. Perhaps the answer should be that at the outset with all our cases there should be a complete split, but as the patients improve, they should then be forced to deal with the therapist as administrator also. They would then be forced to work through the other problems such a relationship would elicit, the aggression, the masochism, the homosexuality, i.e., all aspects of the ambivalence directed to the one person of the therapist.

RESIDENT: What about the suggested technique that the therapist be quite aggressive with the patient? This must provoke the aggression, the masochism or the homosexuality of the patient, all aspects of the ambivalence.

DR. TARACHOW: We have to draw a distinction. In some cases we act aggressively and establish a latent homosexual or masochistic reaction and plan the therapeutic result based on this. This becomes the treatment relationship. To an extent this is Rosen's technique too. You know, he is quite active. He tells his patients that he is father or mother or God, and they should obey him, and they do. In the psychotherapy as we see it, we may not want to use the latent homosexual response as the vehicle of treatment, but only as material to work with. Some patients have a much better and stronger ego structure, so that the homosexual or masochistic response becomes the working material of the psychotherapy. However, this is by no means absolute. In some cases we will want to use the unconscious homosexual attachment as the vehicle or basis of psychotherapeutic "cure."

Do not become involved in collusion with a patient against the administration. There might be occasions when you will be tempted to do so. You will only join the patient in his acting out and you will lose a clear picture of the transference relationship.

RESIDENT: There are situations, though, which make this impossible if one wants to preserve the confidence of the patient. In a therapeutic session a patient might tell me he violated certain administrative rules. I can't turn him in for punishment which would result in certain privileges being taken away. He would never take me into his confidence again.

DR. TARACHOW: As a group you might be interested in hearing about an experience (or unintended experiment) at this hospital several years ago. At one point the Medical Director felt quite dissatisfied with the problem of week-end paroles. It was felt that these week ends at home provided an unsupervised opportunity for the patient to do too much unobserved acting out. The Medical Director decided to cut down drastically the week-end home visits of all patients in the hospital. Furthermore, it was also decided that, contrary to prior procedure, the individual resident, administering the psychotherapy, be the one to inform the patient that his week-end visits were being curtailed. Previously, the administrative head of the hospital had always carried out such unpleasant announcements to the patients, sparing the transference relationship to the therapist this extra burden of the patient's reactions, disappointment, rage, masochism, etc.

The reasoning behind this change was as follows: it was felt that there was too strong a tendency among the therapists (residents) to identify themselves with the patients and become pleaders with the Medical Director for the patients directly in their care. This tendency to become a pleader for the patient was partly due to identification with the patient, but also probably due to a desire to have as strong a positive transference with the patient as possible, and perhaps even an aversion to dealing with the hostile aspects of the patient's reactions. If the patient felt that his therapist was also his defender and pleader with the Director of the hospital (the source of hospital discipline), then the positive feelings would tend to come to the fore and the negative transference might be inhibited from appearing at all.

In the personal psychoanalysis of an extramural psychoneurotic patient, the analyst, through his intimate contact with much data from the patient is able to identify and analyze both the positive and negative sides of the transference relationship without having to provoke the negative by being the messenger of bad news to his patient. But in a hospital, and in psychotherapy, such a thorough analysis may never come to pass, particularly if the patient can separate his doctors into good (his therapist) and bad (the Director of the hospital). Bearing this in mind, it was felt that such a dichotomy exposed the patient to a discharge from the hospital with his hostile transferences unexposed and not worked through, and perhaps even more liable to recurrence of his illness. It also exposed the therapist in training to a one-sided tendency to seek out positive transferences and to rely on the Director to help him avoid negative feelings in his patient.

The new policy regarding week ends brought quick reactions, both from the residents and the patients. If anything, the complaints from the residents were the louder: the psychological burden of the new policy was harder for the residents to bear than for the patients. The residents now had to bear the brunt of the patients' hostility or masochism. At one of the then-current continuous case seminars for the residents, the expressions of rage at the Director were quite vociferous. The entire preceding reasoning was clarified for them, and by and large they were then willing to accept the more complete burden that was being imposed upon them. The clinical material appearing in a patient who was discussed at that seminar served to corroborate that this new policy would bring material into the treatment sessions which otherwise might have remained hidden. This particular patient, immediately after he had been notified by his (resident) therapist that his week-end parole was revoked, responded with a dream which brought out his masochistic homosexual attitudes to the therapist, material which had not appeared until that time.

Resident: We were discussing a patient who reported to his therapist that he had broken a rule, a rule which the therapist did not think would endanger him personally. I think of a specific patient who went off the grounds and had a milk shake in town. The question arises as to what to do about it. I felt I would not report this to the administration on the grounds that if I did, I would also choke off communication between the patient and me. Why should he then tell me what goes on? He feared not only my disapproval but the actual resulting discipline.

Resident: What I've done in cases like that is to tell the patient that if somebody caught him violating a rule, he would then be subject to whatever punishments there were.

Dr. Tarachow: Well, what do most of you do? Do you do the same?

Resident: This patient went out for a milk shake. Another patient is liable to obtain barbiturates. What is to be done in such a situation?

Dr. Tarachow: The absolutely neutral position which a

therapist takes on the outside is not necessarily the only or best position for the therapist to take in an institutional setting. You do not have the same conditions prevailing. With some patients you are neutral, but at the same time you know very well that you're going to exercise your judgment. If the patient went off the grounds and acted out, possibly to his own danger or the danger of another patient, you would have to step in. It is difficult to tell where you should draw the line.

RESIDENT: It seems to me that there is a lot of difference between a patient going out to have a milk shake and one going out in search for barbiturates. On the outside when a patient will come to you and tell you that he has bought a gun, I wonder how neutral the therapist in private practice would be.

DR. TARACHOW: I shall tell you how unneutral a therapist can be. I know of a therapist who practices with a pistol under his seat. It is not funny. It so happens that this therapist is a man who has a gift for treating borderline and psychotic patients, a gift for treating them under ambulatory conditions. But at the same time, he doesn't want to be killed in the process; he knows that once in a while some dangerous transference provocation will arise and he might have to protect himself.

RESIDENT: But he's not acting as the psychiatrist; he's acting in an emergency situation to protect himself.

DR. TARACHOW: That is so, but a patient may walk in with a gun. You may be able to coax the patient to give the gun to you. Years ago at one of the classes at the New York Psychoanalytic Institute, an instructor asked his class, "Supposing your patient gets off the couch and climbs up on the window and is going to jump out. What are you going to do?" Some of them said, "Don't do anything. You'll spoil the transference." "Well, spoil the transference and have a live patient," say I.

You must remember that in an institution, your patients are

sicker; there comes a point at which you may have to step in.

In the treatment of severe problems of acting out on the outside, sometimes the only possibility of success is to permit the patient to run all sorts of risks, even to being arrested. For example, a patient steals in department stores. You will get nowhere if you tell him, "Don't; try not to steal." He will simply go out and steal even more. Successes with such problems are quite limited, but in order to preserve even the limited chance of success, you must be absolutely neutral.

However, do not confuse the ideal unsullied transference relationship of analytic therapy on the outside with the treatment relationship in a hospital. The whole point of raising the issue of administrative vs. therapeutic considerations is to enable you to know what you are doing, i.e., when to divide the roles and when not to divide the roles. In some instances, you may keep the role of the good friend and the good therapist and the good father and the good mother; and in other instances, you will exercise controls. For example, you might have a hypomanic who will go out and commit a variety of irrational or dangerous acts.

RESIDENT: One problem we run into is that the administration itself might not be entirely consistent. Sometimes the patient is caught and punished and sometimes not. Sometimes they're punished in one way, sometimes another. There is a set of rules known to all. No one may break the rules. All sorts of complications result if one patient is punished and another not.

DR. TARACHOW: That would be a real problem. Uniform enforcement of rules helps because it structures the treatment conditions for all the residents in a consistent way, even if the structure might be disagreeable to one resident or another. If it is structured in some consistent way, then that structure can be used as a frame of reference both for resident and patient. You will notice I am emphasizing the uniform structure in terms of the *residents*.

RESIDENT: Patients compare therapists and find that one therapist manages to get more privileges for his patient than another. There is injustice. There are times when some patients get privileges while others do not; but this is the way of the world and of the hospital administration.

DR. TARACHOW: No, that's no good.

RESIDENT: Reality involves injustice at times.

DR. TARACHOW: No, no. That's bad psychotherapeutic technique. You are entering into collusion with the patient in his complaints against the administration and that's terrible technique.

RESIDENT: But we are discussing reality.

DR. TARACHOW: You must stick to the total hospital structure. You are too ready to sympathize with the patient. The patient is in a hospital, and that is the reality he has to understand and to which he has to adapt. You can't say, "It is reality that the administration here vacillates from day to day." You would then be reinforcing whatever unresolved sibling rivalries the patient has. You would be telling him, "Yes, some children are treated better than others." You would be supporting him in his infantile hatreds.

RESIDENT: But the administration may be wrong.

DR. TARACHOW: The administration is wrong in not acting like the administration said it would. *You* have to be consistent in your attitude to the hospital rules. In extramural treatment, the consistency is your neutrality. In a hospital situation, the consistency is with the administrative structure, a certain division of authority. That is the structure you must adhere to, just as in analysis you stick to your absolute neutrality. In a hospital treatment, you stick to something else—a partly custodial and supervisory attitude. That is the structure of a hospital. Don't confuse an extramural analysis or extramural psychotherapy with hospital psychotherapy. Hospital patients have been acting out, have been unable to compose a structure of their own. They have been unable to resist either their impulses or their self-punishment tendencies. You are not an independent therapist. You are an arm of the hospital. The patient lacks ego strength; the hospital supplies a structured situation, and you are an arm of that structured situation. You must stick with the administration, even if administration errs on occasion in the carrying out of its own rules.

RESIDENT: We sometimes discuss these difficulties with our supervisors and try to get them to use their influence to change the rule in question. Or I have asked my supervisor to plead with the administration for an exception.

DR. TARACHOW: The plea to the supervisor to try to get a rule changed is not bad. The rule would then be changed for everybody. The resident must avoid the position of being the patient's advocate. Don't quarrel with the administration for the patient, because to a certain degree you are an arm of the administration, no matter how thoroughly separated the therapeutic and administrative roles might be.

Chapter 10

The Structure of the Treatment Relationship

Today we shall take up some problems arising out of the structure of the treatment relationship. By this I mean the time of appointments, the days, the keeping or breaking of appointments. We shall deal not with physical structure but with the details arising out of the relationship, the time arrangement and the various situations which arise with reference to this structure.

You should be able to make use of all accidental and current events. Perhaps one of the most important of these would be the matter of vacations. Why should you tell a patient in advance that you are going on a vacation? What is the rationale?

RESIDENT: You begin to work through the patient's feeling of rejection or other reactions. In the succeeding sessions he can tell you about it. You will not have the time to get to these reactions if you spring the vacation on the patient at the last moment.

DR. TARACHOW: Yes. Any other?

RESIDENT: In any normal situation where you are working with someone regularly it would be polite to inform him of an impending vacation.

DR. TARACHOW: It's polite, of course, but it has more practical facets too. You give yourself the opportunity to work through the patient's reaction, or to work through something else—the patient's lack of reaction. I would be even more suspicious of a lack of reaction. Patients take your absence in a variety of different ways. The most usual one is rejection, but there are others. In what other way might a patient see your going off on a vacation?

RESIDENT: Great relief.

DR. TARACHOW: Yes, great relief. That's one insult they throw at you, that they'll save trouble or money, but there's another, an even more important issue.

RESIDENT: They are very understanding and happy for you. They understand you need a vacation. You worked so hard.

DR. TARACHOW: Yes, but beware of pity, the moment the patient starts feeling sorry for you, be careful. No, there's another.

RESIDENT: Sexual acting out.

DR. TARACHOW: Sexual or any other type of acting out. Often you come back from a vacation only to find that a patient has married, or had his first sexual experience, or quit a job. You find that every once in a while the patient will take advantage of your vacation in that way. When the cat's away, the mice will play.

RESIDENT: There could be an attempt to provoke you.

DR. TARACHOW: What type of problem would you expect to find when treatment is resumed? There are certain issues that I have seen repeatedly.

RESIDENT: The patient will reproach you. While he suffered, you enjoyed yourself.

DR. TARACHOW: All your answers are correct, but not what I want at this moment. I'll help you out a bit. We will now talk about men patients. Sometimes at the resumption of treatment the patient comes back in a tremendous panic. All his symptoms have violently flared up and there is great anxiety. You find a homosexual panic upon your return. The patient had been relieved of the transference tensions and relieved of his feelings to you; upon the resumption of treatment after your vacation (or the patient's vacation, for that matter), there may be a heightening of all feelings for you. I see this quite regularly and have come to expect it. I have certain expectations when I announce a vacation: there are generally one or two reactions: either that of being abandoned, with depression and hatred, or the impulse to act out, especially sexually. This is upon my leaving. Upon resumption I look for the signs of homosexual panic and fairly undisguised symptoms of homosexual anxieties or sometimes one or another defensive reaction. These might be undue aggressiveness, paranoid feelings, or masochistic symptoms, and a need to break off treatment. Women patients are prone to react with an intensification of their incestuous sexual wishes in your direction.

RESIDENT: Why should the male patients go into a panic when you return?

DR. TARACHOW: Because for the duration of your vacation they've been relieved of their feelings to you; the return is similar to the return to a lover, an unconscious homosexual provocation.

RESIDENT: What sort of patients are you talking about?

DR. TARACHOW: Any male patient, neurotic or psychotic. Voltaire was wrong. He is supposed to have said, "Put two men in a room and they'll talk about women." I would say, "Put two men in a room, and there's a homosexual problem." When the treatment resumes, the homosexual tensions arise.

There is one useful way in which vacations can be utilized structurally in an over-all treatment planning. That is to plan discharges with references to vacations. Years ago I learned from Bertram D. Lewin that vacations are an excellent way of setting up either definite or tentative discharges of patients. Summer vacation is a natural time. I've set up discharges as much as six months in advance, giving the patient plenty of time to work through the problem of feeling abandoned by the termination of treatment. June seems to be a logical month. Patients like discharge in June much better than at Christmastime because everyone's going away at that time and things get broken up anyway. Summertime is also a good testing of the patient's ability to get along without you. If they can't get along without you over the summer, then they come back in the fall. In private practice most of you will find it quite useful to utilize vacations in this way.

Another facet in the structure is the matter of missed sessions. Let us assume a patient misses a session, for a reason that he cannot help, such as a tornado or a storm. At the end of the month you do not charge him for the missed session. What reaction would you expect the patient to have if you excuse the patient and do not include that session in the bill? Would you expect him to be pleased or displeased? This sounds like a trick question, and it is. Give me the reasoning on all sides. Some patients would like it. Some patients are unhappy about it. Can you conceive of why a patient might not like it?

RESIDENT: An orally dependent patient might take it as an affront to his newly found independence.

DR. TARACHOW: That's true. Some patients who are trying very hard to emancipate themselves, to be independent, will insist on paying. They reject all favors.

But there's another type of problem in which a patient wants to pay for that session and feels rejected because you do not let him pay. Some patients have the feeling that if they pay for the missed session, then in a certain sense they have been with you. If you do not accept payment for that session, they feel they have been pushed out of your life for that particular period of time. I have had patients who reacted with great disappointment when I did not charge for a particular missed session. They experienced it as a rejection. They felt that for that time they had *not* had me; they had lost me. They would have willingly paid so that they could have had me in their life, so to speak, for that particular time.

RESIDENT: Would the patient feel this quite consciously or is it deeply buried?

DR. TARACHOW: I got this as an immediate conscious complaint from a patient. "I'm sorry you didn't charge me because I now feel that I had one session less with you last month. I was with you less."

RESIDENT: They must be terribly out of contact with reality.

DR. TARACHOW: Not at all. Do not underestimate your importance to your patient. The moment treatment starts the patient has you in the way that he wants, i.e., in the kind of object relationship he is able to have. He possesses you, and he wants you all to himself, and he wants as much of you as possible. He would like to be your only patient, and if he grudgingly allows you to have a practice apart from him, the least he wants is not to lose any sessions. The actual payment of money becomes a minor matter. The money itself, after a while, becomes quite immaterial and is not brought up often except on an occasion such as we have been discussing, i.e., to reproach you for not having charged for a missed session. You must be prepared for any kind of reaction. That one caught me by surprise.

RESIDENT: In what situation would you forgive the fee for a given session?

DR. TARACHOW: That depends on the type of treatment situation you have and it depends on the severity of the illness. If the patient is in analysis, the patient is expected to pay for all sessions. Some analysts insist on payment, even if the patient is sick, but other analysts do not. There is no absolute rule. If I am convinced a patient was physically sick, I do not charge for the time missed. Patients do pay for sessions missed on account of business commitments or business travel. Every time you do a favor for a patient, you give the patient a burden of guilt. You must remember that. Kindness plays peculiar tricks in analysis or psychotherapy.

The apparent cruelty of an analytic relationship, or of a psychotherapeutic relationship which is carried along interpretive lines, has sense. If you make allowances for every minor illness of the patient, the patient is given a burden of guilt over having robbed you of money. He becomes anxious over whether he is or is not sick. But if he pays for all sessions, the slate is clear and the work proceeds better. He can then be sick without being troubled by it.

Doing favors for a psychiatric patient is a questionable practice, because every favor you do, no matter what it might be, raises some degree of guilt in the patient for being demanding, for being aggressive, for wanting more than someone else might want. It is really best and kindest to be as businesslike as possible. This makes treatment simpler for everybody. This holds for psychotherapy too. I am quite lenient with some types of patients. I operate, I suppose, sometimes on hunches. There are no set rules. I will not give a depressed patient anything further to be guilty about. He already has enough guilt. Doing favors for a depressed patient really gets both you and the patient in trouble. The patient simply becomes more depressed.

Set up a regime with a depressed patient and stick to it, because if you start being overly nice to him, you increase his masochism. He feels guilty; particularly the guilt over greediness mounts. It is difficult to be kind to a depressed patient. You have to find other ways of being kind to your patients than by these direct realities. But at the same time, this does not mean that you can't be flexible. You might have a patient with precisely the opposite problem. He might be unable to make requests which are thoroughly legitimate. He must be helped in this direction.

RESIDENT: How do you present the idea of obligation for payment to the patient?

Dr. Tarachow: At the very beginning, and I give the reason for it. With most patients there is a regular set of appointments. I tell them that in effect they buy this time: if they don't appear, no matter how good the reason is, I can't do much with the time. They are responsible. This has a maturing effect on patients. Basically, they prefer such an arrangement. They are not being "babied" by the psychiatrist.

Resident: What if they ask you in advance if you can arrange another time instead of their regular one?

Dr. Tarachow: I might agree on the basis that it is not my obligation, but would be glad to do it if I can. You have to be very careful about this because the moment the patient starts asking for something you have to be sure this isn't some type of acting out. The patient might be trying to get something from you in spite of your rules, in spite of the arrangements to which he has agreed. It's risky business to make exceptions, although at times it is necessary. You must be careful or you will be drawn into some subtle acting out.

At any rate, these matters of structure in arrangement of treatment all have to be dealt with. You will find material for therapy in everything related to treatment.

I had an experience with a patient which is worth telling because it bears not so much on the patient's ability to tolerate a transference, but the therapist's ability to tolerate his own countertransference impulses.

I had a depressed female patient, for whom I felt it would be very bad if she missed any appointments at all, no matter what the provocation. I needed to cancel several days' appointments to attend a convention, so I cancelled everybody's appointments except this one patient's. I told this patient to come quite early in the morning instead of at her usual time. We could have the session and I would still be able to attend the convention sessions. I knew in advance I would have to get up earlier than usual and have breakfast earlier in order to do this.

That morning I woke up at nine o'clock. I leisurely prepared to go to the convention with the smug feeling I had the day off. I stopped at my office about ten o'clock to pick up my mail only to learn that a frantic woman had been in the lobby early in the morning looking for me. I had completely forgotten the appointment.

I called her up to apologize, which didn't mend matters too much. The patient rightly scolded me. I then said something to the patient which I think was correct. What position do you think you could take, or what could you say to a patient in such a situation?

RESIDENT: I would capitalize on my good intentions in having attempted to give her a substitute appointment and then say, "Well, I overslept."

RESIDENT: If the relationship were good, I would even tell the patient that what you had done this day was to cancel all your appointments except hers, because you were aware how important the appointments were to her. You had responded to your knowledge of this by setting up the one appointment. You could actually tell yourself way down deep that you had a right to cancel the appointment.

DR. TARACHOW: What I said was almost that. First I told her what you said. I mentioned my good intentions and that I had really wanted to do something for her, but then I added, "But I guess there's a limit to the kindness any one person has to another, and I'm no exception;" that apparently in my promise to her to keep that early appointment, I had really promised more than I was able to do. I let my hair down and said that my intentions to be good were there, but I hadn't been quite capable of being that very good; it went off quite satisfactorily.

RESIDENT: If a conference runs over, it's a real problem.

DR. TARACHOW: Well, that's another matter. All we can discuss here is the impact on the interplay between you and the patient. If conferences consistently run overtime, then your appointments should be set up differently, that's all. I have no pat formula that will bail you out with your patients. If you persistently come late to appointments with your patients, it's inexcusable.

RESIDENT: I've had patients waiting upstairs when a conference ran over: all the doctors came upstairs at the same time, so it was quite obvious my delay was legitimate. I apologized to the patient four or five times and she said, "That's alright," and added that she had seen all the doctors coming up the stairs and it's a damn good thing that she did.

RESIDENT: Well then what do you do with the next patient? You hold her over for five minutes, then you're five minutes late for the next one.

RESIDENT: You promise to make up the time to the patient.

RESIDENT: We frequently schedule patients with no leeway between appointments. The succeeding patient is quite jealous of the time taken by the preceding patient, especially if the preceding session runs a few minutes overtime.

DR. TARACHOW: If you are late with one patient it's better to struggle through the responsibility with that one and make it up at some other time rather than having to struggle through it with every patient the rest of the day. It all depends on how much in the way of complaints and hostility you can tolerate. You can put an end to it with one and then have peaceful relations with the rest of your patients, or handle it head on and keep everyone waiting for the rest of the morning or the afternoon and work it out with each one. Your choice will depend on how much you can tolerate.

RESIDENT: I have another question in regard to lateness. If the patient is late, I assume you don't give the patient extra time. How do you start the session and how do you terminate when the time is up?

DR. TARACHOW: Start with his being late.

RESIDENT: You mean you say, "Why are you late?"

DR. TARACHOW: Either ask or tell the patient why he is

late. At the beginning of every session you should have a clear idea of the material of the previous session. If you don't, you are a poor therapist. You should know precisely how your last session ended, and if you cannot rely on your memory, you should make notes. Refresh your memory, so that at the start of a session, you will be able to utilize at once the material of the last session. Even if you are only seeing a patient once a week, he will treat the sessions in continuity, and so should you. The intervening seven days will seem to have had no schismatic effect. At the beginning of any given session your relation to the patient is resumed as of the moment at which you left the last. If the patient is late, he is acting out. *You must assume so.* Otherwise, it is not rational psychotherapy. You may or may not choose to interpret it, but you must assume it is acting out.

First of all if you are familiar with the patient's material, you should have some idea as to the meaning of the patient's tardiness. You should remember what went on in the last session. The most typical issues are fear of emerging material or some angry reaction to you. Your opening gambit might be, "Why are you angry with me?" The patient will often tell you at once. Do not be afraid to play up your omnipotence and your knowledge and your magic by remembering exactly what went on at the last session. You should know it anyway. In addition, the patient is both reassured and flattered by your close interest.

RESIDENT: You mean that you tell the patient?

DR. TARACHOW: If you think it is indicated, yes. This should be done with some wisdom, but if it is indicated you step right in. Several things are accomplished. For one, you prove to the patient that you are interested in his problems. Two, you prove that you remember, that you have been listening. You really do have to contend with the *New Yorker* cartoons. And finally, you are a better therapist. You know what is going on, you are in touch with the patient's mood and material. You can step right in. The simple proof that you remember what the patient has been talking about has astonishing value and power.

Patients will sometimes speak of coming to the psychiatrist as treatments in the plural sense. This should always be corrected. It is singular. It is treatment. It is a continuous process.

RESIDENT: I am wondering what the therapist's attitude should be toward events which occur outside the treatment session. The patients frequently get into situations with other of the therapist's patients or other therapists' patients.

DR. TARACHOW: Under certain circumstances you should very well bring in your knowledge of real situations that have taken place.

Very often, or on occasion at any rate, I will open the session by remarking on the patient's facial expression or manner. I sometimes open up with the previous session's material before the patient says anything. This is not done routinely, of course, but if something of extreme importance in the previous session had been left hanging or might conceivably have led to complications, I might pick it up at once without even waiting for the patient's associations at all. As a rule, it is better to permit the patient to set up the associations first.

RESIDENT: Would you make a comment on following a major theme with a patient? Do you feel you should spend time on one particular problem and try to work it out?

DR. TARACHOW: Yes, that is essential in psychotherapy. I would say that in psychotherapy you make a selection of the areas of the patient's material that should be developed; even in analysis the analyst makes a point of keeping a certain main thread before the eyes of the patient all the time.

I would make a point of it, that is, after you have come to an evaluation of what the major issues are and which are capable of being attacked. With some patients certain areas had best be left untouched. You are asking about sector psychotherapy. By definition, I would say that psychotherapy means sector psychotherapy.

RESIDENT: You stated in one seminar that you felt it is better to permit the patient to set the pace of the session, to start out with what he had in mind.

DR. TARACHOW: Yes.

RESIDENT: I was confused when you suggested bringing the end of the previous session into a session at the outset.

DR. TARACHOW: Once treatment is moving along with a patient, whether it is psychotherapy or analysis, you certainly should give the patient the feeling that it is a continuum. The patient sees you ending with one patient, beginning with another, and you must implicitly reassure the patient that you really listen to him, that you pay attention. Generally, you will find that your memory is more accurate about the patient's material than his. You will be under less need, I trust, to distort or forget what the patient has said. However, it is useful to be able to plunge right into a session. I think the advantages of occasionally doing that far outweigh any disadvantages.

RESIDENT: You mean occasionally, not as a routine.

DR. TARACHOW: Of course. The point is you do it when you think it is called for. However, you must not be so aggressive about it that you open every session this way. That would be ramming something down the patient's throat and not letting the patient talk.

However, if you left off at some extremely important point, the succeeding session can be opened by asking the patient to begin with that subject; most of the time the patient will say that is exactly what he had been thinking of anyway. There is no better proof of your interest.

I have a further remark to make about the matter of forgetting to charge a patient, making a mistake in the bill. Patients are not at all happy about being undercharged. You would think that patients would love to be undercharged. Not at all; I have been soundly reproached by patients for undercharging by one session. The reproach was, in a sense, justified. They said, "But how could you do this to me? How could you forget that I had come to see you?" They were very angry.

The bill becomes not a matter of money but another means of contact between you and the patient.

Another aspect of the contact with the therapist is the setting of appointment days. Let us assume that your working week is Monday through Friday and you have a patient whom you are going to see three times a week. What would influence the days of the appointments you would give this patient? How would you set up the program?

RESIDENT: There are two factors to consider. You might want to space appointments equally for dependent types of patients who can not go a long time without being seen. You might want to have continued sessions one day after another, especially if you have a patient who picks up where he left off. I think there are the two opposing trends.

DR. TARACHOW: Basically that's correct. Even if you are going to see a patient twice a week if you set up Tuesday and Friday, without being explicit about it, you are behaving in a supportive way.

But if you want the relationship to be oriented in the other direction, as a way of implicitly telling the patient that this is not a supportive treatment, the sessions would be set on successive days.

RESIDENT: Do you ever explain this to the patient when they ask you about it?

DR. TARACHOW: Not necessarily, or only rarely.

RESIDENT: Do they get angry at you?

DR. TARACHOW: Yes. A patient whom you set up for Monday and Tuesday will get angry. The patient whom you set up for Tuesday and Friday will not because it is a sign of love. You are doing the best you can to help the patient span the week, so he likes you. The patient with whom you are supportive has been appeased and feels you have given him signs of week-long affection. The patient with whom you keep the accent on interpretation may have many reproaches for being abandoned for so many days at a time. The supportive or nonsupportive, aspects of treatment can be indicated in such indirect ways.

Some patients ask many questions. All they might really want is to hear your voice. They ask questions; you must decide whether you are going to answer the questions. In some cases you will, simply for the sake of speaking. You will answer all questions of some patients, and very few of others.

In some cases you straddle a bit, and by straddle I mean something like this. Even the most dependent patient must be given some task with regard to his need for dependency on you. He must be confronted with that problem at some time. Assume you have a patient who will have to work through the problem of his dependency on you. You have decided this patient is well enough to do so. But at the moment he is not yet ready to tolerate it. Eventually he will have to. What I have done on occasion is to tell the patient I cannot answer his question. I might even go on and give him some kind of general reason why I cannot answer his question. But meanwhile I am talking a great deal to the patient. I might say a great deal to explain why I should not be talking to him at all. By this means the therapeutic goal is kept before the eyes of the patient, but at the same time the technique bends before the patient's weakness of the moment. No matter how much you concede to the patient's weaknesses, you must not altogether relinquish the role of taskmaster to the patient: your function is to hold a therapeutic task before the patient. You have set a basic therapeutic position for yourself and the patient which will guide you in the way you handle him.

In this context I also want to bring up the matter of how a treatment situation may be ended, and discuss variations on the ending of a treatment relationship. In a previous seminar (Chapter 6) I mentioned several, the matter of coming back to you as a lifelong patient. There is another kind of termination: that is to permit a patient to leave owing you money.

There are several ways in which a patient can leave owing you money. Treatment might be terminated with some explicit understanding of how and when the patient will pay up the balance of his bill. Let us consider the patient who leaves and does not pay his last month's bill and does not intend to. There are some cases where you should leave it just that way, undisturbed. But you should be careful. This might be permissible—not with a neurotic, nor with a psychopath who acts out—but with certain types of borderline problems, where this leniency might be your contribution to the patient's stability. The patient is left with a certain piece of acting out which gratifies him. It is a sign of your affection for him which he can carry for the rest of his life. He has something of yours. You didn't think you were going to be in a fix like this when you went into psychiatry, did you?

RESIDENT: How much can one love humanity?

DR. TARACHOW: Don't let everyone get away with it. I have sued patients and collected. But I have also permitted patients to leave owing me money; it contributed to their future stability. It helped them. The debt remained as a bond between us. Occasionally such a patient returns for further treatment years later. In such an event the patient generally pays the long overdue bill without comment as though treatment had not been interrupted and the bill simply referred to the previous month. The patient's capacity for dealing with treatment as a continuous process will on occasion be superior to yours. There is also the element of the denial of any separation, but this is not the only factor.

RESIDENT: It is possible to think about nonpayment of a final bill in a completely opposite manner; instead of having a good effect, may it not have a bad effect in a borderline patient?

DR. TARACHOW: Yes. There is a danger. I am assuming that you know the structure and the workings of the mind in this particular patient, so that when a patient leaves and owes you money and fails to pay, you will decide rationally on the basis of the patient's best interest as to what you should do.

There is also the matter of a patient cheating you. I took on a patient for treatment. He told me what the problem was, we discussed it, decided that he should be treated, and we set up the appointment schedule. Then we came to the fee. I said, "Well, I don't know what the fee should be because I don't know what your income is." He told me what his income was, I set a fee, and we started. For weeks he kept telling me, "What a liar I am. Oh, I'm such a liar." He could not tear himself away from the self-accusation. He gave me many examples of why he was such a liar. Finally, as the trend kept rolling along, it struck me that this must have something to do with me; it occurred to me that what he probably lied about to me was his income.

I broke into his breast-beatings and self-accusations and said, "How much do you really make?" He said, "Doc, am I glad you asked me that!" I raised the fee and we were both happier.

Chapter 11

Education and Reality

I shall turn to a different subject, the place of education and reality in treatment. The therapist assumes the role of helping the patient understand reality, understand other people, and of helping the patient understand psychological principles in general. The patient is educated not so much in terms of his inner neurotic symbolic distortions, but in terms of simple education, for example, education in sexual facts. In this seminar we are discussing that area of treatment which is pitched in terms of education, reality, and interpersonal relationships. This is something which has to be done at times, certainly with hospital patients, certainly with patients in psychotherapy, and occasionally with patients who are in analysis. You will be forced to deal with matters outside of the patient and outside of the patient's neurosis. Sometimes a patient can see his own problem only when it is reflected back to him from the outside. Sometimes the patient must be given actual facts and sometimes he must be given insight into the behavior of others.

For example, you may have to point out to a patient that he is stealing or lying, not from the standpoint of predicting punishment or disaster, but to help surmount denial or psychotic, wishful thinking.

If you have a patient with psychotic wishes you may be forced to point out reality limits, or reality punishments. Certainly this is not the type of education that you have to or wish to carry out. The most general type of intervention is to show the patient the impact of his behavior on another person. This type of explanation is often necessary in obsessive-compulsive people.

I shall give you a clinical example. A male patient of mine is very compulsive, obsessive, procrastinating. Whatever he does is done at the last minute. His income tax return is sent in midnight, April 14th, and so on. I do not have to add more details. He makes a date with his wife to have dinner and to go to a theater on a certain night, let's say Wednesday night, to meet her at Lindy's, at 7:30 in the evening to give them time to eat and make the theater. Of course, he had not made the date until his wife bought the tickets. He forced her to do it; they have a date with two other people. That is the day he gets involved with an unusually long piece of legal work, in finishing papers and briefs that have to be in. At 7:30 he is still in his office and he calls his wife. "I'm terribly sorry, I can't make it. I'm very busy. You go ahead and eat and I'll meet you at the theater." He shows up just at curtain time; he is terribly upset and has been terribly rushed and has been working like a demon all day, and comes expecting his wife to be sympathetic with him, to worry about what hard work he has been doing, to comfort him because he has been harassed all day. He is astonished when his wife indicates that she is enraged at his spoiling the dinner and theater for her. He reports this the next day with a complete lack of understanding of his own sadistic procrastination.

With a patient like that, you have to explain that his behavior, though it was tormenting to him and was keeping him in a state of commotion and turmoil and confusion, at the same time was doing something cruel to his wife. You cannot stop with an interpretation, "You are sadistic," or "This is delaying behavior." You also must show him, "Look what it did to your wife. Your wife was expecting you. You kept her waiting.

You made her uncomfortable with the guests that you had. You made her handle the situation all by herself. You had refused to help her; she had a right to expect you to share the responsibility of having dinner with your friends," etc. "Your behavior was a way of tormenting and torturing and injuring her." Sometimes even a detailed explanation like this does not seem to make the impression it obviously should.

There is another device you sometimes have to use. You try to get your patient to experience the affect of the person with whom he has been dealing. Sometimes the only way in which you can get them to do something like this is to ask them to reverse the roles in the encounter in question. Only then will they realize the impact of their behavior on another person. Often you have to explain the psychology of a wife to a husband, or the expectations that a wife has, or to a young man you have to explain the expectations of a sweetheart.

For example, a young man makes love to a girl, but because of his problems he does it very passively. He is shocked that after the tremendous efforts he has gone through to make love to the girl she hardly seems to respond. He comes to the session complaining bitterly that the girl does not love him, that she does not respond to him, that she does not seem to have any emotion or passion. The therapist has to point out the normal sexual expectations of a girl, that a normal feminine girl expects a certain amount of aggressiveness, expects a certain amount of erotic brutality. He, because of his problems about his aggressiveness, is unable to express this in any way. The girl is left with a tepid lover. He has to be made to understand this. So, in addition to the interpretation to a patient of all the genetic justifications for his behavior, he must also learn the impact of his behavior on other people. Otherwise treatment degenerates into self-pity.

Some patients use the knowledge they have acquired in treatment to justify remaining exactly as they are. A man, for example, never does a thing good for anybody. He just won't do anybody any favors. He won't alter anything to suit anybody's convenience. You point this out to him, and his answer is, "But look how my father treated me. Look at all the deprivations I had." Such patients use insight not to change but to remain as they are. This too has to be shown to patients, but that would lead us away from our main concern. A patient sometimes has to be shown the effects he produces on other people. Occasionally you have to go to some length to develop what seems to you to be the problems or the psychology of a partner, whether it is the patient's child, or business partner, father, mother, brother. I have a man who was depressed and compulsive; his wife was very good to him. She astonished me at the understanding that she had of this man, and how forgiving she was. I had to point out to this man his wife's attributes of which he, in his sadistic and compulsive treatment of her and his demands on her, was entirely unaware. He was unable to recognize that he had a good wife. I went to great length to show him that his wife was intelligent, that she understood him, that she was good to him, that she made many concessions to him.

RESIDENT: Does it help when you do that?

DR. TARACHOW: With some patients it will. Some people reject the insight about themselves, but they may accept insight when it is about somebody else; it is a kind of education. Analysis or psychotherapy can be not only the interpretation of substitutive mechanisms or defensive mechanisms or symbolic mechanisms or ego defenses. Sometimes you actually have to educate your patient to the facts of life, to what other people are. The patient does not look at other people. He is so preoccupied with himself and with his own problems that his impact on someone else and his realistic appreciation of someone else is blurred and confused. This has to be cleared up. Any neurosis leads to a kind of anxious narcissistic self-interest. This has to be overcome.

You have to be not just the therapist. You sometimes have to be an educator for these people, and you sometimes have to stop and explain the meaning of simple words and give basic information, particularly in the sexual area. With some patients you must discuss anatomy, and with others menstruation. It is astonishing to see the extent to which obvious misconceptions about menstruation or masturbation or even sexual intercourse remain unchanged even into adult life.

Another issue which you might have to explain to patients are attitudes of parents, or attitudes of grandparents. On a number of occasions I have found it necessary to explain why grandparents behave the way they do. I would discuss the simple concept of the revival of their parental importance. The parents become irritated with the grandparents because the grandparents are too interested in the grandchildren. Sometimes a simple explanation is very helpful. It is quite traditional. One sees grandparents taking grandchildren to the park and being very proud and sometimes showing more pride in them than the actual parents themselves. A grandparent can be happier about a grandchild than an actual parent. There is less conflict about it. A grandparent can love his grandchildren unambivalently. It is the parents who have the ambivalence about the children. Grandparents experience a revival of youth and mostly pleasure without the day-to-day responsibilities or irritations.

You might have a situation in which a young woman goes into an acute rivalry with her mother over the mother's intense fussing with her own baby. Your young housewife patient might be developing an intense neurotic reaction about a revival of her old hostility to her mother. You can sometimes reach part of this young woman's neurotic problem by pointing out the plight and the gratifications of the grandparent and giving your patient an indulgent rather than a competitive attitude to her own parents. Your patient might then be able to forgive her mother.

I am just picking out a few situations as examples of situations that can arise in which it is useful to interpret somebody else's psychology, to interpret someone else's needs, or someone else's reaction to your patient. This then makes the patient's problem a good deal easier; at the same time it is an education to the patient. It is an expansion of the patient's ego. He knows more, and this strengthens him too.

We have by no means exhausted the types of educative possibilities available to you for your patients. For example, I have one patient who was enormously surprised when I informed him that some children love their parents. He had hated both his father and mother for good reasons; his view of the world was one in which children hate their parents. It had of course dominated everything he did. The only kind of love affair he could have was one of quarreling.

RESIDENT: Would you say something about the approach we might take with regard to different conceptions about treatment which especially some of our disturbed, some of our so-called pseudo-neurotic schizophrenics have? They have misconceptions about what treatment, psychotherapy, really is. These often stem from previous treatment, from years of previous treatment. We are bucking against this misconception in our treatment approach. The patient wants to free associate, but we might feel he needs either education or ego support. Should we explain what we are doing?

DR. TARACHOW: Well, sometimes you have to do that. Sometimes you have to explain the procedure you are following and the procedure you want the patient to follow. Sometimes the patient steals the initiative from you and puts you on a spot in demanding not only that you explain but that you give him a sharp definition of what type of treatment he is getting. Is this psychotherapy or is this analysis? He doesn't want to get the second best variety of treatment. For example, you set up a schedule with a patient of once a week, and he wants to see you five times a week, just as he wants to approach you in one way and you want him to cooperate in another way. You might want to see a patient once a week because you fear that seeing him more frequently will dangerously intensify his transference desires or transference anxieties. He might become psychotic. The best way of rationalizing your regimen is by insisting that you are the psychiatrist, that there are a variety of methods, and that you really know which method suits the patient best. He has to take your judgment about it. Another good answer to such a patient's complaint is that techniques have altered enormously in the past twenty years and that there are modern techniques. You give the patient the idea that he is getting the most modern treatment there is.

RESIDENT: You sometimes run into a complication in the process of educating, of asking the patient to take the other role, how the other persons feel, pointing out the qualities in the other person. The patient simply feels that you are now siding with the other person against him.

DR. TARACHOW: Yes, I occasionally face such accusations, but not by severely detached types of obsessional neurotics. With them I find I have to dramatize the impact of their neurotic behavior on other people. You will find one of two results. Either they say, "By God, you're right." Or else it does not register at all. The isolation continues to work. However, my experience by no means exhausts the possibilities. In a certain number of patients that is the only means of getting them to grasp the meaning of their neurotic behavior. They do not grasp the sadism of the procrastination until you finally tell them, "Put yourself in the position of the person whom you kept waiting, how irritating, how exasperating it would be if someone promised you to keep an appointment and did not show up." A patient of mine exhibited the following behavior. Whenever his wife invited people to spend an evening at their home he suddenly found work to do in his office. He was never at home when they entertained, overlooking the fact that he threw the burden of entertaining completely on his wife's shoulders. He had so isolated himself from his own aggressions that he was unable to see that this was a nasty thing to do to his wife. He did not see it until I *forced* him to see it. I asked, "How would you feel if someone did this repeatedly to you?"

The examples of this type of education which seem to occur to me are all examples of severe obsessional neurotics. Apparently interpretation of the *outside* has to be used when the isolation against the *inside* is too great. Some way of approaching them must be found.

RESIDENT: I found that with one obsessional patient so long as I used the word "you" he never understood what I was saying. I had to deal with him in the third person.

DR. TARACHOW: I can see that. He had so detached himself from his thoughts and feelings that he could be approached only in his own terms. His anxieties about facing his own feelings must have been monumental.

RESIDENT: I even had to say, "This has nothing to do with you. You are at a movie watching the screen."

DR. TARACHOW: One is sometimes driven to such devices to get a patient to admit connections between certain facts or data. But eventually you have to get to the "you," or the treatment will fail.

RESIDENT: The technique being mentioned is similar to the acting-out method of psychodrama. It is interesting to observe patients who cannot say anything concrete about themselves or others. They would first watch others dramatize some idea: this warmed them up to take on a role. Then they would describe and express their own feelings as though coming from another person.

DR. TARACHOW: This is related to what has been said. Work with the detachment, and later they will apply the affect or thought to themselves.

We cannot leave the subject of education and reality in treatment without some discussion of borderline states. It is precisely in these conditions that this educative approach is especially apt and especially necessary. I can refer you to the work of Bychowski (1953) on latent psychosis and the work of Frosch

(1961) on psychotic character. I shall offer a simple characterization before proceeding to the therapeutic and technical aspects of the problem.

In a borderline patient the symptoms might all be neurotic, but the therapist will nevertheless get the feeling that the patient is absorbed in himself and that reality interests have been seriously sacrificed. The tendency to abandon reality is the key to the therapeutic approach to this patient. The technique depends on reality in the following three areas: (1) the reality of the transference, (2) the reality orientation of the treatment, and (3) education of the patient to understand the reality about him.

1. The reality of the transference. For these patients, there is no such thing as understanding the relationship to you. They *have* the relationship to you as a literal and real matter. Your remarks are taken literally. You like them or dislike them. They will have no truck with interpretations. In some respects these remarks hold as well for psychotics as for borderlines. A woman patient had an irresistible habit of always wanting to say something further after I had indicated the end of the session. I fell into the habit of saying, "Please hold it until the next session." This made the patient quite angry. Eventually she told me why she was angry. Her end-of-session remarks were really gifts of feces. In effect I had been asking her to hold a mouthful of feces until the next session. The borderline or psychotic patient might want to give you a gift. These should be accepted. Any interpretation of a gift is simply taken as a rejection. Incidentally, the refusal of gifts is a real burden to the therapist. A woman patient in analysis offered me two tickets to a Broadway hit. I of course refused and indicated I was interested in her associations to her need to give me the gift. The patient raised herself on her elbow, turned around, and said to me, "Doctor, I feel sorry for you."

2. The reality orientation of the treatment. These patients are in a fluid oscillation between absorption in their symptoms

and interest in relationships to people. This oscillation provides the ledge from which you can work. Your therapeutic goal is to develop a greater interest in real objects. My remarks and interventions are pointed, not to the understanding and inner meaning of symptoms, but rather to an understanding of relations to people. Avoid the symptoms and avoid the preoccupation with the body. The emphasis is put on the real relations to people. This emphasis alone has a certain therapeutic value. It is an implicit reminder that the patient is not out of this world, that he is *in* the world along with many others. He is reminded he is a human being. His isolation is thus silently broken down. The borderline is isolated too, though not in the same way as the obsessional. The borderline is encouraged to a reality direction of interest.

3. Helping the borderline patient understand other people. Here the technique of helping the patient understand his impact on others is similar to what I suggested about obsessionals. However, there may be a large difference. A borderline or psychotic patient may *possess* a most accurate understanding of another person, but may *hesitate* and not be certain he is right. His perceptions are accurate, but his ego is too weak to take a stand. A male patient gave me a most penetrating and insightful picture of his adolescent son and his son's relationship to him. At the end of the recital, the patient asked, "Am I right?" I said he was. This was of enormous help to him.

A subsidiary aspect of treatment of such cases is that we must be prepared to offer tension-relieving devices. The most concrete of these is the telephone. The patient must feel free to call you either for some emergency intervention or to set up an extra appointment. We may counsel delay; we must offer minor gratifications; we must offer information. I understand that Federn even offered chocolate to his patients. And in Freud's original record of the Rat Man, we find the terse statement: "He [the patient] was hungry and was fed" (1909, p. 303).

Chapter 12

Values in Psychotherapy

Mowrer (1950) has an interesting approach to the problems of the treatment of a neurotic. He points out that the usual picture drawn of a neurotic is that of a patient imprisoned by a relentless superego, unable to express his natural biological impulses; and that in treatment the therapist allies himself with the ego or the id of the patient in the patient's struggle against his overly strict superego. Mowrer points out that the patient's first impulse in treatment is to identify the therapist with his own conscience. Mowrer then goes on to develop the notion that far from decrying this tendency, this should be welcomed by the therapist as logical, natural, and therapeutically necessary. For Mowrer, the therapist becomes the ally of the patient's conscience, not the patient's ego. His argument is that it is the conscience which is the carrier of the standards, the cultural values of the parents as well as of the larger group. The patient, as a normal social being, must be thoroughly identified with his culture and his group or he will lead a narrow, isolated life. The patient feels his larger and his spiritual identifications through his superego; it is the development of the superego which leads to maturity and cultural development. According to Mowrer, the psychotherapist must therefore align himself with that part of the patient which is most closely related to society, to cultural feelings, to group values, so that the individual will become a more mature and more adjusted member of his group. An interesting and persuasive argument.

Before subjecting Mowrer's approach to criticism we might first look for all possible areas of agreement, and take note of a similar tendency among leading workers in the field of psychoanalysis. Specifically, we might look for signs of a turning from a biological to a social orientation, to an orientation based on object relations. No doubt, there is a turning from emphasis on the biological bases of psychoanalytic thinking to the socially directed aspects of analysis. Michael Balint (1950), in a thoughtful paper, points to this trend. He calls attention to the fact that the instinct theory is a one-body psychology (to use the terminology of Rickman), but he reminds us that in the treatment of a neurotic the problems encountered are not one-body problems, but two-body problems, i.e., the patient is in constant interaction with the analyst or other persons. He points out that what psychoanalysis needs now is to develop a comprehensive theory of the development of object relations to balance the comprehensive theory of instinct development which we already have. This, of course, is the social side of the individual psychology as compared to the biological side of psychology. Instinct development may follow rather stereotyped patterns, but object relations may develop differently though normally in a variety of ways, depending on cultural and group values. There is a certain area of agreement with Mowrer's point of view in Balint's approach, although Mowrer approaches neurosis through the superego, while Balint approaches it through the ego, through relations to objects. Both Mowrer and Balint have freed themselves from attention to the instincts alone. Both approach neurosis from the social side.

The therapeutic approach through the social side, through the ego or superego, if you will, finds its justification from another direction, too. Melitta Sperling (1951) makes a related point in her paper dealing with discipline. She points out that discipline is necessary for normal character development. However, this discipline must be an inner restraint. The only way in which this is developed is by identification with a person the child loves. There is an intimate relationship between the inner discipline and the values which an individual acquires from parental figures. Even in the analysis of adult neurotics and patients with character disturbances, acting out is not permitted within the analytic situation. Sperling points out that a parent who fears his own impulses may fail to control the impulses of the child and thus create a situation fraught with danger for the child. Character formation is interfered with, impulses run rampant, and there may be enormous anxiety about the impulses. Such situations are by no means conducive to lenient superego formation. The child may grow up with the most intense self-punitive attitudes, simply through fear of the uncontrolled instincts. It appears that discipline and values are necessary in child rearing, to regulate the child's life, to give him strength to control his own instincts, and to prevent him from becoming too self-punitive. In the treatment of severe behavior disorders it has recently been found (Geisel, 1951) that absolute permissiveness is not conducive to cure.

Even in the most rigidly orthodox analysis it is a rare analyst who does not at some moment explicitly or implicitly express value judgments about certain aspects of a patient's personality. Permissiveness for fantasy is itself a value judgment. If an analysis is carried far enough, a patient's associations and fantasies (just as in a psychotic) acquire a reality. The analyst's help in uncovering these fantasies (to the unconscious: acts) is a value judgment, often taken by the patient as encouragement or even provocation. In psychotherapy, even more than in psychoanalysis, values are important. In psychotherapy we make a sharper selection of which symptoms to pay attention to, which behavior to interpret; we pay greater attention to current ego attitudes. This selection of elements is accepted by the patient as value judgments on the part of the therapist. The symptoms and actions subjected to interpretation are now treated as, "This is bad." The symptoms and actions left undisturbed are accepted as, "This is alright—this is good."

Both in analysis and in psychotherapy every interpretation is basically felt as a frustration or a criticism. The patient is asked to give something up. This is true in all categories of disorder, though perhaps felt most sharply by certain psychopathic and psychotic patients who act their wishes out or perhaps think their wishes out. Unconsciously the patient fears we want to rob him of the inner infantile impulses from which the symptoms or actions are derived. He then girds himself to preserve the gratifications which he has. Even the entire procedure of analysis is sometimes taken as a valuation. I had a patient in analysis for years; he could not admit he was sick. After many years he still felt offended when I expressed the opinion that the patient did need analysis.

There are certain similarities between psychoanalysis and religion. Both are concerned with systems of relationship to others: both are concerned with judgments about one's own behavior, especially aggressions and sexuality. While generally, though not always, it is religion which tends to hold aggressions and sexuality in check and it is analysis which tries to free these same functions from pathological inhibitions, such a dichotomy is not always the case. Analysis also deals with psychopaths and impulse neurotics who require controls: some religions rationalize libidinal or aggressive excesses.

The matter of values enters the analytic situation when a new level of sexuality and aggression has to be integrated by the patient. In the last analysis the critical factor which motivates the patient to make a change is the transference reason. The therapist offers insight to the patient, but also values. The values are implicit in the character and behavior of the analyst. He helps both the psychopath and the neurotic to modify his superego and ego. It is here that I would differ with Mowrer. Values involve not only the superego, but the ego and ego ideal too.

A therapeutic relationship is by no means an intellectual relationship between patient and doctor. I had a schizophrenic girl patient for whom I was the only link to reality. I cared for her and she cared for me. This was the only factor which kept her oriented toward reality. An interpretation coming from me meant value judgments in fact, a state of affairs which could not be avoided. It is less so in the analysis of a neurotic, but nevertheless still so. It should of course be borne in mind that a patient may accept as value judgments certain aspects of the analytic situation which should be subjected to analysis for the resolution of the underlying problem.

To return to the matter of religion. It is my impression that the more intense the conscious religious feeling in a patient, the greater is the inner problem of hostility to objects. I had a homosexual male patient, intensely Catholic, who literally felt how right it would be to murder all Protestants. The Christians have had their Anti-Christ; the Puritans had their witches. I am most impressed by Simmel's (1946) line of argument about the religious demands on Western man causing him to live "beyond his means," i.e., to sacrifice more aggression than he is really capable of renouncing. The aggressive needs, mainly oral, must according to Simmel, find some expression via hatreds or a system of prejudice. Even the religious system itself must offer an outlet for aggression. The Anti-Christ and Devil are necessary. The overly strict superego of the obsessional neurotic causes the neurotic also to live beyond his means. The aggression finds its way out, disowned and disavowed, in the obsessional symptoms. Just as religion must offer its avenues for aggressions, so must psychoanalysis. The patient has one set of values: we must offer him another. We value his aggressions and his love. He has previously valued only his superego. In the infantile aspects of the patient's feeling, interpretations are either frustration or permission—certainly values. However, an analysis must do two things. It should go deep enough to reach the infantile level of thinking in which the interpretation is felt as a command, a prohibition or a value, and then go on to overcome such infantile valuations so that the analyst's remarks will be accepted as rational and accepted as one's own. Again the paradox: this last rational step will be attained only if the emotional transference relationship is satisfactory, i.e., the patient values his analyst.

A society which plans for peace faces more difficult psychological problems than a society planning for war. Domestic peace and inner personal peace, too, demand great efforts. The more highly developed a culture, the more numerous are the institutions developed for the preservation of domestic peace and inner personal peace, too. Among the institutions developed to regulate relations between men (and women) the most important are law, religion, marriage and divorce, rules of war, work and money, and systems of prejudice. Prejudice is included advisedly. By this is meant much more than problems like anti-Semitism, anti-Catholicism, anti-Negro feeling, and the like. Many more prejudices seem to be necessary for man. The rich have contempt for work, the worker has contempt for capital. The aviator has contempt for the foot soldier; the navy has contempt for the army, the soldier hates his officers. We all seek outlets for aggressions—and we manage to institutionalize our prejudices. It is difficult to place regulatory and other institutions in any definite order of importance. Indeed, several more might even be added, the theater and all varieties of fiction, athletics, music and dancing, gambling, and fraternal and burial societies. Of the various institutions mentioned, the two most important, in my opinion, would be law and religion. It is some of the derivative processes of the latter with which we are concerned in this seminar. Psychoanalysis, which is concerned with ego and superego modifications, as a cultural institution accepted by the patient, is not too far removed as an institution from religion and law. The difference is that analysis is a plastic process, not a static one, and is based on a realistic view of instincts and reality both. The matter of values cannot be entirely avoided by the analyst. If we take no stand on anything, we are not a realistic object for the patient.

Some patients do their best to provoke the analyst into scolding them, and on occasion they succeed. While generally such behavior on the part of a patient should be analyzed (a scolding is considered a violation of correct analytic technique), it may well sometimes serve a useful unintended purpose. The analyst becomes real to the patient, albeit via the parental superego route. By expressing values we have proved our real interest in the patient. The scolding is more readily accepted by the patient as love than many months of permissive neutrality. Before we are accepted by the patient as therapist, we must qualify first as a parent by our reality, moral courage, values, and devotion to the interests of the patient.

Part II

Special Clinical Problems

Chapter 13

The Initial Interview

To begin with, you assume certain obligations. I shall outline what sort of obligations you bear even in the very first one or two interviews. Your first obligation is to present yourself as a helpful person. This is done not by any special action or deed but by the signs of your understanding of the patient as the interview progresses. It is astonishing how quickly and accurately patients will sense whether you understand them or not as they are talking to you and giving you their problems.

Your obligations do *not* include several other aspects which are recommended by some. For example, Gill et al. (1954) emphasize that a warm relationship be established. The G.A.P. report (1961) even emphasizes that therapy begin in the very first session. I would strongly disagree on both counts. A psychiatrist can be interested and empathic without being friendly. Such friendliness may be synthetic or insincere and will be used in the service of the mistrust and anxieties of the patient.

Self-confidence and speedy insight on the part of the therapist are appreciated more than friendliness. Friendliness can be disastrous. So far as beginning therapy in the first interview is concerned, this is unfair to the patient. He is entitled to experience at least one interview to decide whether he wants you to treat him or whether he wants to change his mind and not go into treatment at all. You have no right to disturb his defenses and provoke more anxiety or transference complications than a tactful history-taking interview is going to create. If the patient returns for the second interview, you then have greater liberty.

Colby (1951), in his excellent and orderly presentation of psychotherapy, discusses very nicely the conditions under which the therapist may decide not to treat the patient. His reasoning and suggestions should be read by all beginning psychotherapists. However, he neglects, as do most other writers on this problem, to discuss the problem of the *patient* deciding *not* to be treated by you. The patient's right to this must be preserved—and this enjoins certain technical restrictions on the initial interviewer.

Even though the interviewer carefully avoids assuming the role of therapist in the initial interview and the patient consciously reserves the right of noncommitment to therapy, we must also bear in mind the patient's unconscious wishes in this area. In his unconscious he is already entertaining magical hopes and regards the interview as a cure. Fisher (1954) was able to demonstrate that even when patients are explicitly informed that their cooperation in psychological experiments was sought only for purposes of scientific research and had *no* therapeutic intent, they nevertheless indicated by their dreams and other reactions that they regarded the experiment as treatment. While one cannot restrain the patient's unconscious in the initial interview one should at least control one's own interview behavior.

Your further obligations are to size up the pathology, to size up the possibilities of treatment, to size up the dangers of the illness, and even the dangers of the treatment itself. These are the implicit obligations you accept in the initial interview.

I shall not talk about the standard history or the standard mental status which you find in the Kirby (1921) guide or other state hospital guides (Cheney, 1934; Preu, 1943) indicating the material which you have to cover. For statistical and research purposes there is a wide variety of such material. Certainly your obligation is to be complete for the purposes of records and statistics and for purposes of future research, but also for purposes of your own, of making certain that you have all the data that you need clinically.

The function I am assuming for myself in these seminars is to indicate certain definite lines of thinking that should be open to you and also to give you certain goals. These aims should be systematic and will point your questioning, will make your history taking goal directed in certain specific planned ways. This does not mean that your actual history taking should follow a cut and dried pattern; it can be as liquid as you please and may appear to the patient to be as spontaneous as could be. But in your own thinking there should be a certain organized set of areas of questions and an organized set of directions which you are following. Some histories lend themselves better to one direction or another. We will get to that presently.

Before indicating the specific directions in which your initial interview will be pointing, I want to make a number of remarks about history taking in general.

First, it should not be an undirected interview. I do not believe at all in undirected history taking or undirected initial interviews. The interview should be very much in your hands, certainly with hospital patients and even with any other patient. You should be in control of the situation. There are certain things you have to know, certain things you have to find out, certain impressions you must form, and quickly. You are heading in certain directions; the patient's future is in your hands, and it is up to you to seize the situation, particularly, though not exclusively, with psychotic patients. The patient will be more comfortable if you control the situation, and control it intelligently and tactfully.

In an initial interview you have too many responsibilities to resort to the passive attitude recommended by Deutsch and

Murphy (1955) in their "associative anamnesis." This puts too much of a burden on the patient and risks a great waste of time. It puts the interviewer at the mercy of the initial defenses of the patient. The initial interview is an active assay—it is not an analytic or even psychogenetic interview, except by inference. The interviewer can search actively for various data tending to confirm his hunches without the patient even guessing the connections. However, the patient may well be amazed that the interviewer's questions seem to lead to critical historical data. The patient is encouraged to enter into treatment by this display of magical foreknowledge on the part of the interviewer. Even the initial interview for an analysis should be a guided and searching one (Saul, 1957; Stone, 1954). That is one aspect. You must be in control of the interview.

There is another, a different aspect. History taking is an accusation. You are trying to blame somebody, so the patient thinks. Relatives take it so quite consciously. The areas about which you decide to become curious are the areas which the patient will automatically assume are bad morally or bad in some other mysterious way, bad in some way he does not understand. Though it is up to you to be goal directed and complete, you should also be tactful and gentle; it is astonishing how much information you will be able to get even in a first interview if you leaven your persistence with gentleness.

The problem does not lie so much with the patient's willingness or unwillingness to tell you about himself. The problem lies much more in your own willingness to ask questions, in your own ability to go after material in various directions. If the patient is ashamed to talk about something and you are ashamed to ask about it, your history will not get very far.

You can get a complete and detailed story from your patient if you are willing to go after it and are willing to be curious. At the same time the opposite is also true. A patient, with the best of intentions, cannot tell you everything. You may find that the patient cannot remember events that happened that very day. A day later or a week later or a month later or a year later, depending on the type of contact you have with the patient, the patient will fill out various incidents or details of matters about which in the past he had really been unable to tell a complete story.

So, on the one hand, you have the job of being complete and going after everything. On the other hand, you have to be forgiving of patients and realize that with the best of intentions the patient cannot tell all.

In the matter of details, be sure to go after dates more in terms of chronology of the patient's life than in terms of calendar dates. Be particularly interested in the type of onset of whatever the illness may be, the type of onset and the date of onset. Everything has a meaning if you think in certain directions. For example, supposing we take a slow and insidious onset of a mental disorder as opposed to a sudden onset of a mental disorder. What diagnostic orientation would you have? The slow onset is difficult to dissect away from the ordinary course of his life. Any comments?

RESIDENT: This might have prognostic significance. This might point to some precipitating stress in the patient's environment.

DR. TARACHOW: Possibly. But for the moment I am thinking of a diagnostic direction. It is a straw that points in which direction?

RESIDENT: Whether this might be a reactive psychotic picture or whether it is a chronic one.

DR. TARACHOW: No, we do not even know whether it is psychotic or neurotic. In fact, that is the very point I am interested in at this moment. The story of a neurosis can often not be separated from the story of the patient's life; a neurotic can seldom tell you when his illness began. A psychotic can often tell you the precise moment at which his illness set in. Psychoses have a way of erupting and closing, having a beginning moment, and an ending moment—not that the ending leaves them in a healthy state. However, this is an important difference. Psychoses have process systems of their own. Psychotics can often give you the exact moment at which their illness began. The neurotic seldom can. I mention this simply in connection with history taking. What I am after in the matter of history taking is to have every detail lead you to think in one direction or another and lead you to think in terms of what further material is likely to follow.

For example, a patient gives you a history of an acute sudden onset. What further information of a general nature might you immediately be interested in? If you have something that hints to you that this is the onset of a psychosis, in what other material are you at once interested? I would be alerted to the family history much more than I would otherwise. What I am reviewing for you is the way I would think during the process of taking a history. If something suggests psychosis, my questioning about the family incidence of psychosis would be more pointed and more goal directed.

Again, in connection with the very earliest symptoms, be especially meticulous about taking the history of the very beginning of the illness. That is the point in the clinical history about which you should be most scrupulously curious. The time, the place, the occasion of the onset of phobias should be noted. Where was the patient going, where was he coming from, what was he going to do on that particular subway trip or plane trip or whatever it was? The timing and the events should be carefully noted because they will give you hints as to further details. They will give you further areas of curiosity and point in a couple of directions. They will point inward and they will point outward. They will point to matters within the intrapsychic structure of the patient and they will point to matters outside the patient. The events surrounding it might point to people involved in the patient's illness.

The last among my general remarks about history taking is the suggestion to get a clear picture of what the specific set of circumstances is that brought the patient to treatment or to the hospital. I think one can automatically assume that no patient comes willingly to the hospital or to psychotherapy or to psychoanalysis. Nobody wants to learn about himself. Nobody wants to be analyzed. Nobody wants to be treated. Nobody wants his motivations to be exposed, not even the psychoanalytic candidate. What does bring people to the hospital or to treatment?

RESIDENT: I think the two broad categories, either they personally hurt or they are hurting someone.

DR. TARACHOW: If they hurt someone else, that does not bring them to treatment, not by itself. You mean they get into trouble.

RESIDENT: If they are in a painful situation with the family, then they appear.

DR. TARACHOW: Well, it can be put more sharply: families will tolerate painful situations for a long time. A family might act if the patient is causing an impossible situation, perhaps. But the point I am making is that people come for treatment only if there is a crisis. Nobody comes for treatment without a crisis; the crisis is either precipitated by their having raised cain in the environment and gotten into trouble, or the crisis is something less dramatic, e.g., a marriage is on the rocks or threatening to be on the rocks, or the patient is threatened with divorce or separation or jail unless he accepts treatment. Or the patient may be in great need, in great mental suffering. There is a crisis, either about or in the patient. Be sure to get the picture of this crisis.

Now we can turn to the certain specific areas of interest that I would like you to think about with every history. The first area in history taking is that of heading for a diagnosis. You should have a working diagnosis at the end of your first interview, perhaps even at the end of the first two minutes of your interview.

For example, your patient is a forty-five-year-old man with

one of two sets of clinical conditions. He presents either the acute onset, the first indications of some mental illness, psychotic or neurotic, or he has been a low-grade neurotic or a low-grade psychotic for many, many years. At the age of forty-five he suddenly breaks out with an acute illness. Let us assume the man has been an obsessional all his life and now becomes violently obsessional, or becomes severely and suddenly depressed. What do you think of at once? In the first minute of the interview you know this is the first acute attack of an illness in a forty-five-year-old man. What is the line of your thinking?

RESIDENT: Involutional?

DR. TARACHOW: I left women out. It should certainly be thought of in a woman, less so with a man. Any other ideas? This is the first attack of an illness in a forty-five-year-old person.

RESIDENT: Occupational difficulty?

DR. TARACHOW: No, no. You should at once be alerted to organic brain disease. Alzheimer's presenile dementias, or any other type of organic brain disease can show as its first symptom any of the classical syndromes of psychogenic disorder.

RESIDENT: I have never seen it.

DR. TARACHOW: Well, it is too bad you were born as late as you were. If you had been born twenty or thirty years earlier, you would have seen paresis do just this. But there are other diseases that still present this problem, for example, an organic syndrome such as Alzheimer's. These conditions may begin clinically as apparently psychogenic disorders. I have seen classical syndromes of endogenous manic-depressive psychosis, setting in in paresis in the early forties. I have seen severe depressions in chronic obsessionals suddenly set in as the presenting syndrome in presenile dementia. The symptoms are psychological—and the organic deficit might hardly be in evidence. It might be unnoticeable to you. But once you suspect it and look for it, you will pick up the marginal organic deficit.

If you do not look for it, you are not going to see it. I have seen hysteria as the presenting syndrome in a case of tumor of the base of the brain in a middle-aged female patient.

There are other qualities of the patient that you should observe carefully because they lead in a diagnostic direction. For example, an important sign is the degree of reserve or the degree of intactness which the patient has. If you notice that a woman's fingernail polish is badly cracked and half-fallen away, what would your working impression be?

RESIDENT: She is a woman who has ceased to care about her personal appearance. She has ceased to have normal female vanity about appearance. The fingernails may be the first sign.

DR. TARACHOW: Well, I would say that my thoughts would go in the direction of psychosis. I think women normally are quite attentive to such details. If a women uses fingernail polish, she will neglect it only if there is a really serious disorganization of her personality. I think it is quite rare for a non-psychotic woman to permit badly attended fingernails. I am giving you my own personal impressions: this is not a statistical statement, but it is my clinical impression. I would think very seriously of the problem of a major personality disorganization if a woman is inattentive to a detail such as that.

There is another problem, especially with patients in a closed office. I do not know whether most of your interviews are done in a ward or in an office situation. Which?

RESIDENT: Office.

DR. TARACHOW: In an office, fine. You invite a patient into your office and you go in first, the patient follows. The patient sits down and does not trouble to close the door. What is your impression? The interview has not even started and already you have a diagnostic impression—at least, I have. The patient walks in, sits down, leaves the door open, and is ready to talk.

RESIDENT: The psychiatrist is rude.

DR. TARACHOW: Well, perhaps. The simplest answers are

sometimes the best. If it is a woman patient particularly or perhaps even with a man. But let us bypass the rudeness of the psychiatrist and blame the patient.

RESIDENT: This might indicate a psychosis.

DR. TARACHOW: Yes, what type?

RESIDENT: Organic brain disease.

DR. TARACHOW: Yes, certainly. Such patients can be quite careless and have no interest in privacy.

RESIDENT: Perhaps schizophrenia.

DR. TARACHOW: Yes, especially. This is not yet a diagnosis but simply a direction of thinking. Why? The patient walks in, leaves the door open, and is ready to talk. Why would I be thinking of a schizophrenic process?

RESIDENT: Well, obviously the patient is not nervous or sensitive about what he is going to say, perhaps believes it so completely that he does not fear being thought of as being insane.

DR. TARACHOW: That is true. But you can say even more. You can go much farther than that.

RESIDENT: The reality testing is poor in that he does not separate the door from himself or the outside from himself; on the other hand, the fear of being with the psychiatrist in the interview situation might be sufficiently overwhelming as to outweigh the fear of other people listening in.

DR. TARACHOW: That could all be true.

RESIDENT: I think he is only interested in himself and what he is to say.

DR. TARACHOW: That is absolutely true, he is so preoccupied with himself that it does not make any difference. He could be in the middle of a field. Yes, but there is even more.

RESIDENT: He may be ready to talk, but he has left himself an opening, an out, and he is not really ready to make contact.

DR. TARACHOW: Possibly; some paranoid people will behave just that way. But there is more. Everything that's been said is true, but there are other things that are also true.

RESIDENT: Well, he lacks concern about his environment. He is not concerned, for example, whether people are listening to his personal illness.

DR. TARACHOW: Why is he not concerned about someone listening?

RESIDENT: Because he is wrapped up in his own fantasy.

DR. TARACHOW: That has been said already. He is not concerned for some other very important reason.

RESIDENT: Tremendous desire to exhibit.

DR. TARACHOW: Possibly, but there's something very basic. Think in terms of the fragmented ego boundary of a schizophrenic. What difference does it make to him if the door is open or closed? What are some common delusions that schizophrenics have about their thinking, about their thoughts?

RESIDENT: That every one else knows.

DR. TARACHOW: Yes. What difference does it make whether the door is open or closed? They have no privacy, everything is exposed. Their thoughts are exposed, their genitals are exposed, they will masturbate publicly, they will masturbate in the corridors of the ward, or in the street. Often the latter is the first symptom that brings the schizophrenic to the hospital. They are already "in communication," so they do not bother closing the door.

Now in connection with this problem you ask this same patient a question. You ask him a question and he won't answer. He'll laugh at you; but he won't answer. Or he will look at you very suspiciously. Why doesn't he want to answer?

RESIDENT: He probably thinks you should know the answer.

DR. TARACHOW: Yes. You know it anyway and you are trying to fool him or play tricks on him. Why should he tell you something that you already know?

So, there is a variety of matters immediately visible to you in an initial interview. These have to do with the matters of reserve, the matters of contact with you, with the environment, with dilapidation, with breakdown of the conventional distance between you and the patient. These at once give you some indication of the type of problem you are dealing with and make your questioning and your interest more pointed and more directed in certain specific ways. So much for that; we are not going to spend time on specific diagnosis.

We have dealt with one direction, the diagnostic direction. The next direction I want to highlight is the prognostic direction. You should be thinking of establishing a prognosis during the first interview. The single most important factor in establishing a prognosis—and this is completely apart from the clinical symptomatic picture—is the history of object relations of the patient. You are taking two sets of histories. One is the history in terms of clinical psychiatry, and the other is the history in terms of the life story of the patient. In connection with prognosis, with the life story, the history of object relations is most important. What is the history of intense or affect-laden or emotionally meaningful relationships to people in his family, or to what extent was this individual deprived of close relationships?

Object relations are not synonymous with affectionate relations. The object relations might be sadistic or masochistic, but the richer the history is in terms of individuals in the patient's life with whom there were some important relationships, the better will the prognosis be. A patient's therapeutic future can be salvaged by finding that there had been some one person important to the patient. Often when both father and mother have been very withdrawn from the patient, you may be fortunate enough, or the patient rather is fortunate enough, to have an uncle. A favorite aunt or uncle is sometimes the saving feature of an otherwise bleak family scene.

Would someone try to indicate why this should be so. Why would the history of object relations be so important prognostically? Why is it better to have at least one object than to have none? What is the rationale for this?

RESIDENT: In terms of treatment potential, it might mean

that there is a basis on which the transference can develop.

Dr. Tarachow: Yes, that's precisely the point. The relationship with the one person is the prototype for the transference relationship to you. If you get a history of abondonment, neglect, withdrawal, scan the life of the patient very carefully. You may find someone, you may find a cousin, an aunt, a sister. It is so important for children to have big families. There is quite a difference between having a big family and having a small family, having many relatives as against having few relatives. I have seen children, whose parents were living away from their own families. The parents of the children were a young couple that had moved away from their city of origin and were now living in another city. In this latter city there were no relatives at all. The children had only a father and mother, while their playmates had uncles, aunts, grandparents all about them. These children would make up stories indicating that they had as many relatives as their playmates did. It gave them the feeling of being solidly rooted. This issue also points to other problems, but at the moment we are discussing prototypes for the transference relationship.

The problem of object relations is perhaps of greater interest in problems of depression than in other disorders. In depression the psychology of the illness is closely connected with the loss of an object. In a depressive syndrome I would look back to the history of object relations to try to determine if some *one* person had been especially involved in the personal history or in the history of the present illness. Losing someone later in life always revives the problem of having lost some one person earlier in life.

The matter of object relations is the single most important prognostic element. But we can also turn to various clinical details, historical details, certain types of experiences, which all help determine the prognostic impression. But before I do that I would like to interpolate a specific question about prognosis.

You have a patient in the first interview; he has a right to ask you, "Doctor, can you cure me?" Let us say he asks this at the end of the first interview. You are eager to send the patient away, but the patient is not quite so accommodating and says, "Doctor, can you cure me?" What should you do and what are the principles underlying what you do? Or what should you not do? What is the best way of handling "Can you cure me?"

RESIDENT: Well, medicolegally, you are in trouble if you promise any kind of cure. You have to know what the illness is.

DR. TARACHOW: Well, apart from medicolegal aspects, what else? The patient wants to know his prognosis. How would you handle it?

RESIDENT: If you have already outlined in your own mind what you have planned for the patient, I think you can briefly outline this to the patient, what you plan to do, how; if you do not see him on a regular basis, you refer him somewhere else; or that you are going to give him drug medication as well as psychotherapy.

DR. TARACHOW: You would go into a discussion of the treatment plan?

RESIDENT: Without being too specific, yes.

DR. TARACHOW: Well, I shall point my question a little more in the direction of what I am after. What are the dangers of giving a good prognosis without any reservations or even with qualifications? What are the dangers of giving a prognosis to a patient at the end of the first interview?

RESIDENT: Well, the patient has the need to counteract you, as the person or the therapist; this person may rebel against being helped because it now presents a challenge to him not to be helped, to show you up.

DR. TARACHOW: Yes, that may well be true. A patient who is stubborn and perverse will want to upset your apple cart. On the other hand, a patient may have been afraid to do something. A patient presented himself for treatment; he was afraid to play the saxophone. That was his phobic symptom. In my youthful and enthusiastic fervor I told him, "Why, of course, I'll help you play the saxophone." He never returned because I had simply burdened him with more anxiety. He had had enough anxiety while not even touching the saxophone, before he came to see me. My ready promise of a cure was a threat that he would have to play it; he did not return.

But these are still not the issues I am after.

RESIDENT: I was going to mention the second point, but you apparently are not after that, that you might frighten the patient. He had mixed feelings about coming to treatment in the first place, as you brought up, and if you promise him a cure this may frighten him.

DR. TARACHOW: Well, all of these things are true and you should be aware of them. Premature mention of cure may be disastrous. But something else is more central and you should be aware of it. It is the following: by the end of the first interview the patient has not told you very much. He has perhaps carefully avoided telling you his worst problem. He has avoided telling you why he thinks he is incurable. You know, patients have various levels of thinking. While talking to you they are thinking of something else at the same time. With all the completeness that I say we can attain in the first interview, there is still the other factor. The patient cannot tell you all, either consciously cannot tell you or because he has forgotten or because he is ashamed. But for the moment we shall deal with things he consciously cannot tell you. He cannot tell you the things which he regards as his most shameful problems. So, at the end of this interview in which he has not even told you what bothers him most, you tell him that you can cure him. He regards you as a fool, and correctly so, and he need not return to you. The best attitude is to indicate that you think you can help the patient to help himself.

What have I done when I say, "I think I can help you to help yourself?" I have done a number of very important things when I put it that way.

RESIDENT: You have made it incumbent upon the patient to maintain the therapeutic relationship and to involve himself in the therapy.

DR. TARACHOW: Correct. You have given the patient a number of things. You have given the patient hope, but you have also divided the burden between yourself and the patient. You have assumed some of the burden, but he has also assumed some of the burden and the responsibility. He thus also gets part of the credit in case he gets well. Never rob a patient of that. If you rob a patient of that credit, you will not permit him to be cured. A patient must be able to take as much credit for the improvement as you do. If the cure becomes something you do to the patient or for the patient, you rob him of something that is quite important and he will certainly resent it.

If you take the tack, *I* will help you, *I* will do this for you, the patient will come session after session, week after week, waiting for you to cure him. He will bring his body. You are supposed to *give* him the cure. Patients can become spectators of their own treatment. So, divide the burden, divide the responsibility, divide the credit, divide the blame, and at the same time give the patient hope. Be acutely aware that the patient knows he has not told you everything. If you know the patient knows he has not told you everything, the patient will know that you know. Then you will have an honest relationship to the patient and an honest relationship to yourself. So much for discussing the prognosis with the patient.

Now to turn back again to the matter of prognosis itself. There are some important clinical matters which can easily come up in the first interview and which will help you to come to some prognostic impression. Please remember that these matters we are discussing are in terms of directions of thinking and not as absolute rules of diagnosis or fixed rules of prognosis. You never know in advance how good a worker your patient is or how bad a worker your patient is. But at any rate, the directions in which I think you should think are what we are going to discuss.

One important prognostic issue is the history of masturbation and the date of onset of masturbation. Here, too, if you do not ask questions you are not going to get the answers. Two patients, one whose masturbation set in at age twelve, another patient whose masturbation set in at age twenty-two. What is the difference in prognosis?

RESIDENT: I would certainly think it would be better in cases where it set in at twelve. My first impression of such delayed masturbation is that it is a poor prognostic sign.

DR. TARACHOW: Yes, that is certainly true. The later the masturbation, the more difficult will the problem be of working through the sexual anxieties. Sometimes you will even get histories in which there is no masturbation at all; then it becomes even more difficult and suggests schizophrenia.

RESIDENT: Do you think that such a history is true or do you think that this is material that has been repressed by the patient?

DR. TARACHOW: A perfectly proper question. The history may be inaccurate or even consciously falsified. The patient might have masturbated and forgotten. A patient at thirty can completely forget a history of masturbation at fifteen. Yes, you are quite right. The patient may not be able to tell the correct story. But in terms of the first interview, if the patient forgets, that, too, is a problem. If the patient permits himself to remember it more readily, is more willing to deal with it, is more willing to face it, the degree of anxiety is less and the prognosis more favorable.

RESIDENT: I am wondering about the difference between the male and the female as far as the ability of obtaining the average masturbation history.

DR. TARACHOW: Your question is, is it easier to get it from a male patient than from a female patient?

RESIDENT: Your remarks seemed derived more from a male patient than from a female patient.

DR. TARACHOW: Well, it all depends on your willingness or ability to ask questions. If you are shy about asking a female patient about masturbation, she will also be shy about telling you. You add your shyness to hers and you will never know. There is a masturbation history in both. It should follow the physiological and psychological development in both. However, I do want to express a qualification regarding histories of masturbation in women. They will not follow the pattern of these histories in men. The delayed onset of masturbation or absence of masturbation or greater difficulty in remembering masturbation are not as serious prognostically in women as in men. The masturbation history of women is more complicated. The absence of a penis creates a situation in which the female risks reminder of this absence at every masturbation. Overt masturbation might, as a consequence, be suppressed. In men the history is simpler and can be used prognostically with greater reliability.

RESIDENT: I have another question. Is it not possible that what we consider masturbation may not be so considered by the patient?

DR. TARACHOW: Of course. A patient might have some habitual action or mannerism which unconsciously represents displaced masturbation, a connection which he does not realize. But in the first interview, all we can talk about is the masturbation which the patient recognizes as such. Even so a great deal can be missed readily. For example, I think many residents would be quite content to inquire about masturbation and get the history of the obvious data such as accompanying fantasy or external stimulation employed. This would still leave out a good deal of important information that could be elicited by a few additional questions. The most overlooked data are the specific techniques of masturbation. There is a tremendous difference in how individuals masturbate, both male and female. Either male or female patients may masturbate in a way that acts out a masculine role or they may masturbate in a way that acts out a female role. Or the masturbation might reveal heights of unsuspected narcissism, such as masturbation before a mirror. The male patient may respond, but not inform you that he masturbates with his finger in his anus or masturbates by beating his penis. If you do not ask him he will not tell you. He will be too ashamed to tell you voluntarily. There is a tremendous difference between guilt and shame. Guilt feelings bring material into the interview, shame keeps it out. There are many acts about which patients are ashamed, for example, picking the nose and eating the pickings, playing with the rectum, thumb sucking, and so on. These activities are sometimes kept secret for years even in a thoroughgoing analysis. Obsessional neurotics are especially prone to nose picking, anal masturbation, and direct or displaced coprophagic impulses. A good clinical working assumption is that every severe obsessional neurotic is coprophagic.

So, find out just how your patient, either male or female, masturbates. Does the masturbation fulfill a masculine picture or does the masturbation fulfill a feminine picture? This will help clarify the prognostic picture. If you have a woman who masturbates in a way that indicates masculinity, you have a more difficult issue, and with a man who plays out the female role in masturbation or plays out both male and female roles in masturbation, the problem is more difficult.

RESIDENT: I would be more interested in the time spent in reverie.

DR. TARACHOW: You are quite right in calling attention to this. A patient might masturbate as part of a prolonged reverie, daydream, and withdrawal from reality. Or a patient might deliberately use certain habitual fantasies or practices to promote excitement and facilitate masturbation. Fantasies of beating or being beaten or enslaved are common. The details of these fantasies should be brought forward. Everything will serve a prognostic and eventually therapeutic purpose. Beating fantasies add to the difficulties of treatment.

RESIDENT: Isn't material like this generally considered as not suitable for the first interview?

Dr. Tarachow: It depends on how you do it. One can be tactful and sympathetic and gentle and get all this in the first interview. You can do it and it need not be dangerous or disastrous. I have no intention of promoting headstrong history taking, or getting you to rush into material. What I am interested in is your having a clear conception of your goals, and that in certain specific situations you know in which direction to point your questions. I am not asking you to throw your patient into a panic. But I do want you to have conceptions of what the material should make you think. In the first three minutes you should have a whole series of anticipations of what your fruitful lines of inquiry are going to be.

Resident: If in the first interview you bring out material which is very charged for the patient, could this create so much anxiety that the patient would not return?

Dr. Tarachow: Of course it could. Your judgment about such dangers will develop as you gain experience. You will find that patients are referred to you and never call on you. Patients may come and see you once and never return. And patients will also come and stay for treatment. There is an enormous range depending on anxiety, motivation, and other factors.

The patients will stay if they feel that they can trust their problems to you. They will stay if they feel that you have gotten these issues from them in a sympathetic and friendly way, and that basically you have sympathy for them and for humanity. They will know it, they will sense it, and they will give you tremendous confidences, and they will come back and face you again. But if they sense something else in you, they will not return. But some patients, in the best of hands, may come for an initial interview and never reappear. They are frightened. Of course there is the matter of the anxiety about treatment, about the psychiatrist. But we are not directed toward psychotherapy in our conference today. Today I want to expand your area of curiosity, expand your area of interest, and expand the possibilities in your own mind of how far-ranging your thinking can be and should be in the very first interview.

Before going on I would like to make passing mention of an informal classification of psychiatrists. The poorest group has the least ability and comprehension of their patients. Patients come to them, and they quickly lose these patients. The intermediate group of psychiatrists understands the patients better. They can keep their patients, but never seem able to discharge them. The third and best group is able to hold on to patients and also to discharge them.

To return to prognostic matters. It is interesting to observe the speech patterns of patients, particularly the ways in which they use verbs. There is a great difference between a transitive and an intransitive verb, and between an active and a passive verb. You will learn a great deal about the patient if you make a mental note of what type of verbs he seems to prefer, the transitive or intransitive, the active or passive. There is a marked characterological difference between saying, "I love you," or "I'm in love," or "I'm full of love." These exhibit varying degrees of passivity or activity. The more a patient is addicted to intransitive as against transitive verbs, passive as against active, the more will you find yourself dealing with problems of inhibition, problems of passivity. Another way in which this shows up is the patient's preference for nouns as against verbs. Patients who are passive, who have inhibitions against their active impulse life, will have a tendency to convert verbs into nouns.

I recall a session with a severely obsessional man. One day I referred to how much he hated his father. He protested, "I don't hate him." When I asked what we had been discussing for so many months, he responded, "We were talking about my hostility. I don't hate him." This patient preferred a noun to a verb. Another speech pattern is that of making adjectives indefinite and approximate, for example, "a biggish man," "his age is fortyish," or "a brownish color."

These data do not give you a diagnosis, not at all, but they do give you an idea of the posture your patient has toward his impulse life, whether it is in the direction of activity or passivity. This involves all areas, love-making, ambition, fighting, or whatever the impulse might be.

Symptoms themselves may be a prognostic indication. There are one or two special clinical phenomena I shall mention. There is quite a difference between the symptom of premature ejaculation and retarded ejaculation. Do any of you know in which type of problems you will encounter retarded ejaculation?

RESIDENT: Psychotic depression?

DR. TARACHOW: Possibly. A depressive would not have much sexual interest at all. You will find retarded ejaculation frequently in severe alcoholics and in severe obsessional neurotics. It is a sign of quite deep-seated stubbornness; the therapeutic outlook for these patients leans to the unfavorable side.

Another symptom which should give you pause is blushing or fear of blushing in men. The symptom of blushing or fear of blushing is often connected with important unconscious homosexual problems; especially in men it will be an indication of great difficulty in therapeutic outlook.

Michael Balint, on a visit to Kings County Hospital several years ago, made a prognostic suggestion which I think is most interesting. He suggested that in an initial interview one could get a good idea of the therapeutic outlook for the patient if somewhere in that first session the therapist makes some suggestion which would be a gentle provocation to the patient to think about why he is sick. Some most general psychogenetic reference will do. You give the patient an invitation to respond. The degree of willingness of the patient to engage in some kind of thinking about his illness would be a prognostic sign. Coleman (1949) makes a similar point. If the suggestion brings no response whatever, the outlook is less hopeful. This certainly does not mean that you should plow right in in the first session and try to cure your patient. You are merely trying to get an impression and trying to give the patient a feeling that you are curious about what is going on. If the patient is willing or able to pick up this invitation to be curious himself and do some thinking, the outlook is much better. Before being too harsh with your unwilling patient you might bear in mind that the very concept of "unconscious" could be a severe narcissistic blow.

So much then for (1) the direction of diagnosis, (2) the direction of history of object relations, and (3) the direction of some general and specific prognostic indicators. We shall now turn to a number of other areas which can be structured in the first interview.

We next turn to the history of the sexual identification of the patient, the sexual direction. Another way of putting it would be the direction in which the patient solved his oedipal problem. In other words, did the patient solve his basic problem of his relationship to his father and mother in a masculine direction, or feminine? One important aspect of the patient's relationship to his father and mother is a tendency to a complete macroscopic transmission of the parental relationship into his own life. This can be seen over and over again, a fatalistic tendency of patients to reconstruct in their own lives and in their marriages a precise reduplication of the relationship between their father and mother. Rangell (1952) has given a beautiful description of this phenomenon.

To give the simplest of examples: a few years ago I was treating a morphine addict. During the stormy course of his treatment, I had occasion to speak to his wife a number of times and learned that her mother had also married a morphine addict.

What are some of the easily observed and easily recovered elements which will indicate the basic sexual identification? What would indicate a strong feminine identification in a man patient?

RESIDENT: His vocation?

DR. TARACHOW: Yes.

RESIDENT: Male nurse, interior decorator, beautician.

DR. TARACHOW: Yes. Anything else? Turn to some a bit less obvious. Teaching. Even being a physician requires a strong maternal attitude toward people, psychiatry especially. You have to be able to give and be unwilling to revenge yourself. This is the biggest occupational hazard in psychiatry.

RESIDENT: Creative art, clergymen.

DR. TARACHOW: Yes. How about personal habits or personal appearance? There are all sorts of minor details. I recall a patient who wore a rubber band on his wrist: it unconsciously represented a piece of feminine jewelry to him. I would like to add a word about feminine dress. Normal feminine dress, with all its various points and dangling appendages, such as earrings, pendants, tassels, fringes, etc., is healthy. A healthy woman recognizes the fact of castration and her dress (in addition to childbearing) is the illusory restoration. A woman who dresses too simply or in a masculine fashion has denied knowledge of her castration and acts as though she does not need any substitutes or restoration. There is a two-sentence joke which illustrates this type of woman. A woman presented herself to a psychiatrist for treatment. She complained that she was troubled by a fantasy that she did not possess a penis. Such a woman has failed to admit her femininity. The more neurotically masculine a woman is, the less exhibitionistic will she be. Exhibitionism of clothing and body is healthy in a woman. It indicates the recognition of anatomy (with the pain involved) and a variety of displaced repairs and restorations.

Let's turn to marriage. Can any one of you describe a type of marriage which is relevant?

RESIDENT: An overly dominant female partner who assumes management and domination of the household.

DR. TARACHOW: That might even be within normal limits.

Will someone describe a pathological marital situation? Have any of you read Noel Coward's *Design for Living?* There are two men and a woman. You will encounter marital situations in which there is either an accessory man or accessory woman in the situation. There may be problems of sexual excitability in a man only under the condition that another man be sexually involved with the woman. You will not infrequently see cases in which the sexual excitement of the husband depends precisely on the fact that another man is having an affair with his wife. In one way or another a man will often throw his wife into the arms usually of his best friend or occasionally a stranger.

Years ago I treated a patient who permitted his wife's lover to come into the house and have an affair in the bedroom while the husband was in the house. What he would do (he thought he was expressing great rage at the situation) was to take his violin and play it furiously outside the door of the bedroom, while his wife was enjoying sexual relations with the other man within.

These pathological marital situations are indicators of pathological femininity in men.

While we are on this subject I should like to bring up a related issue. In searching about in a history for homosexual experiences, you will often encounter something similar to the following. The patient will tell you that as a boy he had had an actual traumatic homosexual experience. Some more aggressive boy had inflicted upon your patient a traumatic, overt homosexual act. What effect would this have upon the subsequent normal development of the boy? I am referring to a single homosexual experience which was painful, upsetting, and very traumatic.

RESIDENT: I think it would not have much of an influence on him if everything else in his development were normal. I think he might be depressed about this one instance and that would be that.

Dr. Tarachow: It is not that simple. In normal development we pound out our sexual identification as life experience goes on: we have both masculine and feminine identifications, everyone does. These identifications derive from father, from mother, from teachers, from older brothers, from uncles, from all sorts of experiences. By these I am referring to ego-syntonic experiences in which heterosexual and homosexual love are incorporated into one's normal psychic development.

How could this isolated homosexual experience act as a long-lasting difficulty or become a chronic problem? Why should a single homosexual experience which is remembered readily and so thoroughly rejected create long-lasting problems? What difficulty might it create in addition to being a painful memory?

Resident: If you are going to presume that there is a homosexual element in every person . . .

Dr. Tarachow: Yes, I am making that presumption.

Resident: Then this act will arouse anxiety. That is, if there had been some degree of pleasurable satisfaction from the act, the pleasure becomes anxiety provoking and must be repressed. Later on, during heterosexual identifications there will be this element of . . .

Dr. Tarachow: You had better stop here. You are doing fine up to this point. What I was thinking of was that this traumatic experience would interfere with *normal* sublimation and the *normal* incorporation of homosexual feelings into the healthy personality. Then various other consequences would follow. The homosexual love provoked by the experience would be intense and anxiety provoking but at the same time rejected by the ego; it would not be accepted and incorporated as an ego-syntonic feeling. You may love your father or brother or uncle but not a homosexual seducer.

An experience like that could leave a burden of unsublimated homosexuality and also interfere with the *later* sublimation of homosexual feelings. This would contribute to making the prognosis more difficult.

A picture of the sexual direction, the sexual identification, the sexual direction in marriage, and habits and occupation and pathology, all constitute a cluster of information useful in providing us with a prognostic and a therapeutic index about the patient.

The next area in which we can organize a cluster of information is the issue of degree of regression or the degree of disorganization in the ego structure of the patient. For example, a patient relates a dream which is overtly homosexual or overtly incestuous or overtly cannibalistic. He might have a dream in which a dog was eating a human arm or a human was eating a dog. What can you say about a patient who has this type of dreams?

RESIDENT: Something so overt and obvious might mean something else.

DR. TARACHOW: Quite possibly. I shall interpolate a word or two about dreams. Dreams are a way of both presenting and disguising one's inner mental life. Both are equally important, the presentation of one's inner life as well as the disguise. The disguise is essential. If we grew up without any protection against our infantile and archaic mental life, we would have no adult existence. We would simply be perpetual archaic infants. Dreams, with all their mystery and peculiarities of detail, are an indication of the mental apparatus at work. Organizing, presenting, turning the archaic into something which has some kind of coherence, some kind of representability and expressibility—all these are necessary work. Freud called this the dream work. With this in mind, what can you say about a dream of overt incest, homosexuality, or cannibalism?

RESIDENT: Well, I think it can indicate a person's rather poor ego development or that his ego was not normally developed in the sense that he was not able to transform or disguise these primitive ideas in the dream.

DR. TARACHOW: Yes, in your dreams you should have an ability to hold these archaic elements in check, translate them into relatively civilized conceptions, and certainly to hold these extremely archaic elements in check. This need not hold for someone who has been in analysis for a while. In such an instance the aim has been to uncover and specify these very problems. But if the dream work of an untreated, unanalyzed person indicates that his ego apparatus is not working, is not controlling the inner archaic life, then this patient has a most important ego disturbance.

I am certain you are all familiar with the difference between manifest dream content and latent dream content; one simple rule would be that there should be some difference between the manifest dream and the latent content. If the manifest and latent content are the same, it means that the psychic apparatus has been failing in its work, and it would be a most important and bad prognostic sign.

The character of the symptom is important particularly if the symptoms involve the total behavior of the patient. Examples would be a patient who has a predilection to taking prolonged hot baths, or a patient who insists that her husband massage her body for hours. You will encounter symptoms in which behavior and symptom have fused into a total type of behavior acceptable to the patient. Excessive greed is an example. Can one of you think of other examples of behavior which could be regarded as symptomatic of an extremely childish or infantile acceptance of regressive needs?

Resident: Thumb sucking.

Dr. Tarachow: Excellent. Thumb sucking may go on into adult life, into the thirties or forties. It is a serious symptom. I have seen it in obsessional and depressed patients.

We might take another example, extreme dirtiness. I recall a patient who simply could not bear to flush the toilet. He would finger the stool; he was a severe obsessional neurotic. He suffered an intense sense of pain and loss on watching the stool pass down the toilet bowl. He did not like to pay his bills either. This is part of the total clinical picture, of course.

Another patient complained that the chambermaids were refusing to clean his hotel room; he felt persecuted and upset because no matter how much he complained to the housekeeper of the hotel, no chambermaid would come into his room. Upon close questioning I learned that this man never flushed the toilet; his room was a pigsty. He almost never bathed. I literally had to instruct him to flush his toilet, improve his habits, and I had to impress upon him that he was bringing the neglect upon himself.

At any rate, I mention these data to indicate problems of disintegration of the personality, disintegration of ego functions. In this sense we may group together archaic dreams with problems of personality in which infantile or archaic behavior is completely accepted. They are all prognostic indicators.

Another matter within the province of ego functioning is the type of associations in the patient's thinking. A normal chain of associations should be obvious to you: you should be able to follow the content of a rational line of thought.

Would any of you venture to offer a simple characterization of the thought disorder of schizophrenics? What is the principal issue at work in the thought disorder of schizophrenics?

RESIDENT: The lack of goal?

DR. TARACHOW: You mean the lack of a goal visible to you.

RESIDENT: Or loosening associations?

DR. TARACHOW: Yes?

RESIDENT: Inability to keep thoughts in the unconscious. Everything becomes conscious to them. Therefore their thoughts are disordered.

DR. TARACHOW: Yes, that's a way of putting it.

RESIDENT: I think the general principle is the lack of reality testing.

DR. TARACHOW: Yes, there is a lack of reality testing, there's a lack of goal, as you might see a goal. There is a lack of organization, from the reality standpoint.

RESIDENT: I think there is a private personal autistic nature to their associations.

Dr. Tarachow: Yes, that's what I wanted. I wanted a remark dealing with the positive aspect of what's going on. To the schizophrenic, everything is quite logical. The associations are perceived completely internally, as opposed, for example, to the associations of a manic in whom the associations are determined, for whatever reason, by the external reality. You know the phenomenon of clang associations. In the manic there is a flight from the real content, that is, from what is going on within. The associations are derived from the outside; this helps the patient deny and avoid what is going on within. In a schizophrenic the associations are deeply determined by the inner content, but so deeply and so profoundly and with so little recourse to the organized mental apparatus, that you cannot or barely can follow it.

Here, too, pay attention to the type of associations. Again, I am not interested in diagnosis but rather in terms of outlook, prognosis, and the type of contact that can be made with these patients.

I now turn to another area, the psychogenetic and biogenetic area, the family history. This is a difficult area and what I am going to say is entirely relative; you might be exposed to different points of view from different people. But my own experience has been, in comparing patients with or without a family history of psychosis, regardless of whether the patient is neurotic or psychotic, that a heavy seeding of psychosis in the family history seems to militate against a good prognosis for psychological therapy. When you contend with a family history of psychosis one has to keep two issues apart, prognosiswise. On the one hand there is the genetic factor which is so hard to define and which, some of us have the impression, creates difficulty, and on the other hand there is the psychological factor created by the behavior and impact of the psychotic relatives. The psychological problem of dealing with psychotic relatives is a difficult one because there is an attempt to deny the problem, there is identification with the very sick person. There are all sorts of difficulties; your patient has had to contend with affective experiences which are most intense, which are regressive, which have been very stimulating, may be irresistible and greatly increase the difficulties of treatment. It does not make treatment impossible, but it is a definite factor tending to greater difficulty.

On the biogenetic side I have a general, unsupported impression, namely, that patients with a family history of psychosis have greater difficulty in dealing with their impulse life, and that the patterns they have developed are less amenable to change.

I would also like to view the psychogenetic history in a somewhat different way, that is, start with the symptoms and work back. Symptoms point back in two directions. They point back in the direction of the intrapsychic organization of the patient himself, and they point back to the family. For example, let us consider a symptom of difficulty in swallowing. A young male patient has a problem of difficulty in swallowing. The symptom can point back to within the patient and the symptom can point back toward some environmental factor, to some relevant person. Any suggestions about either of these two directions?

RESIDENT: Perhaps there was a feeding problem, a mother who pushed him to eat too much.

DR. TARACHOW: Yes, there could very well have been an infantile or childhood eating problem; in other words, the symptom points back to the orality of the patient, so far as his own personality construction is concerned, and it could point back to his mother because of that. Putting it differently, the symptoms point to the libidinal level of the patient as well as to the environment. Is there another direction in which your curiosity would be pointed?

RESIDENT: Display of sexuality?

DR. TARACHOW: What kind of sexuality?

RESIDENT: Homosexuality.

DR. TARACHOW: Yes. A feeding problem could be a masked homosexual symptom, a masked fellatio fantasy; it therefore also points back to father. I mention this not because any one symptom should lead you back in some mechanical way to one particular person but rather that the symptoms themselves should provoke your curiosity in specific directions.

For example, you hear of a twenty-year-old boy with paranoid symptomatology. In what direction do you immediately turn, so far as objects in the family are concerned?

RESIDENT: Father.

DR. TARACHOW: The father. Yes, at least at first. You are immediately alerted to the history of the relationship between the patient and his father; you search out a personality picture of the father. Eventually in a deep investigation of homosexuality you will be led to mother too, but in the immediate clinical situation the father is important.

Obesity at once makes you think of the patient's relationship to his mother. Another simple factor to bear in mind is that so much of neurotic and psychotic symptomatology is concerned with anatomy. It is easy to overlook something as simple as that. Symptoms are concerned with anatomy. Dreams are concerned with anatomy. There are important theories of symbolism indicating that anatomy is basic in all symbolism.

I recall a patient who had enormous anxiety about a rather simple action. He had anxiety about lifting up a glass of water for fear of spilling it. Where does your curiosity turn to in reference to such a symptom?

RESIDENT: Urination?

DR. TARACHOW: Yes, urethral problems. This person was full of anxiety about his urethral and sexual life, and had problems of enuresis. Every symptom is a suggestion to you. The history of symptoms, either neurotic or psychotic, should be taken in great detail, both as to time or origin and as to the life situation in which the patient was involved at the time.

I shall now discuss another cluster of data. It centers on the flavor of history taking. The best clinical psychiatric history, including the history of the symptom, the history of the family, the precise dates of all events, may at the same time be miserably dull unless it has a certain quality. It should have the quality of a story. A history should not simply be a history of detailed clinical symptoms, it should be a romance. A history should be a romantic history of the patient. Think of it as a novel. You should think of the history as some individual's personal tragedy or his personal odyssey. If you have that quality in mind, you will be more coherently goal-directed and you will also understand the history more readily.

Recently a resident presented a case to me; it was a complete and thorough presentation of the history of symptoms, relationship to the family, and occupational history. Everything was present except the fact that the girl was in love with the boss's son. All the symptoms and all the facts in the history related to a love affair which had many neurotic vicissitudes. The resident had heard the romance without listening to it. The patient had been trying to tell him the story of her romance, but he had not listened to it as a piece of true fiction. He had been occupied with getting a pedestrian psychiatric history. The fascinating quality of fiction and romance were nowhere to be observed in the case presentation. Once the romance was extrapolated from the material, and then reintroduced in the story, the entire presentation had a quality of life altogether lacking before.

This then is the outline that I am presenting to you for thinking and for curiosity in history taking. Before we close, I want to review in brief what we have covered.

History taking should have a goal-directed purpose; it should have a diagnostic interest and a prognostic interest. You should be able to pull out a history of the object relations of the patient, you should be able to pull out a history of the sexual identification, the sexual direction of the patient, you should be able to pull out a picture of the integration or disintegration of the mental apparatus in terms of the ability to control current behavior as well as organize the archaic past. You should have a conception of genetic and psychogenetic factors that come either from the family history or from the symptoms themselves. The symptoms should be viewed as indicators of the libidinal level of the patient as well as pointing to specific significant individuals in his past. And last of all, and most importantly, you should be able to view the history in terms of a romance, in terms of a story.

You should have these factors in mind even though not every history will lend itself to eliciting all these aspects. One may lend itself particularly to diagnostic curiosity, another to some other direction.

Chapter 14

A History Conference

RESIDENT: The patient is a thirty-nine-year-old American white Jewish woman, mother of four, who is now married for the third time. She is a housewife. She was transferred here from another hospital for continued treatment of paranoid ideas associated with a depression.

The patient is the fourth of five siblings and recalls that she was her father's favorite. The father was shot to death in the home of his mistress when the patient was three years old.

The father had been unfaithful and had been going out with this other woman; the mother had found out about this just before he died. On the night of his death the mother and the father had been quarreling. The father wanted to go back just one last time to break off with the mistress. The mother did not want him to go. The patient was told that she, the patient, was in the next room crying and the mother had to go to her to quiet her. During this time the father sneaked out and went to the mistress' home.

DR. TARACHOW: This begins like a novel.

RESIDENT: It's quite a story. The patient recalls in horror the orphanage where she stayed for three weeks when she was only four years old. The patient apparently had a depression with possible mutism shortly after this stay in the orphanage. The patient's mother did not remarry until the patient was fifteen. Two years after the mother remarried the patient became depressed and worried. The stepfather had made repeated sexual overtures to the patient during this time.

The patient feels that she has been depressed and lonely all her life. The only periods in which she did not feel lonely were her pregnancies.

DR. TARACHOW: The complaint of having been depressed all one's life is an interesting symptom. What are the clinical possibilities about such a complaint?

RESIDENT: She might have suffered something that was extremely traumatic and this traumatic theme may be recurrent and repetitive. Perhaps that is why it came up so soon.

DR. TARACHOW: No, the complaint is: "I've been depressed all my life." I am referring to the clinical symptom itself, simply as a clinical phenomenon, not its psychogenesis. What thoughts do you have about it?

RESIDENT: It's hysterical . . .

DR. TARACHOW: No, no, nothing diagnostic or genetic, simply as a clinical fact. Well, it could be true or it could not be true. She might have been depressed all her life. I doubt it, but it is possible. But in the depths of a depression, a patient says, "I've been depressed all my life." It could have been retrospectively falsified. It is up to you to find out. It is enormously important if it is true. It is somewhat less important if it is, as so often happens, a product of the mood of the moment. They are not lying; they do feel this way.

RESIDENT: During her adult life she had a total of three husbands and has been divorced from the first two.

DR. TARACHOW: Before we go ahead, do you see any similarity between the patient and her father? What similarity do we see even in just the little data we have so far?

RESIDENT: The inability to form a lasting relationship.

DR. TARACHOW: Yes. The father had a wife and a mistress; this woman had one husband, got rid of him, then another husband, got rid of him, then a third husband. She is following part of the pattern of the father in moving from one object to another; she cannot stick with one. How closely similar or maybe identical or how spurious this similarity will turn out to be, we do not yet know. But this is the way I think as the presentation moves on. This is the story, the father had several women; she had several men; there's a strong similarity.

RESIDENT: She complains that these are all weak men, who did not give her the affection and support which she wanted; they were interested mainly in sex.

The present illness began about two years ago when her oldest stepdaughter became engaged and did not inform her. She began to feel depressed and then began to feel suspicious about her other children and her husband. She became suspicious that her husband was having an affair with another woman; this suspicion gradually grew until it had encompassed all the neighbors and anybody that she would meet.

DR. TARACHOW: Let me stop you again. I was going to ask a question, but you have already given me the answer. I was going to ask the group whether there was another possibility, in addition to her possibly repeating her father's pattern. This is one aspect of her personality. But is there something else? Is she repeating her mother's pattern somewhere in having several husbands? I was going to ask whether this woman is repeating the life of her mother in having many men, in finding men who are not interested in her and who get rid of her. Do you see the difference between the two pictures? There could be an identification with her father, she could be following his life pattern and moving from object to object, or she could be following her mother's pattern, who had several men who did not truly love her. Perhaps this is the pattern that lies behind the divorces. You came up with the answer even before I could ask the question. The patient's first husband, either truly or in her own fantasy, either correctly or in her psychotic fantasy, did not love her. So in that sense, whether true or false, she is repeating her mother's pattern, either in delusion or in reality. In a way, it does not even make much difference. There is a short paper by Rangell (1954) that I suggest all of you read. He discusses and gives examples of instances in which the patient recapitulates in detail the life situation of the parents. He presents a very nice discussion of just that issue.

RESIDENT: She felt they were all talking about her or thinking about her. She then became intensely paranoid and beginning about one year ago felt that the television set was broadcasting about her. The instruments in her husband's automobile were recording machines that would report her voice, and in general almost everything pertained to her in some way.

She applied to this hospital because her aunt had been a patient here. This was after the delusions were present for at least nine months.

DR. TARACHOW: Please recapitulate the delusions for me.

RESIDENT: She felt that her husband was going out with another woman. She felt that the television set was telling about her, that her husband's car had some instruments which were recording her voice, and that her children and the neighbors were in on this plot *to keep from her the fact that her husband was going out with another woman.*

DR. TARACHOW: What this makes me think of is that this delusion could be a recapitulation of actual childhood events in which the mother had tried for a long time to keep the child from knowing about the father's infidelity. Then either by accident or by mother's design, the girl found out. This delusion could be a repetition of a real situation. Paranoid delusions can turn out to be a distorted repetition of actual events in the patient's life. You will find this problem beautifully discussed by Niederland (1960) with reference to the classic Schreber case. Niederland goes back to the real history of the subject of the paper, Schreber himself, and illustrates how the delusions repeated in distorted form actual experiences of the patient at the hands of his father.

I mention this to indicate the ways in which you can move back readily from the immediate clinical symptoms and develop leads for possible information. She may or may not be able to give you the information for which you are looking. It is possible that when the patient was older, the mother might have discussed the father with her.

RESIDENT: She was examined here and hospitalization recommended. She was first admitted to another hospital for eleven weeks. There she quickly lost her gross paranoid ideas, but occasionally became suspicious again. She became quite closely attached to her doctor and the threat of separation was overwhelming.

DR. TARACHOW: Was the doctor male or female?

RESIDENT: Male.

DR. TARACHOW: There is one area of the history that was started in this admission note, but not followed through. There was a comment in the admission history about what led to the first divorce. But then the second divorce was neglected. What was the reason for the first divorce? The husband's real infidelity or delusional infidelity?

RESIDENT: It was just that she grew tired of these marriages. Recently what came up was that after about three years she started to grow tired of each of the marriages. The first divorce was occasioned by her being pregnant by the man who became her second husband. She felt her first husband did not love her.

DR. TARACHOW: When did the delusion of infidelity start?

RESIDENT: The third marriage.

DR. TARACHOW: I see. So the first marriage lasted three years.

RESIDENT: Seven years.

DR. TARACHOW: You said that she got tired of both marriages after three years.

RESIDENT: But the marriage started to go sour . . . in about the third year.

DR. TARACHOW: In both of the first two marriages?

RESIDENT: Yes.

DR. TARACHOW: And how many years after the third marriage got started did the delusions begin?

Resident: About four and a half years, although the depressive elements of the present illness set in a year earlier.

Dr. Tarachow: Also not too far from the third . . . how old was she when this traumatic situation with the father occurred?

Resident: Three years.

Dr. Tarachow: Well, we don't know what it means, but it is an interesting coincidence. One should bear these coincidences in mind. All sorts of issues are expressed in cycles or in some temporal pattern.

If you have a female patient in treatment in the hospital who has been here nine months, do not be surprised if the patient comes up with a pregnancy or a childbirth fantasy. It is common, certainly in office practice where you carry patients over a long time. I had a patient who, every nine months, presented me with a baby. I had her several years. She gave me two, three babies. She was schizophrenic, but she was doing her best to be my wife.

We do not know yet what the three-year period means, but you can be reasonably sure that the alteration of the time in the third marriage, when the period was four and a half years, also has some meaning. Something disturbed the time sequence in which some inner fantasy was being lived through. At this point we do not know what it is. But we would be very much interested in finding out.

Resident: She said it was for this reason that her admission to this hospital was delayed.

Dr. Tarachow: What was the reason for the delay?

Resident: Because she was so close to her doctor there.

Dr. Tarachow: Oh, I see.

Resident: At present she feels she does not know why she has come to this hospital and she would really have liked to remain at the first hospital with the former doctor.

During the past year she developed paranoid symptoms with feelings that her husband was going out with another woman and that her whole family was in this plot to keep this from her. These people were everybody except her mother and her siblings. Her children, the neighbors, and her husband were all in this plot.

DR. TARACHOW: But she excepted her mother and she excepted her siblings. How many siblings did she have?

RESIDENT: Four. There are two older brothers, one older sister, and one younger sister.

DR. TARACHOW: In the delusions everybody is taking part except her mother and the four siblings.

RESIDENT: She felt that there were tape recorders in the house and in her husband's car and that the television set was as we noted before. She would get up during the night at about four or five, with anxiety, palpitations, and the feeling that something was going to happen. All this started in the summer of 1960 at which time she went up to a bungalow colony in the mountains. There she met a man who, she said, tried to become friendly with her; she grew a little panicky at this and came back to the city. It was during this time that her suspicions started toward her husband. The paranoid ideas set in one year ago, when her youngest child was three and a half years old.

DR. TARACHOW: Well, what very simple thing can you say about the onset of this delusion.

RESIDENT: It followed her own desires.

DR. TARACHOW: Yes. Someone came along and stimulated her own wishes for infidelity; she then handled it by projection. She attributed it to her husband. So this man stirred the problem in her, and she denied it and projected it.

RESIDENT: Maybe she projected that someone made a play for her.

DR. TARACHOW: Yes, that is a good suggestion. It might well be that she imagined the sexual approach, that she was for some reason which is not clear to us ready for the outbreak of the delusional system. Someone might have said "Good morning" to her and that to her became a sexual overture. That is a good point to make. It could have been brought up by nothing or by a realistic trifle.

We are interested in what determined the onset at this time. Was it accidental? The soil must certainly have been fertile. What suspicion can we have about the two previous marriages, in each of which she got tired of her husband?

RESIDENT: She had been interested in somebody else or had met somebody else.

DR. TARACHOW: Well, I'll put it this way. What we can suspect is that she had some latent psychotic problems which were not quite ready to break out in an overt delusional form. Perhaps we could suspect a latent psychosis going back for many years. It is possible to have latent delusional ideas or a delusional idea even in a dream. It might be interesting if she could recall any dreams during the first two marriages.

At any rate the point I am making now is that there could have been latent psychotic problems at work in the first two marriages. It would be up to the therapist to go back and to get in detail the relationship and the feelings she had to each husband. Do you have anything about that, anything further at all about the type of men she married? You mentioned that they were consistently weak or one of them was a weak man?

RESIDENT: Both of them were, all three of them were and are. Her first husband was fourteen years older than she. She was happy with him for about three years. However, toward the end of the marriage she sought psychiatric help. She was told that she was stable and that she could go through with a divorce.

DR. TARACHOW: Now, do you know anything more specific about her feelings about the marriage, her feelings to the husband, what her loss of interest was based on? What were the grounds for the divorce?

RESIDENT: The grounds for the first divorce were trumped up. Another thing that I do know was that she did not have an orgasm during that marriage. She has had orgasm with the second two husbands.

DR. TARACHOW: What is the child-bearing history?

RESIDENT: She has four children. Two with the first, one with the second, and one with the third husband.

DR. TARACHOW: What's surprising about having four children with this history? Again, I want only clinical observations.

RESIDENT: It's the basic identification with the father, possibly a lack of female identification. Having children is a female function, yet she does not seem to see herself too clearly as a female; but nevertheless she has all these children.

DR. TARACHOW: The question I would ask does not even go as far as your remarks. What is back of her eagerness to have so many children?

RESIDENT: Her mother had many children.

DR. TARACHOW: How many?

RESIDENT: Five.

DR. TARACHOW: My curiosity would turn to her need to have so many children in the face of the fact that her relationships to her various husbands seemed to be so poor.

RESIDENT: Counterphobic?

DR. TARACHOW: Perhaps, but I don't think so. I am just asking general questions. Here is a woman who seems to want to build up a big family, but her husbands do not seem to mean too much. She may have been repeating the whole pattern of her mother's life. She has really lived out the life of her mother. Her mother had five children, now she has four (plus two stepchildren) and an unfaithful husband. Almost exactly like her mother.

Now what happened to her mother's husband, though? What happened to her mother's husband in that traumatic event?

RESIDENT: He was unfaithful.

DR. TARACHOW: No, what was his fate?

RESIDENT: He died.

DR. TARACHOW: That's not the way to put it: *he was killed.* In view of this, what problem can we perhaps anticipate with this patient?

RESIDENT: She hopes, expects, or fears her husband will die now.

DR. TARACHOW: Or *be killed.* Not so much that, but that unconsciously she may be planning to arrange his death. Now we are getting a real mystery story. Perhaps we are closer to the reasons why the illness developed now. How old is her own fourth child?

RESIDENT: Four and a half years.

DR. TARACHOW: And she has been sick for two years.

RESIDENT: The patient remarried five and a half years ago. The present illness set in two years ago at which time the child would have been two and a half. The paranoid ideas set in a year later when the child was three and a half.

DR. TARACHOW: When her last child was about three, the age at which her father was killed, her delusions set in. She lost interest in her first two husbands after three years. Now if we follow this train of events and accept the concept of the macroscopic transmission of the childhood situation, what can we infer she is waiting for? She is waiting for her husband to be killed, which certainly should be enough to throw her into a depression. She is restaging her mother's life in her own. She is the author of the repetitive pattern. In her delusion there is another woman in the picture and she is unconsciously waiting for this woman to kill her husband. The illness, her delusional system, set in just the time when her fourth child was about three. Her delusional system is off by one child in unconscious arithmetic. We might recall that the patient herself is a fourth child.

RESIDENT: Did she have the fantasy that her mother killed her father?

DR. TARACHOW: You never quite know what a child thinks. The mother pleaded with the father to stay home and not visit the woman. The mother then turned away from the father to pay attention to the patient, and while the mother's back was turned, the father went off to the other woman and was killed. The girl at three could well have blamed herself for her father's death.

RESIDENT: This was the feeling that I got when she told me the story.

DR. TARACHOW: She feels she is to blame for her father's death. Now, do you see why it is so important to pay close attention to dates, to position in the family, to time? We do not know whether the story we have built up is true, but at least it is plausible. Do not underestimate the patients' need to create reality to suit the inner fantasy. Orens (1958) wrote a paper emphasizing just this point. And our patient needed a delusion to create it. I would even say that there is a danger of this woman killing her husband. On the basis of the history and our construction, we have to assume there is a danger that she will murder her husband.

RESIDENT: The technique that she was using was projection. If she should have a psychotic break again, I wonder whether the next delusion would be that he is dead as opposed to actually killing him.

DR. TARACHOW: That is a possibility, but do not underestimate the fact that depressed patients are murderers and paranoid patients are murderers. I will never forget a patient I saw as a first-year resident at the Psychiatric Institute, a man who went into an agitated depression because he feared something terrible was going to happen to his eldest son. He was hospitalized and was at the Institute for a number of months. After a time when he seemed calmed down, he was sent home on a week-end pass: he then murdered his son. That was the terrible thing he feared that was going to happen to his son.

I would be interested, in terms of clinical symptoms, what the anxieties were that woke her at four and five in the morning? Did they have any object? Was there any phobia? Had there been any worries or fears about the husband? She seems to develop delusions that people are protecting her husband's good name, concealing his misbehavior from her. Did she have any worries about her husband in any of this time? In the delusion there seems to be an attempt to protect herself from having any hostility to her husband.

RESIDENT: Her nocturnal phobia was that something terrible was going to happen. I wonder at what time of night her father was killed?

DR. TARACHOW: That's a good question.

RESIDENT: I don't know what time.

DR. TARACHOW: Clinically, I am convinced that this woman is reliving that early situation; that unconsciously now is the time for her husband to die, as her father did; and that she has the anxiety about it and that there is a clinical danger of her committing murder. I would really be concerned.

I had a woman patient who was depressed, whose mother had committed suicide after giving birth to a third child. The patient went into a depression and came to see me. The depression set in after the birth of her second child. During the course of treatment she became pregnant a third time and wanted to go ahead with the pregnancy and delivery. The husband wanted it and the patient wanted it, but I refused to permit her to go ahead with the third pregnancy. I insisted on a therapeutic abortion against the patient's wish and against the husband's wishes. I took her to a hospital which is a notoriously difficult place in which to have therapeutic abortions done and gave them precisely these grounds: there was danger of this woman reliving her mother's fate, that is, committing suicide after delivering a third child. The abortion was done.

In our case today we see a beautiful example of an almost perfect repetition. I would certainly oppose this patient's having a fifth child. The possibility of a perfect repetition would then be set up.

RESIDENT: I don't follow her killing her husband. Why would she do the killing?

DR. TARACHOW: In the sense that the fantasy must be carried out.

RESIDENT: I had another thought. There seems to be some identification with this three-year-old child now as herself. She was the cause of her father's death, so to speak. I wonder if she has some feelings about this child?

DR. TARACHOW: So she has to carry it through to prove it, that she is the cause of the death, you see.

RESIDENT: Also if she kills her husband, she becomes the mistress of the father.

DR. TARACHOW: Well, we need not get too speculative. I think as far as we've gone, we're not stretching anything unduly.

RESIDENT: That would be descriptively what was happening. Could you postulate some dynamics for the need to repeat?

DR. TARACHOW: The need to repeat is predicated on the fact that we have an inner set of fantasies as to what life is, what mother is, what father is, what love is, what disappointment is. In a certain sense we cannot act outside the limits of those fantasies. We relentlessly proceed to create a life which conforms to those fantasies. I will give you the simplest example of a fantasy a patient of mine had this morning. He was approaching my office and saw a man walk out of a house which he assumed was my office. His immediate thought was: "That must be Dr. Tarachow's younger brother." Why should he assume that I have a younger brother? He has a younger brother. Look for this kind of transmission of the family pattern; your patients repeat it over and over again. The dynamic force in it is the limit of one's own experience. You are inexorably bound by the limits of your own childhood experience. And to get beyond it really involves quite a struggle. That's one reason why there is so much turmoil in adolescence when attempts are made to break out of the family bonds.

RESIDENT: What about, "I've been depressed all my life?"

DR. TARACHOW: What she has been saying is that she has been carrying a burden of guilt all her life. She was not aware of it before. Oddly enough, what she is telling you is true; in a latent sense, she has been guilty all her life. One gets the impression that she took the blame for her father's death; it was her demand on mother that caused the mother to abandon father: at that moment the father went out and was killed. So when she says, "I've been depressed all my life," in the clinical sense it is not true. I do not think she has had a conscious depression all her life. But in the sense of her total mental content it is true because she has been blaming herself for her father's death. She has had a latent depression all her life.

What is happening in her delusions is perfectly logical and represents a re-creation of earlier reality. I would not want to be in the husband's shoes.

RESIDENT: I was wondering what the grounds were for the second divorce. I think the grounds were mental cruelty. The circumstances were also not very definite. She said that she gradually grew tired, no longer loved him, and wanted to break it off. Again it was about the third year when she started to have these feelings.

DR. TARACHOW: It's fascinating. This woman spent her life preparing for this psychosis. She was building her life for the point at which she could repeat her experience at the age of three. The husbands as individuals did not matter.

RESIDENT: Would you expect, if it is a repetition of early experiences, to find other parallels, for example, the season in which it occurred?

DR. TARACHOW: The seasons in this instance do not match. Depression will often have a relationship to the seasons of the year. Patients will have depressions every spring or every summer, and have a manic attack in the fall. They may react inversely to the biological growth processes in nature. When things are budding and growing, they will go into a depression. When things are dying, they deny it and become manic.

RESIDENT: There might be another repetition involved. I wonder how old the children were when she left the first two husbands and whether or not part of the reason for parting with them was related to this central fantasy?

DR. TARACHOW: Yes, in view of our trying to establish a pattern, that is a good question. Did she flee in defense against the idea of his inevitable death? Did she leave her first husband when one of her children was age three and did she leave her second husband when that child was age three?

RESIDENT: What were their sexes?

DR. TARACHOW: Well, she could not determine that. She has to accept the sexes. But what were they? We'll see. What were the sexes of the first two children?

RESIDENT: The first two, one girl and one boy.

DR. TARACHOW: That marriage lasted seven years, and she had a boy and a girl and we want a three-year-old child, a daughter.

RESIDENT: A two-year-old boy and a six-year-old boy.

DR. TARACHOW: I'm sorry, it doesn't work. But it is a good question. It's a good question because if we believe in intrapsychic determinism, we take a dynamic view of a history, and we accept it (and we certainly have a persuasive picture built up for the onset of the psychosis); we could also look for the same thing, for a similar set of factors that made her get rid of her husbands. But maybe we won't get it. . . .

RESIDENT: Well, there was a girl who was six. She said the marriage was happy for only three years. After three years she started to become upset, from the time the child was three.

DR. TARACHOW: Yes, the three might well have to do with the onset of symptoms. What I am interested in at this moment is the onset of her present illness when her current marriage was three and a half years old. The arithmetical pattern is not perfect. We expect a three-year interval; we're after the half-year difference, as to why trouble began a little bit later than in the earlier marriages. Well, we cannot explain everything. But at any rate the total picture certainly is a persuasive one. I think it is an interesting exercise, to see how clearly the repetition of early life experience comes out, and to pay attention to the histories, and to see to what extent you can work these things out. It is quite dramatic here, even though not perfect. The paranoid delusions set in when the marriage was four and a half years old and the child three and a half.

RESIDENT: I think we should also see how many times this occurs by chance, even though all these things seem to fit in. We are ignoring the areas where they do not fit in and just seem to be glossing over inconsistencies. The patient is thirty-nine, the mother was twenty-nine, and it was four-and-a-half years, not three years. It occurred during the winter, the other one during autumn. The thinking here is *sympatico,* but not precise.

DR. TARACHOW: You are right, it is not a statistical study and we do not have any coefficient of correlation here; the *n* is only one. But in terms of clinical psychiatry, look for this kind of repetition. You are going to find it and you are going to find it over and over again, in practically every patient. If you look for it as a clinician, if you look for the types of marriages, you will not find it filled out in as many details as in this case, but you will find it. And if you bear this idea in mind, it will help you clinically because you will be looking for clinical data and looking for clinical connections that otherwise you won't be alerted to.

I agree with you that this is not statistical; it is a clinical impression. I would like you to check with your own data. You will be amazed at the consistency with which childhood patterns are repeated. Exact repetition should immediately focus your clinical attention.

RESIDENT: I recently read of women who have a psychotic breakdown after the birth of one child. These women lost one parent and their psychotic breaks occurred when their child was the same age that they were when they lost their parent, in a statistically significant number.

DR. TARACHOW: I will refer you to another paper (Tarachow and Fink, 1953), which deals with the loss of a parent as a specific factor in the choice of neurosis. We established a positive statistical correlation between loss of a parent and type of illness. We had an idea that loss of a parent was correlated with a predilection to failure of fusion of ambivalence, as characterized by obsessional symptoms against hysterical. Patients with hysteria tend to have both parents, patients with obsessional neurosis tend to lose a parent before the age of fourteen or fifteen. The hypothesis had to do with the resolution of problems of ambivalence. We studied a group of hysterics and a group of obsessional neurotics. The significant difference in the incidence of presence of both parents as against loss of one parent was remarkable.

At the time of the study, we were quite excited about it. We could look at the diagnosis and we felt we could predict whether there were one or two parents in the family.

RESIDENT: Were you really choosing the correct frame of reference?

DR. TARACHOW: We selected one variable and established a correlation. This seminar is not designed to establish research methods. This is a clinical seminar and we are trying to be clinically helpful. I assure you that the repetition of the early childhood life in the later adult life is a helpful clinical idea. Clinically we are irresistibly driven to repeat our childhood pattern. I think I have previously mentioned a woman who married a morphine addict. Her mother had been married to a morphine addict.

RESIDENT: What happens to a patient who is not able to repeat a pattern? The patient presented today was lucky, she had a stepchild. She may have picked the child as the focus for the delusional repetition.

DR. TARACHOW: We really do not know. Perhaps the delusion would have waited until she had still another baby with the third husband. That would be a clinical presumption; perhaps the delusion would have waited until she rounded out her own family to consist of five of her own children. This is a guess. We do know that this patient's delusional system set in after she had four children of her own. The failure of the precise repetition of her mother's pattern should also interest and alert us. What were the factors influencing this? We cannot answer all the questions. The patient is a fourth child.

Apparently the arithmetic of the patient's childhood does not quite coincide with the arithmetic of the delusion and the adult life. However, for didactic purposes the line of reasoning we followed is still one I recommend to you. This is the type of imaginative thinking which will help you grasp the pattern of a patient's life or delusions; even though there were errors in this patient's unconscious arithmetic.

Chapter 15

Obsessive-Compulsive Defenses

Introduction and Principle of Management

My introductory comment about obsessive-compulsive neurosis will be simply that it is the most severe of all the psychoneuroses. It is a state characterized by marked ambivalence, extreme depths of anal regression, and archaic and magical thinking. Most notably of all, it is a disease of sadism and aggression. The erotic, libidinal component is vehemently denied and suppressed.

In a patient struggling with such problems of aggression and magical thinking, the defenses necessarily take urgent and desperate forms. The treatment of these individuals is extremely lengthy and very taxing to the therapist.

In our seminar we shall be occupied mainly with a discussion of typical obsessive defenses.

The principle in the treatment of obsessional defenses is to bridge the affective isolation. In the compulsives, in the obsessionals, the affect is avoided: one has little trouble uncovering content. The patient thrusts the content at you. For his own comfort and defense the patient has established affective distance from the content. In the approach suggested here the archaic anality and sadism will not be dealt with. Much useful therapeutic work can be done by working only with the superficial derivatives of the archaic problems.

The principal defense is isolation of affect, but there are other important symptomatic defenses. These include rumination, intellectualization, doing and undoing, displacement, reaction formation. These patients are extremely stubborn. They are a prey to indecision and do a great deal of doubting. The doubting goes along with the doing and undoing. It is a way of making something exist that the patient is afraid to own up to; on the other hand, it is a way of undoing something that he has already done, or thought. They are hostile and they tease. These are patients who are very annoying and provoking, sometimes in ways that you do not quite notice: the therapist's mood of irritation might mount and he might not know the reason why.

For example, you ask such a patient a question, "How old were you when your sister was born?" The patient responds, "How old was I when my sister was born? Oh, I was six." What do you make of this? Characterize this patient. He is giving you a great deal of information about himself.

RESIDENT: He was meticulous and restated your question. Or, he could not answer with spontaneity. There is something that interfered with communication, so he had to repeat the question.

RESIDENT: He was obviating your question.

DR. TARACHOW: Possibly, but can you develop your thought a bit more?

RESIDENT: Yes. He was resisting by postponing the answer.

DR. TARACHOW: There is a strong resistance to giving.

RESIDENT: He is stingy.

DR. TARACHOW: But he *did* give me the answer.

RESIDENT: But you were made to wait for it: he controlled the answer.

DR. TARACHOW: There is something else. He was answering

his own question, not yours. He did not answer you, he answered himself. He said, "How old was I when my sister was born?" He became the doctor too: he avoided being simply a patient. Just a bit of behavior like this can give you a world of information about the patient. Repeated often enough such behavior might build up annoyance in the therapist.

You will find this type of behavior in spiteful obsessional people. The marvelously successful element in obsessional and compulsive symptoms is the beautiful union of deference with spitefulness. The Uriah Heep is the most stubborn person under the sun. The most conciliatory is the most stubborn. Ask a question and the patient seems to relish your question and asks it again. You think you have a really cooperative patient, but you do not. He will not even let you ask the questions. But he does it in a very nice and presumably submissive way, in a way you might not even notice.

A few years ago in one of these conferences, a resident presented a patient who would open each session by saying, "How are you today?" I pointed out that the patient was reversing the roles. I suggested that the way to get the patient to see this was perhaps with a remark like, "It's no fun being the patient, is it?"—in other words, to turn it right back again; in a gentle, half-humorous way to remind the patient that *he* is the patient and not the doctor. The following week the resident reported back to the seminar. "A very interesting thing happened. The patient as usual came in and said, 'How are you today?' and I said to him, 'It's not much fun being the patient, is it?' " At the end of the session the patient said, "Well, good-by Mr. M." I thought that was beautiful.

These items come through and tell you with what you are struggling. You are struggling not only with symptoms. You are struggling with a person who has a certain way of life. No matter what the specific symptoms are, the neurosis is a way of approaching people and situations, in this instance a stubborn and spiteful way. Such an issue as the patient's rejection of the role of patient will have to be worked through time and time again.

Isolation from the Therapist

Another aspect is the patient's isolation from the therapist. For example, you have an obsessional patient who is getting along pretty well—for reasons which are not too clear—but he is getting along well, doing better. The patient comes in one day and says, "You know, I'm really feeling much better. Psychiatry is a wonderful thing." I'd like your comments on that remark. The patient is feeling better and is grateful.

RESIDENT: He could be isolating the affect he has for you.

DR. TARACHOW: That's it. He does not say, "You're a good doctor." He says, "Psychiatry is wonderful." Occasionally a patient will say, "I'm feeling much better. Freud was a wonderful man." You are not the wonderful man, Freud was.

RESIDENT: Well, what do you do with a patient who is always telling you that you are a wonderful doctor?

DR. TARACHOW: Look out for the knife.

How would you approach a patient who comes in and says, "Psychiatry is really wonderful". What would be a tactful approach to this patient's difficulty? Why did the patient have to say, "Psychiatry is wonderful," instead of saying, "Dr. R. or Dr. G. or Dr. M., you're wonderful, you really helped me."

RESIDENT: He's afraid of the closeness.

DR. TARACHOW: Yes, but let us say this is psychotherapy. You don't want to stimulate homosexual problems. Try to pitch a response to this patient in a way that is helpful but still will *not* uncover too much material.

RESIDENT: You might say, "As your psychiatrist . . . "—in other words, include yourself in the body of psychiatry.

DR. TARACHOW: Yes, that could be one method, to bridge the isolating gap for the patient. But I am thinking of a reaction on your part that has *some* interpretive function. You suggested a helpful response. You lifted the patient over the problem, which is perfectly good under psychotherapeutic conditions, but I am looking for a gentle interpretive response, as gentle as could be.

RESIDENT: It's difficult for you to give thanks.

DR. TARACHOW: Yes, that's it. I would say, "You really are grateful to me, but you have some trouble expressing gratitude or expressing any sense of obligation." You have given the patient a task and still not pointed too sharply in any intimate direction. Telling the patient that he is afraid of closeness is anxiety provoking. We are trying to stay away from the homosexual problem. You can make a helpful noninterpretive response, or offer a response that has only a little bit of an interpretation to it—enough to help but hopefully not enough to stir up anything too critical.

RESIDENT: I was thinking this might also be a hostile or sarcastic expression.

DR. TARACHOW: We were going on the assumption that the patient was really feeling better, had the problem of gratitude, and was fumbling with expressing his gratitude.

RESIDENT: Would the following question be appropriate? "Would I be included in psychiatry?" and in this way find out whether you were included, then say, "You seem to have some difficulty in giving thanks."

DR. TARACHOW: It all depends on how much you think the patient can tolerate, because the response,, "Am I included?" points to the patient's hostility. If you say "Am I included?" then you are implicitly saying, "But you might not be including me." Then you are pointing to the patient's ambivalence, i.e., his hostility. You would be responding to a patient's feeble effort to give thanks by labeling it hostility.

All I was looking for was the gentlest kind of interpretation and assistance. The issue of shame or difficulty in expressing gratitude or friendliness is a very useful pathway for patients, particularly in the early months of treatment. You should sympathize with their difficulty in communication. They are ashamed of their feelings. They are ashamed even of being in treatment. They are ashamed of having to expose themselves. They are ashamed even of being helped by you.

RESIDENT: How about asking the patient, "What is there about psychiatry that you think was of help to you and—?" If he answers in a personal way, you have helped him bridge the emotional gap.

DR. TARACHOW: In many instances, "What do you think?" is a perfectly good follow-through. But it is not the tangent I wanted you to notice. There never is just one correct intervention.

RESIDENT: Do you think there could be a situation where the patient states that he feels better and psychiatry is wonderful and does not feel gratitude toward you? I mean he really does not feel that you played an active role.

DR. TARACHOW: If you are looking for gratitude, stay out of psychiatry! He might not really feel grateful to you; it's possible.

The lesson of the day is, the patient is better and grateful, but he cannot express his gratitude. If *you* try to bring yourself in, the patient will demolish you with, "Why do you think you had anything to do with it?"

We frequently see a certain type of patient who gets a great deal of help from his psychiatrist but cannot permit this psychiatrist to feel that he has accomplished anything. He must rob the psychiatrist of pleasure; you finally have to transfer this patient to another psychiatrist. Then in a matter of a few weeks or months the real improvement will reassert itself. At that point these patients need not be grateful to any one person; they have outwitted two doctors. The first one who really helped the patient does not know that he helped him, and the second one who thinks he helped him really did not. So the patient gets away from the situation of ever having to be appreciative to anybody. These people are embittered. It takes a great deal of tolerance on the part of the therapist to help them overcome this.

The following situation will often present itself. The patient will develop some ideas entirely in agreement with what you are thinking. He knows this. When he has completed his trend of thought he will say, "This is what you think doctor, don't you? Well, I don't believe a word of it."

If you are looking for gratitude, avoid obsessional patients. If you need it, work only with hysterics. A frequent response from an obsessional to an interpretation is, "Oh, yes, I heard that yesterday," or "Someone told me that two weeks ago." They do not let you enjoy your work. But what I also wanted to stress is the following situation: you work through something that is very convincing to everybody but the patient. Nothing can be more convincing than a certain sequence of experiences or dreams. Though the meaning is quite obvious, the patient is not convinced. Months later he will read it in a book and come back and tell you he accepts the idea since an authority who wrote a book said so. They will not accept the idea from you, but they will from an *impersonal* source, and/or *not* the therapist. Some patients simply will not get well during treatment. In despair you discharge a patient as unimproved. To your amazement he will come back a year or two later to tell you how much better he is.

Another patient starts a session as follows: "You called me into your office and the moment the door opened I had a sensation in my genitals." What is that patient trying to tell me?

RESIDENT: He is having sexual feelings toward you.

DR. TARACHOW: No, the answer simply is, "I like you." In this instance, the defense is to take a total attitude or total feeling and convert it into a local feeling, one which can even be disowned. This patient would rather admit to a sexual feeling than say, "I was glad to see you." Furthermore, the sexual feeling is not even recognized as a sexual feeling.

With patients of this type, you have to find the simplest kinds of relationships that you can think of. This elementary type of interpretation in these highly intellectualized people will eventually reach them. You will be astonished at the emotional outburst or emotional capacity that these people will show eventually.

Isolation of the Treatment Session

Now let us turn to another problem. Some time back I compared two ways of isolating the treatment session. On the one hand, there is the patient who isolates his session by making some remark to you, either when he comes in or when he leaves, or at both times. By implication, this is his way of saying, "This remark is my real contact with you. Everything else was just nonsense." The patient uses a device like that to render the treatment meaningless. In this instance you have to interfere with the patient's making these remarks and interpret them. You must establish the connection between the treatment session and the patient's life.

On the other hand, I described other patients who are isolated from you in a more total way. They do not make any remarks to you at the beginning or at the end of a session: they are completely isolated from you. Even though they talk to you during the session, you have the feeling that they are isolated; and they regard the entire treatment and relationship to you in a detached and isolated manner. With such patients you should go out of your way to reach out with some words and establish contact with them, before or after the session if necessary. You must establish that you are in the patient's life. So with these two types of patients you behave quite differently, even though both have tried to isolate themselves from you. Your purpose is the same in both.

RESIDENT: With the first type who makes the opening or closing remarks, would you interpret this even with a schizophrenic patient?

DR. TARACHOW: Yes and no. The isolation aspect can safely be interpreted, but do not rob the schizophrenic of any of his devices of attachment to you. It is not too dangerous to interpret this to any other type of patient. With regard to a schizophrenic patient, though, it might be unwise to forbid the before and after contact even though this contact has a defensive purpose; he might feel rebuffed or pushed away. A schizophrenic patient might want to isolate his session, but also want to preserve his contact with you by means of the remarks at the beginning and at the end of the session. You would have to be sure what you think this means to the patient. I would hesitate to forbid any kind of contact that a psychotic has with me. I permit psychotic patients to talk to me both before and after the session "officially" opens and closes, so to speak. You must weigh the helpful importance of the contact against the isolating purpose of the devices used by the patient. With a psychotic patient I would not interfere with his attempts at establishing contacts. If he talks about the weather, I talk about the weather. If he talks about my cold, I'll tell him about it. With psychotics, I would in general tend to answer and treat everything in a realistic way. Do not push your psychotic patient away from you.

A Variety of Isolation

I now want to read a letter a patient sent me recently. He had been in treatment with me for about a year and then broke off. I had not heard from him for about a year when I received the letter. In the meantime I learned he had been seeing another analyst. The letter is as follows: "Dear Doctor: I have discussed with Dr. X a return to your office for a sincere attempt to complete the work we started. It is with his understanding that I write and tell you that after September 5th, I would like to have the first 8:30 A.M. five times a week that occurs. I will look forward to hearing from you."

Which features of the letter give you diagnostic clues?

RESIDENT: He is obviously obsessive-compulsive. He uses, "return to your office" instead of return to treatment.

DR. TARACHOW: Yes, the word office instead of the personal reference.

RESIDENT: He said Doctor. Did he say Dr. Tarachow?

DR. TARACHOW: Good. He did not say Dr. Tarachow. He said, "Dear Doctor." He was not as specific as he might have been.

RESIDENT: The word "sincere." Is he indicating that he has not been sincere in the past?

DR. TARACHOW: Well, the "sincere attempt" I think is his attempt to struggle against all the isolating devices he had used in the past. This man spent about twelve or fourteen months with me. After about eight or nine months, he said one day: "You know, people have been telling me, 'Compared to six months ago you're a changed fellow. Something's happening to you and there's something different about you. It's much easier to get along with you.' " Then he stopped and said, "I know what you're thinking. You're thinking that he's going to say that son of a bitch in back of the couch doesn't have a God damn thing to do with my improvement, and you're right."

RESIDENT: Well, there's another point. He does not call you. He writes. If you actually wanted to indicate to him that you could take him, you would still have to talk to him. You would still have to get in touch with him and say, "Well, now I have such and such an hour available."

DR. TARACHOW: That's right. He did not actually ask me in person. He forced me to come to him, which I did. I called him and I told him I was very glad to get his letter.

RESIDENT: I was struck by something else. I do not know whether he left you for this other person or whether he saw you and the other fellow simultaneously.

DR. TARACHOW: He did not see us at the same time, though patients will do that on occasion; they will be in treatment with two psychiatrists concurrently. This has happened to me twice. This is an interesting subject in itself. In one such instance it was clear that one psychiatrist was the good parent and the other was the bad parent. (I was the bad one in that case: I tried to analyze the patient.)

RESIDENT: He makes it easy for you to turn him down.

DR. TARACHOW: Yes. He reduced the personal risk to a minimum in this letter. He did not ask me directly. It is only an exchange of letters; and he makes it as impersonal as possible. The address or the salutation is Dear Doctor, not Dear Doctor Tarachow. The signature is his first name and his last initial. He does not even sign his entire name.

RESIDENT: Also, "I would appreciate," instead of "Will you please." He is making a statement.

DR. TARACHOW: The whole thing looks like a very formal business letter. This man is formal all the time except when he is telling me what a jerk I am. Then he speaks in plain English. But otherwise he is extremely formal.

RESIDENT: I think his attempt to control the situation is indicated by the manner in which he says, "If you want me, I will be available to you at 8:30 five times a week." He does not say, "When can you see me?"

I would like to ask you a technical question. You said that this patient is neurotic, not psychotic. When you called him, why did you tell him you were glad to hear from him?

DR. TARACHOW: This man's isolation was so great that I really wanted to welcome him back and make the return to me as easy for him as possible. This man creates injuries for himself. I did not want to react to him with the formality with which he approached me. If I came back to him and said, "Dear Sir: I would be pleased to see you on January 15," we would be two business men discussing some third party or two neurotics both using the same compulsive defenses. I tried to make it as personal as possible—something which incidentally he always resisted. For example, if he came late on a certain day, he would go to enormous pains to show that his reactions to me had nothing to do with his coming late. I, of course, took just the opposite tack. We sometimes had bitter tussles because this man would always try to show me that these bits of acting out had nothing to do with the treatment, nothing to do with the analysis. So when he wrote the letter, which was very difficult for him to do, I rewarded him. This man is not psychotic, but he is a severe neurotic.

RESIDENT: He will leave you again.

DR. TARACHOW: He did eventually. I was this man's fifth analyst. He had been to four other analysts. So I consider that this wasn't bad. He left me but came back. He left all the others and went to someone else. One of the reasons why he leaves is that, having gained something from one analyst, he has to flee from his sense of obligation.

RESIDENT: Has this been interpreted, this sort of reaction?

DR. TARACHOW: To be sure, but don't overestimate the power of your words. You may interpret something quite accurately, but that does not mean the patient is going to accept it. This is a man who would throw back at me in the most bitter and sarcastic fashion almost everything I would say.

What kind of toilet training do you think this man had?

RESIDENT: Early and severe.

DR. TARACHOW: That's right. This was so. Early and severe. Do you think this man had an affectionate or unaffectionate relationship to his parents?

RESIDENT: Unaffectionate.

DR. TARACHOW: Yes. He wanted to kill his parents. Well, I won't go into that, but it should be possible to work out family structure from just this. Sometimes one can take a bit of data and work out an entire family structure.

RESIDENT: I have noticed that obsessive-compulsive patients always have a prodding mother, one who pries into their affairs, looks through their drawers, listens in on telephone conversations, opens their mail. Is this something you have noted?

DR. TARACHOW: I do not recall prying mothers, but prodding, yes, in the sense of controlling. If you add the word "disciplining," you begin to cover the attitude of the parent a little better than the word "prodding." They discipline. They go through their children's drawers to make sure that everything is clean and orderly, and they count up the pairs of socks. They count their underwear, count their shirts. They see that their things are in the right place, that sort of thing. That provokes hatred and compulsiveness and compulsiveness in return, but there are also compulsive people whose family background has been very lenient. Neurotic symptoms can arise from two areas of difficulty. In a classic paper, Freud (1937) indicated that either development has been very traumatic or the instincts themselves were too intense, too powerful. If you have a patient who has been subject to no discipline whatever, the instincts, the inner emotions and impulses tend to overwhelm the child, and he has to erect powerful neurotic defenses against them. Pathological parental leniency is a source of difficulty too.

Isolated Memories

Another kind of isolation that one sometimes encounters is isolation of memories. It is always interesting to discover what a patient's early memories are; many patients have several memories which they recall from early periods of their lives. I would say that it is especially interesting to ask about the memories that cluster around the ages of four, five, and six. Especially in obsessional neurotics, an effort should be made to get these memories. Patients will reveal these memories readily: they might seem disconnected and unrelated. Sometimes one finds a connection between them. These isolated memories often state certain cause and effect relationships. One might be a memory of a crime, the other might be a memory of the punishment. One might be a memory involving excitement, and one might be a memory concerning reprisal or defeat. Sometimes these memories state the essential activity or activities of the patient of this particular age period. The patient is able to remember them clearly because he sees no connection between them. These clusters of disconnected memories can sometimes be put together.

For example, one patient had a memory of a brutal beating at the hands of his mother, and another memory of climbing up on a freshly made bed and having a bowel movement right in the center of a clean white bedspread. The two memories, the two incidents had actually taken place at separate times. They might have occurred six months or a year apart. These isolated memories tell something about this period of the patient's life, his struggle against a very harsh mother and the punishment.

These isolated memories may be telling you a consecutive story; they are really giving you cause and effect. They are like two dreams in one night: one dream is cause, the other is effect.

Isolated Love-Making

There are all sorts of defenses. For example, there is a certain kind of psychopathic behavior which is also a variety of obsessional defense. We have talked about splitting love from hatred, one mixed feeling from another. We talked about splitting sexual from tender feelings. There are all sorts of splits that compulsive individuals set up.

I want to mention the subway love-maker. I do not know how familiar you are with this disorder. The only patients I know who do this are men, although I presume there are women who go at this actively too, since these men always find women to respond to them. These patients press up against women in crowded subways or buses. There seems to be a proper way of doing it; the proper way is never to let on to the woman that anything is going on, and the woman never lets on to the man that she knows what is going on. Meanwhile there is a romance going on with a good deal of sexual excitement and gratification. The cardinal rule is that there be no speech, no motion, no verbal personal contact. The man makes contact from behind. He does not see or touch the front of the woman's body. What is the isolating element here?

Resident: The anonymity?

Dr. Tarachow: Yes, the anonymity is preserved. These patients never date the girls and never speak to them. I do not want you to get an oversimplified notion of this disorder just because I am trying to highlight one defensive aspect. I would like to take a moment to indicate briefly the various levels and areas of problems at work in such cases. I have treated two such patients. The usual precipitant for this recurrent, compulsive behavior is some disappointment in real life. Such a provocation points to the reassuring, consoling aspect which this love-making represents to the patient. In the act itself, the most characteristic feature is the anonymity and isolation from the woman. No personal relationship is permitted to develop. This aspect points to the spiteful, vengeful component in the patient's make-up. He will not admit to the woman that she is comforting or loving to the patient. A further area of interest lies in the specifically sexual aspects of the symptomatology. The approach is from behind and there is no contact with the vagina or vaginal region. Looking at the front of the woman is excluded. What was most exciting to one of my patients were bare, rough women's legs. His image of a subway crowded with women was that of a huge mass above with many legs extending below; this has some of the characteristics of a Medusa fantasy. In other words, the symptomatology leads us in the direction of the problem of castration denial. The actual sight of the vagina was disgusting. Another striking characteristic of this type of love-making was immobility. There was no movement and there were no sounds. It is rather paradoxical that these patients seek out a private mode of love-making characterized by no motion and no sound in the midst of a crowded, jammed, noisy subway. At any rate, the immobility was related to an aversion to motion and movement in the sexual act; it was a defense against violence and aggression in sexuality.

I point out all these aspects to indicate that no case is as simple as our discussions might be leading you to believe. We have been dealing with defenses one by one, isolation in this case. Isolation is a factor in *one* aspect of this patient's problem.

On the other hand, isolation can be a factor in a variety of ways, too. It can be a factor in the patient's methods of dealing with his own impulse and emotional life; it may be part of his symptoms, his relationship to the therapist, his relationship to reality; and it may even be a factor in the way in which he remembers his past.

Split Object Choice

Another difficulty in obsessional neurotics is not only the split away from feelings but a split of object choice. A fairly common type of compulsive disorder is that of a patient falling in love with two people at the same time. This may follow one of several patterns. One common pattern is to be tender and loving to one and cruel to the other. Another common pattern is to be both married and have a mistress or lover, to have no sexual feelings to the spouse and be capable of intense sexual passion only with the lover. Any comments?

RESIDENT: The man has been unable to fuse the two images of women. They are either pure or debased sexual objects. This is normal in adolescence, but not in adult life.

DR. TARACHOW: Correct. Now take it a bit farther back than adolescence.

RESIDENT: There is a split of the two views of mother, either as pure and beloved or the degraded sexual object.

DR. TARACHOW: The mother is the desexualized, idealized person. Characteristically men develop the need for a mistress only after their wives have had the first baby, i.e., have become mothers. Then they find they are incapable of sexual interest in their wives. They find themselves falling in love with mistresses as the only way to mobilize sexual passion; it is the struggle between the two images of mother, the idealized image of mother and the degraded image of the mother submitting to the revolting experience with the father.

In varying degrees this split image is present in everybody. In which type of case would you think treatment will move along more smoothly, more easily, the one in which the neurotic has both a wife with whom he cannot have intercourse plus a mistress with whom he can, or a neurotic who has his mixed feelings directed to his wife?

RESIDENT: The second one would be easier.

DR. TARACHOW: Yes, when all the feelings are still directed to one object you're better off and the patient is better off. The technical problem in cases of splits in object choice is to find the original infantile object to whom both sets of feelings were directed. So long as each relationship is regarded as a separate problem, the treatment will go on indefinitely. You will find traces of the opposite in either relationship. This gives the therapist a foothold for treatment. If the man has a split object choice, he also has split feelings to all women, although one side of the ambivalence might be almost completely latent. In a murderer one may find passive feelings, and in a very passive man you will find murderous feelings.

RESIDENT: Actually the man with a mistress has much more affect toward the mistress than toward the wife. That would be a displacement in a way.

DR. TARACHOW: No. He has as much affect to his wife as to the mistress. This is precisely the error to avoid. Don't fall into the patient's trap. The patient has split feelings about all women and has relieved himself of the conflict by finding what seems to be a wonderful and easy way out. He loves this one and hates the other one, or is interested in one and not the other. However, he both loves and hates *all* women: the therapist has to find the original object to whom this mixture of love and hate was directed. Finding this conflict between two opposing feelings intolerable, the patient finally had to split his feelings or his objects. This is isolation too, but it is isolation of one feeling from another feeling. Your job as a therapist is to produce a fusion of the two feelings; no love is ever absolutely pure. When a patient tells you, "I never quarrel with my wife," you can be sure he is very sick; or when he says, "I never had an angry thought about my wife," there is something the matter. There is a mixture of ambivalent feeling in all normal relationships. The fact that a patient can get sexually excited by a mistress and remain completely inert to his wife should not mislead you.

RESIDENT: The movie *Captain's Paradise* is an example of just this thing.

DR. TARACHOW: Yes, you're absolutely to the point. Not only is that movie a good portrayal of a man who split his object choice, but the women also showed the split in their own characters. Before the movie is over, it is clear that both women wanted both sides. The wife wanted the Bikini bathing suit and the mistress wanted to cook. There is a paper by Helene Deutsch (1933) which discusses precisely this subject. It deals with a story by Balzac consisting of a series of letters. Two women write letters to one another; one woman is a prostitute and the other is a respectable bourgeois married woman with a number of children. These two women had apparently been schoolgirl companions; in spite of their diverse ways, they had remained intimate friends, even though they were in separate cities and lived far apart. The book presents the contents of the letters; it develops that the prostitute finally comes forward with a great desire to have children and a home, and the woman who had made such a wonderful home and brought up children had tremendous cravings to be a prostitute.

RESIDENT: Do you think that there is something specific in the wife which would lead a man to choose her as his madonna-like creature?

DR. TARACHOW: Oh, yes. The wife generally has some characteristics of what the husband is seeking. She might be frigid. The man's desire to keep his wife asexual and the wife's tendency to be frigid would enter into collusion, the marriage bed thus remaining quite unruffled.

Images and Clouds of Obsessions

A patient of mine is a publisher. He prepared a plan to do a certain piece of work. He presented it to his editor. As he was telling this to me he had a visual fantasy. In the fantasy his editor was holding his nose. He had not yet told me what the Editor thought of his projected piece of work, so I interrupted to say, "You mean the Editor thinks that what you did stinks." He said, "Yes, that's right." All he was capable of having was a visual fantasy of his editor holding his nose. I had to supply the affect for him. Surprising as it might seem, it was a visual image which had no conscious meaning to the patient. This man was a severe obsessional neurotic. At the moment of the fantasy he could establish no meaning or connection. Your therapeutic function is to establish the affect and the meaning. In fact, the interpretation was given simply by supplying the emotion. You cannot be emotionally flat when you supply the missing link. The patient's response then was, "Yes, I was afraid he would think it might stink."

Sometimes the compulsive or obsessive thoughts operate to protect the patient from simple elementary feelings or simple elementary reactions. Patients may have mountainous loads of obsessional thinking. For example, a patient related that when he got out of the subway on the way to my office, he looked up and noticed a man in front of him. The man was wearing a hat and an overcoat and the patient began to think, "What is that? Is it a hat? Is it an overcoat? What is it made of? It's made of cellulose." He then went on into a minute chemical analysis of the man's clothing and his body. He reduced that man and everybody around him to molecules and atoms.

Well, what's the clue?

RESIDENT: He reduces you to molecules.

DR. TARACHOW: No, what's the clue to the understanding of this story?

RESIDENT: He was on his way to see you.

DR. TARACHOW: Yes, that's the clue. He was on his way to see me. He was very angry with me and via this displacement was dissecting me and taking me apart. His hostility was expressed with no affect at all. At other times he would become tremendously involved in looking up at windows where he might see someone. He would then speculate whether that person was a homosexual and go into all sorts of involved thinking. I would take my cue from the situation in which this took place. What it generally turned out to be was the following: he might have been confronted by some simple elementary feeling which he had to conceal behind a florid outburst of obsessional thinking. The obsession was an elaborate hyper-development of the original feeling, so overdeveloped that the original feeling would be lost, in the mountain of thought. If I could find the critical moment for a particular burst of symptoms, the entire obsessive cloud would vanish. The patient could then be confronted by some simple thought or affect. It might be the first of the month and he had to pay my bill.

But at any rate, the basic therapeutic technique is to bridge the affective isolation which the patient has put between himself and his thoughts, between himself and the simple elementary feelings. The number of elementary feelings is really quite small.

RESIDENT: What does stating the emotion do within or to the patient?

DR. TARACHOW: It *might* then be possible for the patient to deal with the feeling of the day.

RESIDENT: Do you deal with it?

DR. TARACHOW: Well that depends on a variety of factors. It depends on whether the treatment is going well or badly. You cannot help or cure everybody, you know; if the treatment is moving in the right direction, the patient can absorb the feeling as his feeling to you, but you have to show him what it is. If he then hides behind another bank of clouds, you are both worse off.

I recall working for years with an obsessive-compulsive patient. This man had florid outbursts, mountains of obsessional thought. I worked with him for years and considered myself successful when I got him, not to solve his problems or to understand why he hated women or why he hated bosses, but simply to the point where he saw he hated them. It took years of work to get this man to work through the isolation from his resentments. He was always getting into trouble with coworkers and never realized how angrily and how sadistically and bitterly he was behaving to them. Consciously he was preoccupied with fantasies of molecular dissolution of human beings and with fantastically intricate evaluations of international politics. He was consciously preoccupied with trying to understand relations between people and chemical analyses of bodies and movements. But in his obsessional absorption, he completely overlooked his actual gestures and actions to other persons.

It took years to get him to see that he could be or was angry at somebody. This was a tremendous accomplishment for this man. He was quite grateful to be able to recover the feeling of anger to somebody or the feeling of liking somebody. Originally, if he liked someone, he immediately became involved in obsessional ruminations about being a homosexual. The moment he liked a man he promptly felt that he was walking like a pansy, and that his hips were wiggling. If two men spoke to each other in a friendly way, they were both homosexuals. He could not tolerate a simple, elementary, positive or negative feeling.

I did not cure this man; but at least I got him to realize that if he liked somebody, he did not need to take flight into homosexual preoccupations; and if he hated somebody, he did not have to take flight into intricate chemical and physical dissolutions. He was not cured, but his feelings had become more real. Instead of being preoccupied and worried about obsessions, he is now preoccupied and worried about his likes and dislikes. I consider this a satisfactory result.

Resident: Other than defining the affect in a given situation, how else would you go about attempting to do this? Would encouraging a patient to express emotion as much as possible or a directive approach be useful? How else do you attempt to break this isolation?

Dr. Tarachow: Well, you break it every time you help the patient bridge his obsessional distance. We were talking about the use of words. If a patient talks about his genital apparatus, you get him to talk about his penis. A man who was very jealous of his brother saw his brother at a party. The patient told me how he noticed that his brother's digital extremities began to palpate a girl's mammary glands. I said, "You mean your brother was feeling this girl's breasts." He said, "Yes, that's right." This is what I mean by bridging the affective gap. Such patients insulate themselves, and they use language particularly suited for this purpose. Another method of insulation is to have the patient refer to his visits as "treatments." It is treatment: it is a continuum. Such a semantic difference is most important. The therapist should always know at the beginning of a treatment session how the previous session had ended. The patient isolates one session from another by such a defense.

The General As a Defense

Another type of defensive behavior seen not only in obsessionals but also in schizoid characters and schizophrenics is the general as a defense. Let me give a typical question and answer. "Did you sleep well last night?" Answer: "I never sleep well at night." You were given a general answer to a specific question. One must be alert to such qualities in responses. Every such instance does not necessarily indicate severe psychopathology, but you should be alerted to look for severe pathology.

A compulsive male patient who never referred to his penis as "my penis" had problems of impotence. He always referred to it as "the penis". *The* penis was erect, or *the* penis was soft. He was in bed with a girl and *the* penis was doing this and *the* penis was doing that, but it was never "my penis." It was "the penis." He had certainly isolated himself from his sexual apparatus.

RESIDENT: I was going to point out that in a group therapy situation, where the discussion is usually general because it is safer, I observed one patient make personal references. The group descended upon that patient. He had violated the rule, so to speak. The implied rule was to talk about problems only in a very general way.

DR. TARACHOW: Well, I suppose the meaning under such conditions depends on the way in which the leader of the group is pointing the work of the group. Some group leaders will encourage, at least with certain kinds of patients, very specific exposure of personal historical material or symptoms. I have no experience of my own with group therapy. But I presume a group indoctrinated in one direction would behave in that way.

RESIDENT: I have had patients in whom translation from one language to another served the purpose of isolation from the affect involved.

A patient reported a furious argument with her mother. Her mother had said something to her in Yiddish which infuriated her. I asked what her mother had said and she told me, but in a very bland, matter-of-fact, narrative way. The furious argument did not make sense to me. So I asked her, "What did your mother actually say in Yiddish?" She refused to tell me. This refusal lasted a week. When she finally did give me the Yiddish expression, the affect was with it. The actual use of the Yiddish seemed to carry both the affect and the meaning, whereas when she gave her English version of it, she was in control and could express it in a very isolated and cold fashion.

DR. TARACHOW: In the seminar on Acting Out (Chapter 16) we shall discuss the function of the use of foreign expressions. With your patient the rendering of Yiddish into English robbed it of its zest.

Your patient at least, reported an argument. Patients often report arguments as discussions. "I had a discussion with my wife last night." What they really mean is they had an argument. There are all kinds of euphemistic defensive expressions in speech. You will encounter them especially in the reporting of sexual behavior. You must push the patient beyond the euphemism. "Kissing" is a common euphemism for "sucking."

"It's Unconscious"

Another favorite device certain patients exhibit in response to an interpretation is to say, "Oh, that must be unconscious."

RESIDENT: Well, you can point to logical inconsistency there. The patient tells you that it must have been unconscious hostility; but you can point out the fact that since they can talk about it, there must be some awareness.

DR. TARACHOW: If you stick to pure rational thought and logic, you soon become embroiled in a fruitless argument with the patient. The simplest device I have for handling this is to point out to the patient that it is really not as unconscious as he likes to think. Many patients have a certain insight into their own attitudes and their own actions. When you point out something obvious to a patient, for example, that a woman hates her mother-in-law, she will say, "Oh, that must be unconscious." It is your job to demonstrate that it is not nearly as unconscious as they try to lead themselves to believe. They try to render their existence more comfortable by saying, "Oh, it's unconscious." They then have less guilt. If they can label something as unconscious, they are at liberty to have any kind of feeling and also not to recognize it. Another similar, but somewhat more pathological device serving the same purpose is simulation of insanity (Tarachow, 1945). Insanity leaves you free of guilt over any action.

Prefaces

I want to call your attention to a few other types of obsessional symptomatology that lend themselves to interpretation in simple ways. I will mention first the circumlocution of many obsessionals. Obsessionals will say, "I want to tell you what happened to me this morning." Then they launch into one preface after another. They never get to tell you what they started to. They keep you waiting, they tease and tantalize.

This is a common device that should be cut through. Attack the teasing, the sadistic, the delaying, the disappointing, attempts to overwhelm you. This attitude should be and can be interpreted.

RESIDENT: I thought that if you interrupt the patient, you're being hostile; that's what an interruption is. Even if you do not intend it this way, they will interpret it this way nevertheless.

DR. TARACHOW: Not at all. Your interruption is helpful, not hostile. Of course, a patient clinging stubbornly to this type of speech pattern might accuse you of hostility. But if you are making your interruption in a helpful and not an irritated mood, the patient will recognize this. In general, do not permit your patients to throw you on the defensive. The patient's devices of procrastination and circumlocution must be dealt with, equably, though.

RESIDENT: A patient will speak in such a fashion with anyone, not only his therapist.

DR. TARACHOW: That is correct. But you should nevertheless cut into it with your interpretation of what you think it means.

I can mention another common device. The patient might say, "I read yesterday about the British Prime Minister, you know his name, uh, uh, uh." They do not utter the name. Your natural impulse is to supply the name. Then they have made you do their work. They have forced you to give something to them when they should be giving something to you. This is a complicated character trait. It is a mixture of oral greed and anal stubbornness. They want you to put words in their mouths. It is an attempt to convert what should be an active communication into a passive communication. It is a stubborn holding back on the part of the patient. It is like the child who will have only a partial bowel movement; he gives you part and keeps part. I had one adult patient who would not have bowel movements on schooldays: he saved them for the week end at which time he had enormous stools. Beginning Friday afternoons he felt he was his own master; school was out.

So, you have to resist your natural impulse to fill in for the patient and immediately call the patient's attention to what he is doing. This depends on what you think the main current problem is. You can interpret the orality, or you can interpret the anality of it. You can interpret whichever side you think requires interpretation. If it is a patient who is always greedy and always parasitic, and it is the greediness and the parasitism which is the problem, you interpret it that way. If it is a patient who is stubborn and unwilling to give, you interpret that. There is no standard interpretation.

RESIDENT: I have a question about this business of a preface and then another preface. You tell the patient that his endless prefaces represent hostility, and the patient says, "No. I have to tell you these things so that you'll understand and appreciate what I'm going to say and appreciate the significance of it."

DR. TARACHOW: You must stick to your guns and not engage in a quarrel. But I am sure you can find other instances to prove your point, and, if necessary, simply wait and see. You will find the patient doing the same thing again and again.

Simultaneous Trains of Thought

Then there are several other ways, too, in which patients betray their ambivalence and their lack of cooperation. You will sometimes find, particularly in obsessional patients, that "Two or three things come to me all at once and I don't know which to tell you." The patients wish to give you the job of selecting from among their thoughts that which they should tell you. Or the patient may make the choice himself, but forget the other trains of thought. In this way the patient gives you something and holds back something.

Patients will often tell you the most important thought on their way out of the consulting room. This generally indicates they regard this as their only "real" communication. The other communication, within the bounds of the session, is regarded as artificial, unreal, and not spontaneous or voluntary.

Agreement

RESIDENT: I have a patient who, in reaction to every interpretation, says, "That sounds logical." I don't know what to do with that. It's exasperating.

DR. TARACHOW: Such agreement is a marvelous resistance.

RESIDENT: What would you do? I see the compulsive mechanism, but I get lost with it really because it does sound logical to me.

DR. TARACHOW: The psychotherapeutic effort with such a patient is to get him disturbed by what you are saying, even if you have to quarrel with him. The patient might even be challenged. "I'm not so sure you really agree." He has offered you a compliance which renders everything you say completely meaningless. You might tell the patient, "I have a notion that you say this to me regardless of whether you really believe it or not, just to pacify me, to get me to think you are a good patient." I have had patients who could sense what I was going to say and would start giving me confirmatory data before I had even completed my remarks. There is also such a thing as spite by overcompliance. I recall a patient who, as a boy, had been instructed by his harsh mother to report all his activities. One day, while his mother was entertaining several lady friends at tea, he announced in a loud voice he was going to the toilet for a bowel movement.

RESIDENT: I have one patient whose favorite rejoinder is, "I thought you would come to that some day."

DR. TARACHOW: Such a patient is trying desperately to avoid the need for help and certainly to avoid acknowledging openly his need for help. Your psychotherapeutic intervention follows upon that idea.

Tricks

Some of these patients set all kinds of traps and play tricks on you. I had one patient who would tell me the first half of each dream and would not tell me the second half unless she was satisfied that my remarks about the first half were intelligent or suited her. Then she would say, "Well, I think that's right." Then she would tell me the rest.

There are other kinds of tricks. A patient might start talking about Joe, someone you had not heard of before. The patient is trying to see if you are alert; he wants to discover if you are listening. Patients will throw in characters sometimes and throw in incidents quite deliberately to see if you are paying attention.

And, of course, patients can also lie; but if a patient lies, you need not take the responsibility. If the patient comes to you for treatment, you presume he wants to cooperate. However, one may encounter varying degrees of concealment of material, often through shame, sometimes for other reasons. Patients expect you to guess the truth through their circumstantiality.

Compulsive Character and Prognosis

RESIDENT: When you say that these characteristics apply to obsessionals or obsessional-compulsive neurotics, do these not also apply to people who have a certain kind of compulsive character formations?

DR. TARACHOW: It is simply a matter of how solidly the character structure has been built up or whether it is ragged at the edges. In the latter case it starts breaking down into specific obsessions or compulsive thoughts. Some of the most successful people are severely compulsive. The compulsive-obsessive defenses are built into an entire character structure and can be completely sufficient and efficient. I had a patient who did his work promptly. He was very bright and capable; when a task came across his desk, he could not rest. He had to do it right away. He was a most efficient, effective, aggressive person. At work he displayed an uncompromising steamroller type of zeal. He was a fantastic success. I could not in any way question his compulsive need to do things efficiently, speedily, in response to clients' requests. His entire life and professional career had been a success because of his compulsive structure: it was impossible to question or undermine it.

RESIDENT: Why did you want to?

DR. TARACHOW: Because he had other problems too, which did not, to him, seem to have any connection to the obsessional system itself. He had phobias and gastric symptoms. That is where the ragged edges were. He had phobias and hypochondriacal symptoms. (I would like to register a passing clinical observation on phobias. There is an astonishingly high incidence of gastric symptoms as prodromal symptoms of phobias no matter what the phobias. Before various displacements occur, the first phobia is usually a fear of the gastric disorder, which in itself had been the first symptom.) But the obsessional character structure was in the center; it was an immovable structure, it could not be breached.

He did not come to me because he was an efficient professional man. Time and again, I retired bleeding from the fray because it was impossible to shake the mountainous defenses of his very successful, aggressive, and orderly personality structure.

Sometimes the underlying bitterness and spitefulness and aggressiveness are so enormous that the defenses they erect are really indispensable. The patient cannot really tolerate the underlying aggressions without chaos or a psychotic break. Pious (1950) warns of the danger of underlying psychosis. Both Miller (1950) and Stephen (1950) agree that there may be cases in which the underlying aggressions are so powerful, the defenses best be left undisturbed.

The Therapist's Difficulty

The most important interfering reaction in the therapist is his own reaction of annoyance and hostility. These patients are spiteful and they do tease and they do provoke and they do conceal and they are stubborn.

RESIDENT: Isn't it to some degree reality testing to permit them to see that they evoke anger?

DR. TARACHOW: Only in a limited way. You can rationalize such a position for your own comfort over letting yourself be annoyed and say, "Well, it's good for them. It helps them test reality." But it is better not to. If you do get annoyed, then the patient has succeeded in re-creating a transference situation with you which is identical with the original infantile or childhood ones: they tease mother, mother gets angry, punishes. They tease you, you get angry, you punish. The patient may then conclude you are no better than his father or mother.

With some patients the provocation is irresistible and you cannot help but explode. Then and only then, this is an exception in technique, not a rule, if you have been driven beyond your endurance and you do show your anger, the best you can do is to say, "Well, you have succeeded in doing with me what you have done so often with X, Y, and Z." On rare occasions, you might even have to give the patient up. I have had to do that twice. I was unable to master my hatred of an especially trying patient.

RESIDENT: I had a patient who had been in the hospital only a few days; she had had psychotherapy for a long time. She would get me to the point where I would react to her, and would then ask whether I was annoyed. I answered it by saying, "This is my problem, not yours."

DR. TARACHOW: That's one way, but not a very good one. You might have asked her why she was warning you in advance and why she expected you to be annoyed. Eventually you might have been able to deal with her wish and need to provoke you.

Search for Affection

The analysis of the defenses against the archaic sadism is not enough to help these patients back to normal human relations. In the daily struggle with the hostilities the psychotherapist is liable to overlook the problem of the desire for love and the capacity for love. In fact, he may be sufficiently irritated with these patients not to credit them with the capacity for love.

At the proper point the therapist must introduce this theme.

If done properly the therapist will be amazed at the real gratitude the patient will have for being so credited by his therapist. This area will round out and complete the work with the obsessive-compulsive patient. My remarks in this area are grossly inadequate, but if you have survived all the sadistic assaults which the obsessional patient will hurl in your direction and have managed to retain your sympathy for his sufferings, you will be able to help the patient recover his desire for love and his capacity for love. Put in more general terms, if you have not been defeated by the patient's sadism, you will be able to resurrect his libidinal and affectionate qualities.

Chapter 16

Acting Out and Psychopathy

The subject today is "acting out." I should like to spend some time describing it, some time discussing the dynamic nature of it, and also enter into some discussion of the treatment issues that have to be faced in handling this problem. We might start with the working definition that acting out is the solution of an inner psychological problem by some external action, as opposed to an internal solution such as hysteria or an obsessional thought; it is the solution of an intrapsychic problem by action.

In terms of symptoms it might be telling lies or stealing. As I go on, I will and perhaps you will be able to add further clinical examples.

What types of acting out are there? Our discussion today is mainly from the standpoint of office treatment rather than hospital treatment. We have already discussed acting out in the hospital (Chapter 5). I do not know just how my remarks might apply to your specific experiences, but in office psychotherapy, or in the office practice of psychoanalysis, acting out occurs in several ways.

First of all there is a type which is most difficult to recognize. I think of it as built-in acting out. A patient who tends to act out sneaks in some acting out of his problem into the very treatment situation. For example: I took on a patient, a young lawyer who had symptoms of a compulsion neurosis. When we made the arrangements for treatment, he made what seemed a reasonable request of me. He said, "I'm a lawyer. My income isn't very stable. I know what I earn during the course of the year, but from month to month I'm not certain. Would you mind if I pay when I can? I know that during the course of the year, I can handle the bill, but sometimes one month I might have no income, another month I would have a larger income." So I said, "That's perfectly alright." We left it at that.

As treatment went on, it developed that this arrangement, which seemed so rational and sensible, was really a piece of acting out on the part of the patient; he always kept me waiting for the money. Just as he kept his wife waiting for appointments, he kept his clients waiting; he spent his life disappointing people and keeping people waiting. He was happier when a judge rendered a verdict against his client than for him. His personality is perhaps best expressed by a story which he remembered reading as a little boy.

Parenthetically, it is interesting that certain stories remain in our memories from childhood. Of all the books and all the stories we read, we may remember one unusually well. The story we remember generally tells something important about us.

It was the story of a French colonial governor who had been sent to govern some small island possession of France. This man was an efficient governor, but he never turned in his annual report to the French government. Finally, after a number of years the French government insisted that he must submit the annual report for his colonial administration or he would be asked to resign. So he sat down, wrote out and submitted his first report and then shot himself!

This story was a fit description of this man's basic personality. He was very stubborn, very bitter, very unyielding. I mention this instance as an illustration of built-in acting out. Some call this "acting in" the treatment; the problem of the patient is expressed in some action involving the therapist and in the treatment relationship. On occasion we find that we do something for the patient or we accept some arrangement or we set up some circumstances in the treatment relationship, which seem quite reasonable and harmless. Somehow the problem of the patient is insinuated and most impossible to locate.

There are other types of acting out with reference to the treatment situation. For example, patients may act out even before treatment starts. A patient may come to you for a consultation. You agree to take the patient on but cannot begin treatment until some time later.

At the appointed time the patient appears; during that period he has done all sorts of things. He married, he gave up his job, he started music lessons, etc. This is a type of acting out with reference to *you*. It is the patient's way of indicating that he does not want to be changed *by you*. It is a way of saying, "I don't need you." He has agreed to start treatment with you but found this way of acting out in advance of the treatment·to say very defiantly (albeit implicitly) to you, "You're not going to do a thing to me and I don't need your help. I can make any changes in my own life without any help or coercion from you."

This is one of the dangers of keeping a patient waiting too long to begin treatment. On the other hand, a patient who has this characteristic does not need much time to act out. He can do something catastrophic overnight.

I have had patients quit their jobs in the first week of treatment. This is a way of thrusting themselves upon you, of making you responsible for them, of creating emergencies for you. There are further kinds of acting out which illustrate something in their relationship to you.

For example: on several occasions I have had patients who immediately upon beginning treatment became pregnant. This is an attempt at forcing you to enter into their lives in a way that you had not planned. They will catch you off guard.

They attempt to force you into some emergency action. They try to confront you with perpetual emergencies which demand your action, advice, and, in effect, an active role in their lives. They also try to alter your technique of treatment. They want you to do things the way they want, at their own pace, at their speed. This is their way of getting something from you that you had not intended to give and is not really in the structure of the psychotherapeutic relationship.

RESIDENT: I wonder if these types of coercive control of the therapist can in some way be correlated with depressive attitudes?

DR. TARACHOW: Not directly, though in a way, yes. One way of seeing a depression is as stubborn blackmail of those about the patient. In a sense it is the technique of getting onself into a deep paralysis and thrusting oneself onto somebody's doorstep. This is similar to the extreme masochistic technique. By his misery the depressive and masochist both try to squeeze you for care, reassurance, interest, and support.

Depression does enter in the problem of acting out, especially in the sense of the need to *conceal* the depression. Denial of a depression is one of the most important aspects of pathological lying. Mania is not the only defense against depression; a pathological lie can serve the same purpose.

In a basic sense, acting out outside of the treatment relationship and acting in or acting out within the treatment relationship are the same. Just forbidding these actions is of no avail. For example: a very stubborn obsessional patient is in analysis. The elementary routine of beginning the session is converted into a kind of battleground by the patient. I put a piece of Kleenex on the pillow when the patient comes in. But he never really lets me do it for him. If I put it down, he must move the pillow again. If I say something, if I make some interpretation, he says, "Oh, I thought of that already." He won't let me do anything for him. This is part of the pattern of his entire life.

The type of acting out outside of the treatment situation which will concern us most has to do with stealing and pathological lying. Pathological lying is interesting if the therapist does not become angry or worried about the patient. If you can overcome your own hostility and worry, you can be helpful.

A patient, for example, told me in her Monday morning session that she had been to see a football game at Yale the previous Saturday afternoon and had had a wonderful time. In great detail she described the trip to the college, the football game, and dinner afterwards. The only fly in the ointment was the fact that on that Saturday afternoon I had been out for a stroll and had seen her on the street shopping for groceries; she could not possibly have been at the football game and buying groceries at the same time.

I said, "This last Saturday I was on Madison Avenue and I saw you walk into a grocery store." She refused to admit that she had not attended the football game. She insisted on trying to so bend the story that the football game was still possible. This patient was creating an illusion of happiness. She was not spending the Saturday afternoon alone. Her lying and stealing have the quality of comforting self-love and illusory happiness. The basic problem is the inability to admit the underlying depression or unhappiness. This patient would buy clothes and charge them to her parents' account, whether she needed them or not. Such patients cannot tolerate the pain of deprivation. The lying has an oral, magical quality. They have to deny the very existence of disappointment. Another woman patient with a similar problem which involved acting out expressed it as follows, "The idea of *no* just does not exist for me."

Of crucial significance in the treatment of these patients is the task of getting them to the point of realizing they are depressed or unhappy. These patients have an early background characterized by severe deprivation, generally at the hands of the mother.

Acting out is a defense. It is not that such patients are impulsive or hostile when they steal or lie. It is that they cannot face the task of recognizing disappointment. The principal defensive mechanism is the magical oral denial. It is closely related to mania, to the defense that everything is wonderful, a denial of the depression underneath which they would proclaim, "I am unworthy and I am unloved."

The basic problem in pathological lying and stealing is the defense by denial against the knowledge of being unhappy. The treatment of these patients is difficult; there are certain principles that have to be followed. Following the principles is no guarantee of success, but abandonment of the principles will guarantee failure. So if one maintains certain attitudes toward these people, one can at least rescue the *possibility* of success.

In the usual situation, in the treatment of a neurotic and sometimes even the treatment of a psychotic, under office conditions, the patient comes to you with a symptom that makes him miserable. It is a migraine headache, or a paralyzed arm, or a work inhibition; or it is a phobia that locks him in his house, that makes it impossible for him to go to work; or it is impotence which could ruin a marriage. To most patients who come for help the symptom is ego dystonic. They do not like the symptom. It is troublesome. But not so with symptomatic acting out, because here the symptom is specifically designed to make the patient happy. The patient is not in conscious conflict with his symptoms, in fact he is delighted with his symptoms.

A patient, for example, would send herself orchids, and make up a story that she got the orchids from some boy friend. The symptom made her happy. And the analysis of this symptom threatened to reduce her to a less illusory type of existence, to the feeling of lonesomeness and unhappiness. The therapist is a threat; he will take something away from these people. This is in contrast to the situation with a neurotic for whom you are trying to relieve the pain of a symptom. In the acting-out patient the symptom *relieves* the pain.

There is a long preparatory period in the treatment of such

patients. The therapist has to live through a good deal with his patient before he can begin to interpret at all. Put most simply, the patient must first develop an attachment to you. In a sense, he must fall in love with you. It will be an infantile demanding love; it is not going to be a mature love. You must have the patience, tolerance, and good will to endure a long period of transference testing. Only on the basis of the patient's love and attachment to you will he even begin to consider any interpretive remarks you make. The patient will test you over and over again to make certain you deserve his love. Every interpretation is a deprivation. You rub salt in the patient's wounds. He might have to be confronted with the fact that his mother was a cold, barren woman. He wants to deny this.

The therapist has to live through a peculiar paradox. The patient who is a confirmed liar is precisely the one who demands that his therapist be scrupulously honest.

Generally these patients come to treatment quite unwillingly. They come either because a father or husband or wife has threatened legal action. Occasionally some criminal action is impending. At the outset the therapist is certainly classed with the enemies. The patient will exert himself to prove you are an enemy.

I have had a patient do the following: she went home for a holiday; her behavior was quite exemplary, except that at the last minute before she left home she stole some money from her father. The father did not find out until after she was gone. By the time the girl came to see me the next day there would have been time enough for the father to notify me that she had stolen the money. The series of traps this patient laid for me to try to find out whether I knew that she had stolen the hundred dollars was simply endless. Patients are interested in the parent's communication with you, but they are even more interested in your communication with the parent. They expect their parents will complain to you. But they lie in wait watchfully to see if you give away their secrets to the parent.

How well you keep their secrets is the test you have to pass. If you do not pass this test, the treatment will certainly fail.

There is this initial period of transference testing. They want to see how faithful you are to their interest. You must be on their side. There is this role playing that has to be lived through. The transference is really the vehicle of treatment. *With this type of psychopathy, the vehicle of treatment is your fidelity to the patient.* This lays the basis for what has to be done; namely, the patient must give up his illusion of being loved, and he can only do so when he has a reality of some kind to fall back upon in his relationship to you. He also must face his own depression and his own unhappiness that lies underneath it, and he can only do that if you offer him your love in return.

RESIDENT: Isn't the secrecy of communication guarded in any therapeutic relationship anyway?

DR. TARACHOW: Oh, yes. This is true with every patient, but with these patients it is a special problem because these patients sometimes get in trouble with the law. They engage in real actions with external consequences. These people are doing something. They try to provoke action or worry or role playing in you. There is a strong similarity to the treatment of a child.

This is not a matter of the patient telling you that he had a homosexual experience in college and does not want you to tell this to his father. This is a matter of the patient doing something potentially dangerous *now*. You have a natural impulse to protect the patient and call the father and say, "You had better do something, your son or daughter is in trouble with the local department store." But you must keep hands off. The very impulse even to protect your patient against reality and to interfere in the reality is part of the patient's unconscious transference design—to draw you in as a real figure. But you must not be drawn in.

No matter how much trouble these patients get into, you must not worry about the overt consequences of the act. You must not butt in. They must face the legal consequences of their acts without your involvement. You must not say, "You'll get into trouble if you do that, you know." Or, "If you do that again, you know you're liable to be arrested." The moment you speak like the police and the moment you speak with the police, the moment you speak like the father or the moment you speak with the father, you are the authority and you are hostile. The therapy must run this risk.

Now, what is gained by running these risks? It might seem there is no gain whatever. But there is a gain. *You have not robbed the patient of his own responsibility for himself.* We are doctors and have humanitarian feelings and we want to help our patients, but as soon as we enter and take responsibility off the patient's shoulders, we have infantilized and robbed him of some degree of self-respect.

In psychotherapy, with some problems you do have to step in in just that way. You have to protect the patient, and in the more serious cases you put them in hospitals and so on. But if you have a patient with whom you are trying to work in an ideal way, or psychopaths for whom the sense of responsibility is a central issue, you permit the patient to keep the responsibility even for his mistakes. If you try to help too much or to warn the parents or even to warn the patient, the patient is belittled and reduced to having a childlike relationship to you.

RESIDENT: Could you get the patient to admit she sent the orchids to herself?

DR. TARACHOW: Oh, no. She insisted that somebody sent her the orchids.

RESIDENT: How did you find out about it?

DR. TARACHOW: Well, this was part of the original history obtained from the parents. When she was with me, she did many things about which I did not learn until many months later. One often works in the dark.

Pathological liars will often try to tell you the truth through a mountain of lies. For example: to oversimplify it, let us say the patient is trying to tell me she went into a store and made a $50 purchase that her mother did not know about and charged it to her mother. The patient really wants to be close to me. The patient really wants to tell me, but if she does tell me it would create a self-imposed crack in her illusions. But she still wants to tell me about herself. So she might tell me of taking a shoelace from her sister twenty years ago. She will tell me something. It is like telling me a tiny fragment of the truth. They try to tell you the truth; but if the truth conflicts with the need to deny pain, they can't. Still they do try to tell you something of the truth.

The therapist's job is to get this fragment of truth to grow as the patient's feeling for you grows. Incidentally, a great deal can be learned from the lies themselves. The lies tell what the patient wishes were true. The child wishes to be happy. The child wishes to have someone that loves him. But the underlying depression stands in the way. Even the cure stands in the way of happiness because these patients will not be cured until they go through a depression.

I have said a good deal about the need of the therapist to become important to the patient, to become an object to the patient. But this is not easily attained. In some respects these psychopaths have no objects. They substitute their illusions for objects. They have narcissistically created illusions as a substitute for objects. They do not want to run the risk of your replacing the illusion, because you might disappoint them. They do not want to run the risk of pain or depression, and they do run that risk if you become important to them. A crucial forward step in treatment is the patient's move to permit you to become an object to him. To do this is to risk object loss and depression and pain. The narcissism and impaired object relations are central qualities in the acting-out patient. Even the apparent objects in the patient's life are not true objects. The patient is simply using characters to dramatize certain problems in his life. A distinction can be made between acting out and action. I would say that action is object directed. Acting out uses apparent objects to dramatize certain problems, but without real object relations. Acting out has some of the characteristics of the restitutive phase of delusion formation.

The patient I have mentioned would have certain swings. There were times when she would draw away from me. She would react with outbursts of additional feeling, or with further psychopathic acting out, or she would come to her sessions progressively later. She rarely missed any sessions altogether.

I had one way of drawing this patient back to me again; it had its dangers, but I had to encourage a close tie to me. Her only ties to people were in terms of what she could get. I found through trial and error that interpretations of past injuries, particularly at the hands of mother, would draw the patient closer to me. This put me back on the patient's side, in sympathy with her; I was helping her justify her behavior and that made us friends again. For a period she would then come on time, cooperate better. This patient had excellent insight into her behavior, but the insight had no effect on her behavior.

She was doing her best to force everybody in her environment to become a good mother to her. Whoever had any dealings with her lost money in some way, sooner or later. Everybody managed to give her something. She managed to get something from everybody; she was perpetually transforming everybody into mothers; she created a world in which everyone was good to her, a total denial of any experience of deprivation.

One of the main things I was trying to get this girl to do was to overcome this fantastic denial of deprivation, to get her to try to admit that she was unhappy, to get her to cry. It was almost impossible to get her to admit to any current frustration or deprivation. A frustration could not exist in this girl's conscious mind. The moment a deprivation faced her, it was immediately covered over with stories, with lies, with stealing, with acting out. She simply could not tolerate it. I was trying desperately to get this girl to cry, to admit that something hurt her, that she wanted something, that she needed something, that she was missing something. In two and a half years she cried in only one session, and then it was not through my work at all. She managed to get a young man to propose marriage to her. The moment he had, she went off on such an enormous binge of telling him lies that he became terrified. He could see that something was wrong and he dropped her. At that point she recognized reality a little bit and cried.

Every time a new person appeared in her life she was provoked into new acting out, new symptoms. Each new person, each new object that appeared could be handled only in the one typical way. Each new object was expected anew to be but a source of deprivation. She immediately had to test it and suck it dry. Everyone who came into her orbit suffered the same fate. Any attempt to stop her acting out provoked the most violent rage, further lies, and further acting out. It is precisely this factor that leads to flare-ups of symptoms at the beginning of treatment. The therapist himself is the newly presented object at the beginning of treatment.

Patients suffering with pathological lying and stealing never come in voluntarily, but there are some types of psychopathy that sometimes will. Homosexuals will occasionally come for treatment, but oddly enough, never for the homosexuality. They will come for something else that makes them unhappy. Homosexuality, too, can have some of the qualities of this other type of psychopathy. For example, it is very easy to get lost in the details of one or another particular homosexual practice and to look for its unconscious meaning. But there are some simpler elements that are sometimes overlooked. To many homosexuals, the experience which gives them the greatest pleasure is simply to be held in the arms of the other man. They want to be cuddled like a child; these men would go through any sort of perversion demanded by the other partner, provided the partner would agree to cuddle them like a baby.

Another facet of these patients who act out either outside

or inside the treatment is the tendency to find an accomplice. The sadist will find his masochist. Patients sometimes try to make you their accomplice; if the patient tries to make you an accomplice in large ways, this is quite easy to avoid. There is the dishonest patient who cheats the government. He will offer you an income-tax deal. I have had an even more ridiculous proposition. A woman patient suggested to me that I give her larger bills than was correct: her husband would pay them and she and I would split the difference.

It is so ridiculous that it is laughable. But nevertheless this was one of this woman's important problems. Her mother had cheated her father. The patient repeated the pattern: she had to steal money from her husband. She came for treatment to overcome this problem and wanted to convert the treatment into the very problems from which she suffered. Sometimes the seduction to become an accomplice of the patient is so gross and obvious that it can be rejected easily. But sometimes it is quite subtle. There is a good rule to follow, a rule which will help you spot the impact of a patient upon you. The rule is as follows: if you find that your behavior is changing in any way, even in the slightest detail, with regard to any one patient, ask yourself in what way you are responding to the patient. Have you become an accomplice of this patient?

I start sessions precisely at certain times and finish them precisely at certain times. If I would find that with one patient I tended to extend the session an extra one or two minutes, I look to myself: I am probably responding to the patient. Or if I find that I am sending one patient out a minute or two early. Or if I alter my behavior with respect to greeting or departures.

At any rate you will find this caution in Glover's (1928) lectures on the Technique of Psychoanalysis. I find that it is a fascinatingly useful caution. You may be acting in collusion with the patient's neurosis in some way. Typical situations are: the patient has either seduced you and you give him too much, or the patient has irritated you and you have entered a sadomasochistic or a hostile relationship. You might forget to bill a patient. The patient might be activating guilt in you. The patient has succeeded in getting you to join him in acting out, in living out his neurosis. You have lost your therapeutic leverage: you have accepted the patient's conditions for a relationship.

RESIDENT: Do you have better results with depressions than with your psychopaths?

DR. TARACHOW: Yes. I have had better results with openly depressed patients. When the depression is denied with this type of overlay, the results are poor. Nevertheless, one should make the effort, particularly be willing to undergo the transference testing. I have done better with patients who did not deny the depression, those who were able to face the hostility as well as the loss and the deprivation. They were able to struggle with their problems, even though in a painful way. When the patient denies the depression with narcissistic illusions, then the task of getting him to face the underlying pain is almost impossible of accomplishment. You have to recover the depression and throw the patient into pain. You must get the patient to say, "I was not loved." In fact, it takes a certain amount of masochism on any patient's part to stay in treatment.

RESIDENT: How old was the patient who presented pathological lying?

DR. TARACHOW: About twenty. This had started at the age of thirteen, which is a characteristic age of onset for this psychopathy. It seems to have some relationship to the onset of menstruation.

There may be factors which specifically influence the superego of these patients. Perhaps the best work to refer you to is the work of Johnson and Szurek (1952) who were able to demonstrate quite clearly the transmission of superego defects from mother to children. They worked with mothers and children and found that the superego defects in the mothers were quickly realized and absorbed by the children.

For example, I treated a psychopathic girl whose principal problem was stealing; her mother had done the same thing. While the mother, a very cold and depriving woman, clamped down on her daughter, at the same time there must have been some subtle transmission of the mother's own superego defect.

RESIDENT: What are the main problems in the therapist's reaction to these people?

DR. TARACHOW: The principal reactions are hatred and envy. You are a hard-working physician. You get up early in the morning and work hard and see patient after patient; the joys of your own life are regulated and controlled. But these people get whatever they want to get, they do whatever they want; as a result you hate them. These people are self-indulgent; they refuse to admit the harsh facts of reality to themselves; unhappiness is brushed off; responsibility is brushed off. If they want something they borrow or steal it from someone. The principal hazard is envy or hatred of the patient.

Sometimes the hatred is quite direct. You are annoyed with them. You want to scold them. You want to get angry. You want to tell them, "Don't do that, you'll get into trouble." Your hatred becomes disciplinary. This reaction is easy enough to understand but hard to control. The hatred can also be expressed by the therapist in a different way. He can worry about the patient. When instead of being angry at the patient you start worrying about him, it simply means that your hatred is even greater than when you are overtly angry. You are defending yourself even more against the hatred. Worry is the masochistic refuge of sadism. Worry is basically a sadistic attitude, just as pity is. It is easy to become resentful or worried. Then you are lost.

There are more psychopathological phenomena growing out of hatred than out of love. So when you are struggling with a patient like this, just assume that you are jealous and angry at this patient's defense; the patient's defense is so pleasant.

RESIDENT: The psychopath is a kind of extreme. Can one be

more optimistic about alcoholics or perversions which are more common conditions?

Dr. Tarachow: These will turn out to be neither so common nor less serious. They are all very difficult. The two you mentioned—addictions, alcohol or other drug addictions, and homosexuality—are both very difficult to treat and the results, I would say, are poor. I doubt that in the literature you will find any large-scale statistics about the treatment in the setting of a private practice of psychotherapy or psychoanalysis.

Addictions are most difficult to treat. I have been in private practice almost twenty-five years and I have treated only three drug addicts (exclusive of alcohol) in all that time. One was a morphine addict who was treated by a number of doctors, and he stayed with me a month, which was a long time. He was a doctor, as many of these patients are doctors or doctors' wives. In the old days a very high percentage of drug addicts were doctors, nurses or doctor's wives. In my experience, the severe drug addict can be treated successfully only in a hospital, although Savitt (1954) has reported good results in office treatment.

In the same period of time, I have had only an extremely small number of homosexuals of either sex come for treatment. I am certainly not giving you any statistically reliable data. I achieved a satisfactory result with one woman patient, but the results with the men were uniformly failures. I would be inclined to think that good results in any hands would be scarce.

The absolute prerequisite for treatment is a willingness of the patient to come. If the patient is forced to, e.g., by impending court actions, your efforts are doomed to failure.

Resident: What position do you take about emergencies created by the patient?

Dr. Tarachow: Don't ever be upset by emergencies. If you put yourself in the patient's shoes, then all is lost. Patients have a way of re-creating their emergencies year after year. So, never be upset by patients' emergencies. It is bad enough that the patients are frightened by them. At least one of you should not be worried.

About the current emergency situation, never consider it an emergency. Consider the patient's emergency as a chronic problem. The patient will re-create the emergency again tomorrow, to keep his conflict alive, to keep alive the picture of either a bad father or a bad mother, or "I am being abused," or "The world is mistreating me," or as atonement for his aggression or what not. He needs it. So, an emergency is a chronic thing.

You know a patient will present himself and say, "I'm going to be married next week, and I still don't know if I should get married. Doctor, tell me what to do." Well, this problem is many years old, so don't get rattled.

One must not be misled by apparent reality. There are times when you have to pay attention to reality, but often you must pay no attention to reality at all. The reality is simply the inner fantasy realized. The best tack to take is to tell the patient, "Well, you must have done this many times before. This is nothing new to you." The patient will confirm this time after time. The edge of the emergency is lifted and treatment can be more considered and deliberate.

Patients are always consistent. Do not expect patients to behave differently tomorrow than they do today unless the treatment has effected some change. Everyone behaves according to his own pattern: every patient has his own favorite and typical defensive structure. Once you grasp the patient's chief line of defense, then you have a key to his dreams, to his behavior, and to his symptoms, to all his chief actions. You have the patient's style. Patients do not use many different defenses. Patients have one chief defense. You must be deliberate about your patients' emergencies. Look for the chronic pattern. The police know this very well regarding criminals. Each criminal sticks to his own specific type and style of crime.

RESIDENT: Would you comment on a statement that has

been made quite frequently: when you are dealing with a character disorder, you have to convert this into a depression or into anxiety, and then treat the depression or anxiety.

DR. TARACHOW: That's true. It is not easy to put it into more specific terms without a concrete case at hand. The therapeutic effort is to try to get a grasp of the manner in which the patient re-creates his problem with you in the transference. The problem will be brought forward in the treatment because you will not behave the way the patient's original objects behaved. You are on a search for the original painful set of relationships. You must help the patient recover psychic pain and the neurotic problem underlying the psychopathy. There is no other approach to it than through the transference. You stay with the patient until you become important to him, and when you are important you play out some role that has been assigned you. You must not gratify the demand, the claim. Let's try and be more specific.

For example, a woman is extremely greedy, forces her husband to do everything for her, shows no gratitude, shows no appreciation. Her husband supports her and she really abandons all responsibilities to the husband. This is a kind of oral psychopathy, if you will. This patient comes into treatment. It becomes clear that the patient wants you to kiss her. She wants you to do favors for her. She wants you to change appointments for her. She wants you to make adjustments to her. She wants you to start feeding her and giving her, and she wants to exhaust you the way she has exhausted her husband or her mother or any other antecedent character. She wants to live out with you the life that is typical of her.

The thing to do, after she has formed a strong attachment to you, is to interfere with the construction of her pattern with you. Everybody has given in to her, but you do not. Then perhaps you can provoke rage or depression or anxiety. You assume that behind the greediness is a potential depression. Behind the orality is a potential depression. The patient protects herself from the psychosis or the neurotic depression by an insatiable greed which she has been successfully living out. You, transferencewise, frustrate her, and you try to provoke the rage which she avoids by being greedy, or the depression that she has avoided. If you can provoke rage or depression, in relation to her feelings to you, you are provoking a conflict in place of the acting out. This is quite an accomplishment.

A patient tells a joke, but you don't laugh. The patient is thus promptly brought face to face with his motivation. It is quite an effort not to laugh. Not laughing is a good illustration of not playing ball with the patient's acting out. The patient may be a seducer, always seducing, winning everybody, telling jokes, clowning, directing jokes at himself. By his masochistic appeal he says, "Love me, love me, I'm not dangerous, I'm making a fool of myself." The patient makes this appeal via a joke. But you don't laugh. Now, instead of getting what he is accustomed to get, laughter and praise, he is confronted by his own depression.

Since his joke has fallen flat, he feels deflated and unhappy. Your psychotherapeutic technique is successful, the unhappiness has been brought to the fore. It is a wonderful technical device to bring out the concealed depression, the concealed need for love. If you laugh at a patient's joke, you have lost your chance of analyzing or interpreting his need to tell jokes. He has won you over. He has gotten you to act out along with him. He has not been confronted with his own need for love, nor with the masochistic approach he takes to get it. There is no therapeutic task brought to the patient. His neurosis has simply been gratified.

A patient may start a sentence and leave it unfinished; he will want you to finish it. If you finish it, you are either feeding the patient or converting him into a passive homosexual partner. You have put words into the patient's mouth. This has quite a loaded meaning.

You will provoke and bring forward the neurotic feelings

and the neurotic craving and the neurotic conflict by not entering into the acting out of the patient. If the patient does something to provoke your anger, you must not scold. If the patient does something to provoke your approval, you must not offer love. The psychopathies are simply massive ways of doing just this.

RESIDENT: Is this technique followed with all patients or just with certain psychopaths?

DR. TARACHOW: You should behave this way to most patients in psychotherapy. The patient in psychotherapy tells you a joke. You need not laugh. You will see how disappointed the patient will be. Instead of laughing you might say, "Are you trying to make a hit with me?"

RESIDENT: First you must have a friendly relationship.

DR. TARACHOW: Yes, particularly in psychotherapy.

RESIDENT: If you first build up a friendly relationship, then take a frustrating action, wouldn't that be inconsistent with your previous behavior?

DR. TARACHOW: You are right, and the patient may accuse you of the inconsistency. But you have to take that chance. You take the rap and simply insist on interpreting because you feel that the time has come to start interpretation. At some point the therapeutic task must be thrust upon the patient. The honeymoon has to end.

I would now like to turn to another type of minor acting out which could occur either in or out of treatment.

This is the case of a female patient in treatment with another psychiatrist.[1] The patient had two foreign languages at her command, as did the psychiatrist. Both were also at ease in English. Once in a while the patient would break in with an expression in either French or German. For awhile this was passed by, ostensibly because they both understood the reference to German or French so readily that it was accepted by

[1] I am indebted to Dr. Herbert J. Urbach for permission to cite the material of this patient.

them as the ordinary communication of treatment.

The therapist began to suspect that this was acting out. To abandon spoken English for any other mode of communication should by definition be regarded as acting out. He decided that this acting out must be interfered with.

Interference with acting out is bound to produce consequences. What do you think the lapses into foreign expressions could mean? What purposes could they have served the patient?

RESIDENT: It could be an attempt to deny the fact that the therapist is a doctor; he is really a buddy, a friend.

DR. TARACHOW: Yes, any other? It turned out to mean many things. It had a variety of implications.

RESIDENT: I think it has transference implications.

DR. TARACHOW: Well, specify. The whole behavior had a transference implication, but what was it doing in the transference?

RESIDENT: She is substituting for him father or brother.

DR. TARACHOW: Yes, going back to more familiar, older, comfortable objects—it's closer.

RESIDENT: The mother tongue, father tongue.

DR. TARACHOW: It's the mother tongue. It's closer to a real intimacy with each other. It's a "We know this and no one else does" kind of bond.

RESIDENT: The use of the French language in addressing a German could have hostile implications, because of the antagonism which has existed for so many years between the two countries.

DR. TARACHOW: I hadn't thought of that. The background of these people is German; they don't seem to object to the French language. These are not French people who are using German, but German people who are using French, and they don't mind it at all.

RESIDENT: It paints an intellectual picture of both. It puts the patient on the level of the intellectual standing of the doctor.

DR. TARACHOW: That's an interesting observation because one of the meanings this had to the patient was: "These are things the average person doesn't know. You and I are superior to everyone else."

RESIDENT: Testing out whether or not the physician is more comfortable using the mother tongue.

DR. TARACHOW: That could be. It hadn't developed in this particular instance. I'm going into this because it could be quite easy for the therapist to regard this behavior as a charming attribute, and neglect to study it.

RESIDENT: In terms of technique, it would be very detrimental to respond to the patient in that foreign language. It would be a type of acting out of the therapist.

DR. TARACHOW: Oh, yes. It's bad enough simply to accept it at face value, because you lose so much that requires interpretation.

RESIDENT: Was the patient aware of the doctor's background?

DR. TARACHOW: Presumably—the doctor had a faint accent. An important element that came through was that the patient had the fantasy: "This is a very elegant thing to do, to use French and German expressions." It was very elegant; it was as though she went around dropping elegant pearls, these pearls of elegant language. But this was a very obsessional and depressed patient. What do you think the further material about these elegant droppings turned out to be?

RESIDENT: The droppings were not so elegant.

DR. TARACHOW: Precisely. The droppings were not so elegant. She would space and pace the droppings. In each session she would drop one or two. I tried to give you a clue when I said it was an obsessive and depressed patient.

RESIDENT: You said droppings?

DR. TARACHOW: Of course. Then, to make it easier, I added that the patient was obsessional and depressed. This was a way of daintily having part of her bowel movement in the doctor's office. The idea of dropping things was connected in the patient's association with dropping a bowel movement in the toilet. At one level she had the feeling that she was being elegant and dropping an occasional elegant expression. At another level she was moving her bowels in the presence of the therapist.

The therapist stopped the patient at every foreign expression. As soon as the therapist and patient really began to pay attention to this, the other connotations of the dropping began to appear; it referred largely to the toilet. Much of the patient's behavior had the connotations of holding back material from her doctor, of giving him material and holding back; it was a struggle. Like a mother struggling with her unwilling baby or with an unwilling child, the doctor had a struggle with this patient. The patient delivered, dropped, or held back to suit herself.

This behavior had persisted for a period without the therapist realizing it. She was unconsciously having fun. She was unconsciously laughing at her doctor. "I just come in and I elegantly have my bowel movement here and leave." Greenson (1950) makes the point that the original mother tongue is the bearer of pregenital conflicts. The new, second language has offered the patient a chance to build up a new defensive system against the infantile relationships. As we see in this patient the reversion to the older languages represented a regression to a stubborn, anal embroilment with the mother.

I am going into all this just to give you another example of a kind of acting out that you might encounter. Acting out is not confined to crime and perversions. Did one of you indicate you had a patient who used Yiddish with you?

Resident: Yes, at first, I thought the patient was trying to determine whether or not I was Jewish, because she had previously asked. When I did not answer, she went on to explain it as being closer together. That is about all it came to.

Dr. Tarachow: So then that was to establish your identity and to establish a bond. Has this patient tried to continue to use Yiddish with you?

RESIDENT: Yes, but rather indifferently. I never brought it up.

DR. TARACHOW: Has the patient occasionally reverted?

RESIDENT: Occasionally.

DR. TARACHOW: Well, here is a suggestion. The next time this or any other patient switches to a foreign language you must regard it in the following way; the patient has been in communication with you; at a certain point the patient runs into anxiety or some painful affect: the patient switches to Yiddish, and then goes back to English. Your working assumption *must* be that there was some interference to continuing the train of thought, and that the patient at that point adopted a *different* means of communication. You can *not* regard it as a continuing communication. If the patient switches to Yiddish or French or German, it is *not* a continuing communication. It is an *interrupted* communication, a different type of communication, a regression of some kind. If it is an attempt to create a bond from the old country, it is a regression. If you really stop and pursue it, you will find that it is a regression which has a variety of additional meanings too. The patient will not like the scrutiny. The patient I described wept when her use of French and German expressions was interfered with; she wept bitterly because she was robbed of this closeness, the intimacy, the superiority, the defense—she was robbed of a great deal.

RESIDENT: Could it have the flavor "*I* know who you really are" and communicating in the doctor's presumed mother tongue?

DR. TARACHOW: Well, in a paranoid patient it could be. Paranoid patients are given to such remarks indicating private or secret communication. A paranoid patient of mine would follow a long recital of events with the remark, "You know what I mean?"

About a year before, without saying so to me, she had experienced the feeling that she really had some warm and friendly feelings to me, feelings which she could not reveal. This self-knowledge struck her while she was telling me something else.

At the end of the story she had said, "Do you know what I mean?" She was really asking if I knew what her unspoken thoughts were. When I answered in the affirmative it meant to her that I knew what she was secretly thinking, even though in actuality I had been responding only to what she had actually said.

This went on for many months. So far as she was concerned, she was telling me of her love for me every time she said, "Do you know what I mean?"—no matter what else she was talking about. If I simply said "Yes" (because I understood the spoken part), it made her quite happy.

Resident: When someone speaks Yiddish in some ordinary conversation, is it different from a patient doing so in a treatment session?

Dr. Tarachow: No, in principle it is not at all different. When someone drops French or German or Latin or Yiddish expressions in an ordinary conversation, it could have the same unconscious meaning as it would in therapy. It could serve one or another of all the functions we discussed. It so happens that what we discussed occurred in an analysis and was a resistance in the analysis. The therapist (and the patient too, of course) had to know what this woman was trying to express and feel. She was hiding her wishes, her intense attachment, her childish relationship, her anality, her toilet approach to the treatment situation. All this was hidden in the speech and language pattern. She wept bitterly when it was interrupted.

Let us assume that this same girl is not in treatment, and is at a party; she drops French and German expressions. It serves the same purpose to her, except that nobody at the party is trying to cure her. At the party she is elegant: in treatment it is a resistance stemming from anal stubbornness. You don't go to a cocktail party to be cured, but to have a good time. Acting out is not limited to psychotherapeutic or to analytic situations; transference, in a broad sense, is not limited to an analytic or psychotherapeutic situation. In therapy, when one mode of communication is abandoned for a regressive kind of communication, the therapist should regard it as a technical problem. Why should the patient abandon English even for a moment?

There is another kind of abandonment of communication via the spoken word. It could be the following: a patient may say, "My thoughts seemed to stop, but I have pictures in my head." I think you will find this particularly in obsessional patients, who may describe images rather than thoughts.

You will find a helpful paper by Kanzer (1958) about this subject. Just as switching to another language indicates a resistance, so does switching to imagery indicate a resistance. Go back to the last point in the spoken word where the thoughts had been thoughts and not pictures, and find up to what point the patient had been able to tell you his thoughts. You will see that the point of abandonment of words is a point which provoked resistance.

So whenever there is an interruption in communication, whether it is by protracted silence, a fit of coughing, a loud rumbling in the stomach, there has been an interference in communication. Physical restlessness, a switch to a foreign language, a switch to imagery, pain in the stomach, headache, are all examples of the abandonment of speech for a more regressive communication.

This regressive communication can occur in yourself, too. The on-the-spot analysis of regressive references that occur in the therapist can be used by the therapist in understanding what the patient is up to at the time.

RESIDENT: I've noticed recently that if my stomach starts gurgling, my patient's stomach starts gurgling.

DR. TARACHOW: That's regressed communication between the two of you. You know the joke about the patient's tape recorder talking to the psychiatrist's tape recorder. Well, your stomach was talking to the patient's stomach, and the patient's stomach responded.

RESIDENT: A patient of mine who knew that I had a foreign background assumed I knew Greek. She has a Greek background. On many occasions she started to talk Greek to me. I stopped her on many occasions. I observed that when she's talking Greek with me it is at a time when she is breaking up a relationship with a boy friend or she has some difficulties at home with her mother and father.

DR. TARACHOW: At moments of distress she tried to be closer to you.

RESIDENT: Yes. I then learned that she had a close relationship with her grandfather, who was Greek, and she used to speak Greek with her grandfather. When I interfered with her use of Greek, she wept, she cried bitterly, and told me that I was stupid. This patient used to tell the other patients that we had things in common because I knew Greek; she always told the other patients that she was more acceptable to me and that she was my favorite patient.

DR. TARACHOW: It was her fantasy of being a favorite child. In treatment you should persistently interrupt this. Apparently you did.

RESIDENT: She is speaking English now.

DR. TARACHOW: We have just been given a nice example of the abandonment of English and the use of another language; it illustrated two things: one, it represented a flight from disappointment in reality to her resident physician who in the patient's fantasy was going to solace and comfort her; and two, it was a pointer in the psychogenic direction. The therapist represented not only her physician but perhaps her grandfather too.

This reminds us of the conception that an interpretation robs the patient of something. Patients do not welcome interpretations because you take something away from them, you take away some defensive structure or some disguised method of finding happiness. You are helpful but you are mean. In effect, you said, "I'm not going to act like your grandfather,

I'm not going to act like your comforter—you've got problems, you have to work them out."

RESIDENT: That's why she cursed me.

DR. TARACHOW: From her neurotic standpoint she was right. You were stupid in not understanding her childish and infantile wishes. And you were mean because you refused to take her childish wishes as real and exert yourself to make her happy.

RESIDENT: In terms of language usage though, the foreign language need not be the only type of acting out. The patient's use of slang or of obscene words could be a type of acting out.

DR. TARACHOW: Of course. The guideline for you is the continuity of communication. If anything alters the stream or mode of communication, look for a meaning. Look for a meaning, whether it is a relapse into an earlier language, to slang, to vulgarity. Sometimes there may be a vulgarity that suits your patient or a vulgarity that does not suit your patient. Sometimes patients are pseudo vulgar, they think they have to be vulgar to be cured. They are not really vulgar; they are simply trying to please you. But at any rate, the communication is disturbed, and that is the signal to you.

Chapter 17

Depression and Suicidal Risks

The central issues in the management of the suicidal patient are the solution of the problem of aggression and the presence or absence of object relations. We shall discuss this subject in these terms, and shall also deal with the related problems of grief and mourning. I shall open with a clinical example.

I am treating a depressed woman patient, a classical manic-depressive, quite agitated and with strong suicidal impulses. She also presents the problem of homicidal impulses. We might take note of the important clinical fact that the only act of violence in a depressive patient may be an act of homicide. Many depressives succeed in murder, but fail in suicide. One has only to note the many suicide pacts in which the instigator of the pact somehow manages to survive. I have already mentioned in a previous seminar (Chapter 14) the agitated patient who murdered his son on a week-end pass from the hospital. The problem of homicide is important in every severe depression. Every depressive is a potential murderer. Among my depressive patients who did *not* attempt suicide was one who made an abortive attempt to suffocate his child and another who broke his son's arm. Recent medical reports indicate the ubiquity of serious attacks on children by their parents (Kempe et al., 1962).

The depressed woman patient I referred to had strong impulses to kill herself and her two children. One day she described in detail just how she was going to accomplish this. I permitted her to return home without calling either her husband or her physician. The next day the patient returned for her session and thanked me. Why?

RESIDENT: You trusted her.

DR. TARACHOW: Precisely. She thanked me for trusting her. Of course, you have to know when to trust a patient. They might not return the next day to thank you. Having once decided on the therapeutic position, you take a calculated risk. Trusting such a patient is a risk; the patient knows it, and will sometimes torment you with this knowledge. A patient will say, "You're trusting me, but suppose I double-cross you?" One must avoid involvement in this form of torture. The very expression of hostility in such teasing is already the saving factor in the situation. Aggression is the only alternate response available to the depressive: he can rarely be grateful even if he wants to be.

Perhaps we can state a principle which can guide us in evaluating suicidal risks. Depressives who have retained some external outlet for their aggressions are lesser risks. A depressive who does not show any outward-directed aggression is in danger of suicide. The principle can be restated in another way. If the depressive shows any trace of working out his murderous impulses with an object, you may take the risk of suicide. How does one judge whether the patient in question is working out his problems with an object? When the patient has completely lost object attachments, then you may not take any risk. Put in another way, if the depression is not quite total, if the patient is still involved to some degree with an object, it is still possible to trust the patient. Will someone put my last remarks into the simplest possible terms.

RESIDENT: The patient hates someone.

DR. TARACHOW: Yes, that's it. The hatred is a safety vent for the self-directed murderous impulse. The moment the outside object is completely abandoned and the object entirely cannibalized the patient's life is in danger. You must then act quickly. In terms of the transference, what could be taken as a favorable development in the treatment of a depressive?

RESIDENT: The patient tells you you are too young to be a doctor.

DR. TARACHOW: Yes, the patient shows signs of hating you. If the depressed patient shows no interest in you, then suicide is an imminent risk. The patient planning on killing herself and her children was the most abusive patient I had had in years. She had almost to be dragged to my office by her physician, and she then poured out torrents of abuse at me, criticizing every possible aspect of me and my surroundings. She scolded constantly. This saved the patient's life and was my clue as to whether I could safely take the suicidal (and in this case also homicidal) risk. The patient, although in a deep depression, was nevertheless capable of some object relationship. She was saved from suicide by the hostile transference.

RESIDENT: Does there have to be insight into the hostility to save the patient?

DR. TARACHOW: Oh, no. As a matter of fact, that would probably spoil it.

RESIDENT: It must be a real relationship?

DR. TARACHOW: Yes, real to the patient. One must not believe too much in the strength of the word. The patient must simply hate you. I had one severely depressed patient who would put his cigarettes out on the table top of a small ashtray stand next to the couch. This table is quite a useful aggression thermometer. It is a rather small table and easily knocked over. Patients not acting out their aggressions never knock it over. This table takes an occasional beating. One's narcissism has to be likewise sacrificed to the interests of technique.

RESIDENT: Or you go back to your own psychiatrist.

DR. TARACHOW: Freud said every analyst should go back into analysis at five-year intervals.

RESIDENT: The depressed patient's failure to be outwardly aggressive is like the lull before the storm.

DR. TARACHOW: I suppose that is a way of putting it, though I do not think of it as the lull before the storm. The point is that a storm is safer than a lull. The storm, the outward aggression is safer.

RESIDENT: You were talking about your aggression thermometer. Does your trust in it hold even if the patient is overtly friendly?

DR. TARACHOW: I always feel more comfortable if the aggression is delivered directly and overtly. At least you are kept in touch with the patient's aggressions. It is the sadistic side of the depressed patient that is the source of trouble, and if you lose touch with it there may be difficulties.

RESIDENT: A patient said to me, "You're a very good psychiatrist, for someone so young and inexperienced."

DR. TARACHOW: That's naked hostility. It isn't even disguised.

RESIDENT: We don't doubt that the patient is expressing hostility, but the patient would deny it. Should one try to bring the patient's hostilities out into the open as soon as possible?

DR. TARACHOW: Very good. If you do this at the wrong time, especially prematurely, you may drive the patient into a deeper depression. This has to be done with some wisdom. If the patient is not yet at a point where he can cope with it, the guilt and suicidal risk may be intensified.

RESIDENT: Zilboorg once made the point that a depressed patient is more suicidal when not at the height of the depression. The greatest risk appears when the patient is coming out of his depression.

DR. TARACHOW: There is a good deal of truth to that. In the depth of a severe depression the patient might be so paralyzed that he cannot carry out any action whatever, even his suicidal wish. Suicides will frequently occur in the first stages of the hypomanic reaction as patients begin pulling out of the depression.

Severe depressions, even those with some degree of retardation, can be treated in office practice. If a case presents itself in which the genetic weight is relatively minimal and the psychogenetic factors seem to loom large, I would take on a depressive for treatment. These patients can be carried on an ambulatory basis, even though they may be seriously suicidal. However, they must conform to my criteria of the type of depression with whom the risk can be taken. We are discussing the factors which would permit us to take the risk. I remember one week end I had three suicidal risks walking the streets of New York. I had a bad week end, but on Monday they all showed up very much alive.

RESIDENT: Would it not be better to get the depressed patient to work through problems of loss, grief, and being unloved before one looks for the aggressions? It seems to me the aggressions would then come out in the wake of the grief. He may not be ready to express the aggression first.

DR. TARACHOW: This is an excellent question. From the standpoint of ego tolerance, grief is much more bearable than the impulse to murder. In grief there is no guilt. It is quite a worth-while and commendable feeling. You may be able to get a patient to work through his grief over a loss, but the important point is to get the patient to identify the lost object. In a severe depression the object is internalized. It has been unconsciously introjected, swallowed up. In terms of clinical differentiation the patient who can come up with his grief first is not nearly as deeply depressed as the patient who is struggling with aggression and guilt. The more severely depressed patient is more ambivalent and more hostile. His problem is expressed not as grief over someone he has lost but over the self- destructive tendencies let loose by introjecting someone whom he loves very ambivalently, that is, with a great deal of hatred. This is where the danger to the patient's life lies. The aggression and guilt are in the forefront. The grief is quite out of reach. Depression solves the problem of grief. In grief, there is recognition of the object relationship and recognition of the loss of the object, with an attempt to work through the loss and give up the object. In depression, there is a more tenacious attachment; the object loss is not recognized.

Grief and depression are derived from the two sides of the ambivalence, grief from love and depression from hatred. No two depressed patients will be exactly alike; each has his own defensive style, as all patients have their characteristic defensive styles. One patient will be relieved by working through his aggression, another by working through his grief. In principle, the psychotherapeutic maneuver is to help the patient work through his more tolerable feelings first and the intolerable ones later. Murder is not the first subject to bring up to an already-depressed patient. One need not work through all sides of the ambivalence to get a good clinical result. The clinical symptomatology might be derived primarily from one side of the ambivalence. In psychotherapy one works out only as much as one is forced to, not everything one would like to from the academic or theoretical standpoint.

RESIDENT: What do you think of the suicidal risk in the following case? The patient is depressed and self-derogatory; he feels he is worse than Hitler. He seems to express hostility to the introjected object.

DR. TARACHOW: Do not confuse attack on the introjected object with attack on the object in reality, on the outside. This patient is not expressing hostility outwardly. He is a murderous, suicidal risk. He is telling you he is a murderer.

RESIDENT: I have heard that at some centers they make bankers scrub floors to work out their sense of guilt.

DR. TARACHOW: There certainly is a rationale for that. Call it the mental hygiene of the depressive. This leads us to another aspect of the therapeutic position needed to be taken with depressives. Even though you might be working interpretively with the patient, you must take a strong authoritative position. The patient is seeking to punish himself. If you do not supply some element of this punishment, he will seek it elsewhere. He requires the punishment; his guilt is so enormous.

I would like to develop this discussion by citing a case of my own. This man made a serious suicidal attempt and almost succeeded. This was a patient with whom I did not take a strong enough position. The secret of ambulatory treatment of severe depressions is the strong authoritative position of the psychotherapist. I will describe the error into which I fell. At one point the patient suggested to me that perhaps he required electroshock therapy. My response was, "Yes, I've been thinking about it and perhaps we will do so." The error was in accepting a suggestion from him. That night he disappeared and twenty-four hours later was found almost dead in a hotel room. His not being held in check by me served as an acute aggravation of his guilt over his aggressions. I was no longer of any help to him in controlling himself. The moment I was not in absolute control over him the patient was in danger from his own aggressions.

The therapist must take into account the masochism of the patient. When dealing with a neurotic masochist one must not too directly gratify these needs. The therapist should remember that it takes a certain degree of masochism to subject oneself to any type of mental treatment, especially the painful aspects of any interpretation. But one certainly should not act along with a patient's masochism outside the absolute needs of the treatment effort. However, with a depressive, a *psychotic masochist* if you will, the therapist must act along with the patient's needs in order to save the life of the patient. The therapist must be sadistic enough to save the patient's life. You are his protector and must be stronger than he. The serious suicidal attempt in the patient mentioned above occurred when I showed some weakness to him.

RESIDENT: The patient felt he had pushed some person around. He had added another person to his list of victims, increasing his guilt.

DR. TARACHOW: Yes. If I give in to him, I burden him with the unconscious problem of having killed me. It is up to the therapist to adopt such a therapeutic attitude that the patient's pathological superego will not become more active and destructive than it already is. A depressed woman patient came to me for treatment after leaving another therapist. She had asked the previous therapist for permission to take a month's vacation and interrupt treatment for that month. The therapist had (kindly) agreed. She promptly broke off treatment and sought another therapist. She felt rejected, of course ("He doesn't care"); but, more importantly, he had allowed the patient too much liberty; he had given up his control over her. The patient feared the success of her own aggression and sought someone stronger to keep her in check.

RESIDENT: You spoke of the hostility. What is the usual course? Is it worked out? If the patient expressed hostility without insight, would it do him any good?

DR. TARACHOW: It certainly would. The turning outward, with or without insight, does two important things. It re-establishes contact with objects, and it relieves the pressure toward self-destruction. The therapist aims for relief of the psychotic mechanism: absence of insight would not disturb me. Indeed, most psychotics recover without insight.

RESIDENT: I take it the patient might leave you still hostile and aggressive, but feeling much better in terms of his depression.

DR. TARACHOW: Oh, yes. Many psychotics recover without insight, depressives as well as schizophrenics. Only at certain stages of an illness will the patient have insight, often spontaneous, into himself. Some schizophrenics have frighteningly clear insight into all their deepest and most archaic needs. A depressive, at a point at which the depression is mild, though he might be motivated by a masochistic need to know only the most painful qualities in himself, might have accurate and deep insight into his cannibalistic and murderous feelings to his objects.

RESIDENT: In an ideal case, would you try to give the patient insight?

DR. TARACHOW: Of course. In cases in which the psychogenetic aspects are predominant, you would really try to work out the patient's ambivalence, both the problem of hostility and the need for love.

RESIDENT: Is there a danger that such a patient might go into a paranoid state, projecting the aggression?

DR. TARACHOW: Theoretically yes, but clinically this rarely ever happens. Everyone has his own style of illness. The patient who introjects sticks to that pattern. You will seldom see switches from depression to paranoia. In fact, you will seldom see paranoid trends in a depression. If there are paranoid trends, it would indicate some special extra factors arising from a homosexual problem. The one important exception is involutional melancholia. This is a type of depression strongly characterized by paranoid trends.

RESIDENT: We have a depressed woman on the ward who has been given electroshock. Her symptoms now are primarily paranoid.

DR. TARACHOW: This might well happen in shock which produces transient ego disintegration and other physiological issues not too well understood. You would profit by reading Frosch (1945) and Frosch and Impastato (1948) on this subject. The question we are asking is somewhat different. In the attempt to get the patient to redirect his hostility to an external object, do we run the danger of the patient requiring another defense against the aggression, namely, projection, with consequent paranoid complications? The reaction to electroshock is an interesting clinical matter, but is not the subject at hand. Under the impact and conditions of shock no attempt is made to give the patient insight into his aggressions; furthermore, something additional has taken place, the organic ego disturbance, the organic mental deficit. We are discussing the dangers of insight into the aggression.

One likely danger is that of making the depression worse by premature insight. We are now discussing the dangers of certain psychotherapeutic measures.

RESIDENT: Are externalization and projection the same?

Dr. Tarachow: I did not use the expression externalization, but it could refer to the turning outward of the inwardly directed aggression. We are discussing the task of helping the patient locate the real object that has been hated, lost, and introjected. We are helping the patient to find the external real target of his aggressions. We are reversing the introjection. Reversing the introjection is not projection. We are seeking a return of feelings and the object to which they belong, not another defense against them. The basic problem in depression is the cannibalism, the oral aggression against the mother. In the cure via psychotherapy the aggression against mother must be clearly regained. Sometimes the patient cannot tolerate the cure. They become more deeply depressed. Projection is another matter. In projection the patient imputes his *own* aggression to *someone else,* either to the object of his aggression or to a third party.

Resident: As a patient comes out of a depression, is it possible that he will then handle his fear of the hostile impulses by compulsive rumination?

Dr. Tarachow: Oh, yes. The patient may overcome the depression and then erect new or old defenses against the selfsame hostile impulses. The chief problems in a depression are the enormous oral greed, oral demands and hatred. If the depressive defense is eliminated, this does not necessarily eliminate these personality traits. The patient may then have recourse to obsessive defenses, to isolation. I recall one male depressed patient who recovered from a severe depression and then suffered from a severe compulsive neurosis, the central compulsion of which was an urge to cut off his father's penis.

Incidentally, I will prescribe medication for a psychotic depression, but not for a neurotic depression. With regard to a psychotic depression I assume that the patient's ego is sufficiently fragile, the hungers are sufficiently great, and the intolerance to frustration sufficiently sensitive, that I consider it warranted to indulge the patient in a certain degree of derivative feeding. The treatment of a neurotic depression proceeds much more along interpretive lines, greater demands are put upon the patient, and I would not indulge in this type of derivative feeding. This indulgence with a psychotic depressive might seem contradictory to the authoritative role I recommended in the attitude to the depressed patient. But this is not a contradiction. In the treatment of the psychotic depressive the psychotherapeutic principle is to take into account both the enormous strength of the oral demands and the enormous strength of the superego. The therapist must act to prevent a catastrophe originating from either side.

In order for a neurotic to realize the intensity or enormity of his childish desires these desires must be permitted to reach a certain level of insistence. Without this pressure of insistence any interpretive effort is doomed to failure. This is the frustration imposed on patients in analysis or intensive psychotherapy. Without frustration in the therapeutic situation and under the conditions of the therapist gratifying the wishes of the patient, the relationship is closer to an adoption than to therapy. However, some of this adoption may be necessary under certain conditions.

I would like to return to a clinical quality of depression and suicidal risk. I always try to get an estimate of the emotional fluidity or lability of the depressed patient, particularly the ability to cry. I am rarely concerned about the safety of a depressive who is able to cry. A certain degree of fluidity and lability improves the prognosis. In very severe depressions there is enormous rigidity and embitterment. Everything might be rigidly frozen, the entire body posture, the gastrointestinal tract, and the affects. These patients do not talk, eat, defecate, or cry. They are colossally spiteful; in fact, they often will not even admit that they are depressed. They refuse help and have no interest in anything. These are the suicidal risks, especially if there is any tendency to remission of the motor paralysis.

Incidentally, the therapist should always be in touch with

some member of the family. The suicidal risk should be shared by you with the family.

RESIDENT: How does the principle of granting requests, e.g., prescribing medication, square with the principle of attempting to arouse their hostilities so that they can be directed outward?

DR. TARACHOW: I have already mentioned the reconciliation. The depressive is buffeted by strong oral needs as well as by a strict superego. He must be saved from being damaged by either extreme. Neither side should be permitted to become too dangerously insistent. I had expressed a reconciliation of the indulgence with the authoritarian role. You are raising something a bit different. You are asking for a reconciliation of the indulgence with provocation of hostility. To begin with, I do not think that the therapist should do anything to provoke the patient's hostility. However, he may so deal with the patient's tendencies that in a sense he permits the patient's hostilities. The authoritative role is for the sickest of the depressions; it serves to hold the patient's aggressions in check. As treatment progresses the therapist will permit (or encourage) the patient to take the therapist or others as the target for the patient's underlying aggressions. The safest state is for the therapist to be the target—in other words, the hostile transference. As I mentioned before, these patients are deeply ambivalent. Their libidinal needs for love as well as their sadistic needs must be granted some gratification. When a patient is very deeply depressed, our authority helps to keep the aggressions in check. As they improve, or as a relationship to the therapist develops, the aggressions are permitted outlet. In either case the patient is saved from his overly strict superego. Our authority holds the aggression in check and our indulgence permits safe gratification of the aggression.

If the depressive is willing to make demands on you, you should try to fulfill the demands. The depressive who refuses to be greedy is the suicidal risk. The depressive who makes demands has an object relationship which may save his life. The therapist supplies himself as an object to the patient; in fact, he should even thrust himself upon the patient as an object.

Chapter 18

Masochism and Paranoia

We shall attempt to discuss masochism and paranoia in the simplest possible way. The most well-trod formulations of masochism deal with the problem of aggression and guilt, and the subsequent turning inward of the aggression. The aggression turns into self-punishment. However, masochism can be understood in other ways, too. Newer conceptions have given us further psychotherapeutic leverage in our approach to the masochist.

The masochist can be considered as someone who is struggling with a need for love, but has been saddled with a perverted technique in this quest. Let us consider an example. A little girl who had recently been blessed with the arrival of a newborn sister was walking about her home. Her mother was occupied with the baby; no one was paying attention to the little girl. Suddenly she burst into tears, turned to her mother and said, "You hit me." This is a model for masochism. The quest for love is processed through suffering. The accusation, "You hit me," was another way of saying, "You don't love me enough; and this hurts." Every masochist says in effect, "I don't think you like me." This is masochistic bait. The automatic response this is designed to elicit is one or another variety of reassurance.

The feeling or statement, "I am unloved," is a reverse or perverse way of saying, "I want love." There is an implied claim. The claim is made by the statement of the deprivation:

this statement can be made with varying degrees of intensity. For example, when asking for food, one could say, "May I have something to eat?" One could also say, "I'm dying of hunger." The statement of the deprivation is the request. This is the technique of the masochist. The masochist exaggerates and advertises his deprivations. This is a perverse technique of asking for love. We can thus consider masochism as a *deformed* technique in the pursuit of love. The masochist is a blackmailer. His statement of deprivation is coercive and makes it difficult for the object to refuse.

We can now detect the sadistic note in the humble masochist. He coerces love by thrusting his suffering under the nose of his object. There is an interesting series of papers on masochism by Bernhard Berliner (1940, 1942, 1947). He was the first analyst on the current scene to emphasize these aspects of masochism. He discussed it in terms of the deformity of the approach to the object. The path of love goes through a bypass of excessive suffering, of excessive claim.

RESIDENT: Some time back you said that the masochist denies. Does he deny his love or his need for love?

DR. TARACHOW: The masochist will deny in the sense that he does not admit he is asking for love. His aim is to get love, but he does not really consciously admit this aim. There is a stubborn, hostile, blackmailing quality to him. But he denies the direct search or the direct plea. Masochism is the technique of someone who cannot be direct.

There is an old, worn-out joke which is relevant to this. It is the story of the man who gets a flat tire on a country road and finds he has no jack. He walks to the nearest farmhouse; on the way he builds up an anticipation of refusal on the part of the farmer. By the time he reaches the farmhouse he is in such a rage that he greets the farmer with, "To hell with you and your jack."

RESIDENT: A patient of mine shows this beautifully, because she demands so much of her husband's love. She keeps on asking for more and more. She engulfs him and then she fights him because he does not give her enough.

DR. TARACHOW: I am glad you mentioned this patient because it brings up another important aspect of masochism. There is the other side to the humble masochist. On the one hand the masochist is unable to ask for love directly and approaches love via the deformed path of suffering. But on the other hand the masochist makes enormous demands: he is the greediest of all. This very greed insures disappointment and suffering. He demands so much that no one can ever really give him everything he wants. The masochist demands so much love, so much reassurance that his objects finally get to hate him. The masochist finally creates the very situation he fears. The patient you mentioned does just this. One of the difficult things to do in the treatment of a masochist is to get him to see how *much* he is really asking for, how greedy he is. He suffers from a kind of hypocritical virtue. He must be made to see this. The very sensitivity to rejection which plagues the masochist is a sign of his greed. If he were not so greedy, he would not feel rejected at every turn.

RESIDENT: My patient shows another characteristic, too. She says, "I don't want to be selfish."

DR. TARACHOW: Yes, and then she goes on to be selfish.

RESIDENT: What's the incidence of gross perversion among masochists of this type?

DR. TARACHOW: I don't know, though it probably is a substantial percentage. The patients in the Havelock Ellis sense, in whom suffering leads to orgasm, do not come for treatment, just as very few homosexuals come for treatment. However, of the social varieties of masochism, of moral masochism, you will see a great deal. The masochism will be present in social and marital relations, in life patterns. Patients will present themselves complaining about unhappy marriages, unhappy work situations, a great variety of suffering apparently due to a difficult environment. You will rarely see full-blown perversions, though you certainly will see many patients with various degrees of one perversion or another.

RESIDENT: Is every masochist also a sadist?

DR. TARACHOW: In a sense, yes. The masochist is ambivalent: he is sadomasochistic. However, one side of the ambivalence may be quite prominent, while the other side is latent. In intensive psychotherapy, both sides of the ambivalence should be worked through. The masochist must recognize his aggressions. Today, I wanted to emphasize the deformity in the search for love.

RESIDENT: By definition, the masochist is unable to share the pleasure of his pain. In that sense he is completely narcissistic. I have a patient who repeatedly says, "I'm ugly. I'm horrible. I have no abilities." What puzzled me was her saying to me, "I like you better when you are mean to me." It puzzled me, but at the same time I can see that it has the quality of an object relationship.

DR. TARACHOW: Were you trying to say that they cannot share their pleasures and in that sense they are narcissists, but at the same time they do show some perverse object relationships?

RESIDENT: I am wondering about the social quality or the object-related quality of perversions, especially masochism. Even the full-blown sexual pervert who hands the whip to a prostitute seems to have an object relationship.

DR. TARACHOW: Let us go back to your patient who said, "I like you better when you're mean to me." Patients will often provoke you to scold them: after they have succeeded they are quite content. It is only by the scolding that you have demonstrated proper parental interest. This is a bit of masochistic excitement. It is a search for proof that you love them. If you love them in the ordinary sense, the ego of such a patient is incapable of recognizing it. The path to object relationship is via sadism.

RESIDENT: I wonder if masochists always need such narcissistic types of object relationships?

DR. TARACHOW: It is not narcissistic. It is very much object directed, deviously, but object directed.

Even a paranoiac has reconstituted a path to the object. The paranoiac says, "You hate me." He is also expressing a crippled plea for love. He says, *latently,* "I want him to love me, but he hates me." This, too, is a way of asking for love. The paranoid accusation and delusion are a plea for love. He says what the little girl said. The paranoid attitude shows a greater degree of defeat than the masochistic one does. The masochist says, "You are abusing me." The paranoiac says, "You hate me." Another way of contrasting the two is to say that the masochist arranges to suffer *in reality*. He finds real people and constructs real situations. The paranoiac suffers at the hands of *imagined* distant persecutors. Yet this very delusion is the paranoiac's attempt to get back to objects. It is the devious statement of his claim for love. With all this in mind we can open up an avenue of psychotherapeutic approach to the paranoiac. This might even give the therapist a feeling of sympathy for the paranoid patient.

RESIDENT: Paranoiacs and masochists manage to bring their complaints to the attention of the object. A young girl patient who was secretly vomiting her medication told another patient, "Don't tell the nurses." Of course, the nurses were promptly summoned.

DR. TARACHOW: Even the most regressed and withdrawn schizophrenic is object directed, too. You can hurt the feelings of a schizophrenic. Everyone is object directed, even suicides. Jensen and Petty (1958) have done some interesting work on suicide notes, the plea to the object to save them. They show very nicely that a suicidal patient is very much object directed. He tries to provoke something in the rescuer. Even when he does not want to be rescued, the sadism of the suicidal patient is specifically object directed. He is trying to inflict perpetual guilt and pain on someone.

I believe I mentioned a fantasy one of my patients had. He was toying with a suicidal fantasy and had the thought he would leave a suicide note saying, "Dr. Tarachow has nothing to do with this." Such a note would of course immediately pin everyone's interest on me. I suppose the only patients not object directed are patients suffering from marasmus. They show an absolute suicidal loss of interest.

RESIDENT: There are several patients who will act out only when the supervisor and the entire staff are on rounds. One man, especially, behaves well most of the time except when the supervisor comes on the ward. Then he will pace outside in rain or snow.

DR. TARACHOW: A number of years ago I took on a depressed woman patient who made me promise at the beginning of treatment that I would kiss her at the end of treatment. I promised. (You won't get anywhere with a patient unless you have the patient in treatment.) She released me from the promise subsequently. At any rate, during the course of treatment she would often station herself across the street outside my office and cry loudly for hours.

The point I am highlighting is the search for love, apart from the sadistic problems. The masochist, with all his deformities and pain, has an object relationship and wants love. What he wants is reasonably normal. His technique is perverse.

RESIDENT: Is a masochistic syndrome related as much to homoerotic strivings as are paranoid ones?

DR. TARACHOW: This is a difficult question to answer. I have the impression that there are varying degrees of the same psychopathological solution in both instances. The masochist, you will notice, has passive, not active, techniques. He presents himself to a woman and says, implicitly, "I am your victim." The masochist accepts a passive role in life. The paranoiac accepts a passive role in his unconscious fantasy. In real life he is more often pathologically aggressive and sadistic. The passivity seems to be more ego syntonic to the masochist than to the paranoiac. The passive techniques seem to have taken over for the masochist.

My answer to your question would be to respond with my

working clinical orientation. In a paranoiac I am alerted to the latent passive homosexuality; in a masochist I am alerted to the aggressions and the deformed search for love. These are by no means mutually exclusive. One does not rule out the other. Neither does this mean that paranoid reactions are based solely on problems of unconscious passive homosexuality or the problems of a masochist. Macalpine and Hunter (1956) have put forward some stimulating ideas about the Schreber case. They feel that the paranoid psychosis is based on problems of archaic bisexuality. Their book is very much worth reading.

RESIDENT: Is masochism related to problems an individual faces in dealing with extremely aggressive or brutal objects, leading to a technique of maintaining a relationship to the object at all costs?

DR. TARACHOW: Quite so. Bak (1946), in his excellent paper on masochism in paranoia, describes the case of a young man who suffered brutal beatings at the hands of his father. I do not recall whether the patient became masochistic or paranoid, or both. It is really only a matter of degree in differentiating between them. On the other hand some individuals in whose background there was an absent or passive father do become homosexual or paranoid. The passivity in the patient might be engendered by the absence of the male figure or by an environmental predominance of feminine figures. Frequently, the homosexual or paranoid patient gives a history of the father being dead or absent. The critical period at which the father has died or abandoned the family is when the patient was either aged five or aged twelve.

Bak highlights the other type of background. In these instances the father is brutal and aggressive, too strong to be overcome by the patient. In such cases the path to identification with the father is so blocked by the father's aggression that the son can only adopt a passive orientation to him. It is impossible to work through the rivalry and aggression against the father.

There is more than one path to homosexuality, masochism,

and paranoia. What we have noted are the vicissitudes of the relationship to the object, the perversions in the search for love from the object, and the similarity of the search in both masochist and paranoiac.

What is the disadvantage to a boy of having a father who is away a great deal? What opportunity does the boy *not* have?

RESIDENT: The opportunity to identify with him.

DR. TARACHOW: That is one important factor. He is left with the women of the household. But there is another factor.

RESIDENT: When this boy has an upsurge of aggressive feelings and expresses them, he is at least assured that the father can take it and is not destroyed by it.

DR. TARACHOW: Exactly. He is reassured that his aggressive fantasies have not borne fruit: his father is still alive. There is yet another aspect. He has an opportunity actually to carry out some of his aggressions against his father. Those of you who have sons in the oedipal period will know how much your sons enjoy not only imitating you but also punching and hitting and beating you in some competition. In the absence of the father there is lack of this opportunity to work through this competition by a positive identification, which is a mixture of love and rivalry.

RESIDENT: At the Adolescent Pavilion there are epidemics of wrist-scratching and self-mutilation of various kinds. Some patients become angry at the self-destructive patients for the attention they get. They will openly criticize them, for using self-injury as an attention-getting device.

DR. TARACHOW: There certainly can be an element of attention getting in a suicidal attempt, but there is more to it than that. I will mention the most recent suicidal attempt that occurred in my practice. A young married woman attempted suicide by taking quite a handful of pills: she promptly called her mother on the telephone to tell her what she had done. The point of this is that the mother lives in California and could not possibly get to her in time to be of help. The patient's act was an act of revenge against the mother, and also against others. As you can note, the suicidal attempt and the phone call were both very much object directed.

RESIDENT: I wonder if masochism can be separated into the following: one group growing out of inverted aggression and the other being somewhat regarded as a mold for erotic gratification.

DR. TARACHOW: I said at the outset of this discussion that we would add to the problem of masochism as an expression of aggression the conception of masochism as a perverted search for love. One can suffer for a variety of reasons. I might suffer because I want you to love me, or I might suffer to make you feel guilty and miserable. The motives could be either to extract love or to inflict punishment, two quite differing motives. The two motives may exist in one patient, though one side of the ambivalence will generally predominate.

RESIDENT: I would like to mention a patient who scratched another patient's name on her own skin. She consciously felt she was giving pleasure to the other patient, since she had given the other patient control over her by virtue of the name being scratched on herself.

DR. TARACHOW: This strikes me as voodoo, or rather a reverse voodoo, or passive voodoo. The patient was using herself as a voodoo object and indulging in the same type of magical thinking which is involved in the sadistic voodoo act. This patient was using voodoo for masochistic and passive aims.

RESIDENT: You mentioned the factor of the inability of boys to work through their aggressions toward their fathers. Perhaps an additional factor could be that the boy retains an early image of a large father. This image remains uncorrected by reality and may therefore assume strong pathogenic features.

DR. TARACHOW: Yes, I agree. In fact, this issue reminds me of an interesting aspect of that phenomenon known as "the good old days." In the good old days everything was wonderful. One facet of this is the image of the parent which may remain uncorrected by reality under certain special conditions. One such special condition was the emigration of the father of a family from one country to another. A good number of years later he sends for his wife and children. The reunion of the children with their father is unfailingly a disappointing experience for them. Over the years they had carried an enlarged, idealized picture of the father. When they finally meet him he invariably seems small in size and not very attractive.

RESIDENT: I would also add a further construction. There are families in which through the absence of the father, the boy is prematurely thrown into the position of the man in the family. The mother encourages him in this position making the oedipal situation too real and too anxiety provoking.

DR. TARACHOW: Such a situation would provoke more guilt than if the father were on the scene. When the real father is present, the guilt does not reach such high proportions because the boy does not permit his fantasies to go as far as they might otherwise. Reality inhibits and corrects the fantasy with its associated guilt or symptom derivatives.

RESIDENT: There is something puzzling to me about homosexuality being the basis of paranoia. As a psychotic symptom I would assume it is based on pregenital problems, and yet it seems to derive from the reverse oedipus complex, putting it at the genital level.

DR. TARACHOW: An excellent question. The concept of homosexuality as deriving from the negative oedipal configuration is the classical concept described by Freud. It is certainly true, and can be verified clinically. But other things can also be true. There are instances of homosexuality which grow out of other issues. Suppose we consider homosexuality in which fellatio is the outstanding symptom. (Incidentally, do not automatically equate homosexuality with paranoia.) We can take another variety of symptom: the patient has a persistent sensation of something stuck in his throat. What can you tell me about this? Your response to my question should be imaginative and also controlled. The one symptom gives you a great deal of information about this man.

RESIDENT: It is a hysterical symptom. I would assume it has something to do with a problem at the genital level.

DR. TARACHOW: You are passing up the most obvious clue. You asked me a question and in return I gave you a problem. You asked about pregenital homosexuality.

RESIDENT: I would speculate he was having an oral fantasy of fellatio.

DR. TARACHOW: You asked about pregenital varieties of homosexuality, so I mentioned one. As soon as you hear of such a symptom you think of a homosexual component. Which parent would you think of first?

RESIDENT: The mother.

DR. TARACHOW: Of course.

RESIDENT: Speaking of paranoia, why would the critical period be especially the ages of five and twelve? I am thinking of a homosexual with a large pregenital element.

DR. TARACHOW: The answer is clinical and empirical. The pregenital, the preoedipal, and oedipal problems all reinforce one another. When the father vanishes at the time oedipal guilts are at their highest, the growing boy is in trouble. There is no counterbalance to the aggression and guilt.

Reality is important. The reality relationship with the father will check the inner problems. The intrapsychic problems do not simply persist unchanged by or independent of reality. And in therapy, there are times when reality can and must be manipulated for the benefit of the patient, especially the young patient.

RESIDENT: I have a practical question. How can you tell a man's principal sexual identification? It is easy enough when the femininity is obvious or when the occupation is an obvious clue. But one does not always have these obvious clues. A homosexual might be a truck driver. How can we tell if an apparent high degree of masculinity is only a compensation for the inner passivity and femininity?

Dr. Tarachow: Sometimes you cannot tell at the outset. The best indicators are the signs of sensitivity to passivity, e.g., quarrelsomeness, irritability in traffic situations, irritability with employers, with having to wait in line, overreactions to being jostled or pushed in crowds or in subways. Other indicators are excessive shame at having to see a psychiatrist; difficulty in tolerating a collaborator or a partner; the need to do things alone. Many young men with high degrees of pathological femininity were able to function within sets of circumstances which they could at least partially control. When they were drafted into the army there were large numbers of paranoid breakdowns, because such men were thrust into situations of intimacy and of obedience, situations which they had managed to avoid in the past. A man might present himself to you in a marital situation which seems obviously homosexual to us. The situation might be one of tolerating a close friend in a relationship to his wife. The passive qualities are obvious to us, but not to the patient. The passive *content* might be quite difficult to establish. The *defensive* maneuvers or the defensive irritability to the passive homosexuality might be easy to see.

I recall one patient who presented himself for analysis. He was an extremely successful and ruthless business man, yet one of his symptoms was fear of blushing (a certain indicator of latent homosexual problems). This patient almost fainted when I asked him to lie down on the couch. To assume a recumbent position with me above him was a disaster of the first magnitude.

In the management of the latent homosexual-paranoid type of patient one must learn to distinguish between several varieties of aggressiveness. There is more than one kind of aggressiveness. There is a real aggressiveness and there is a paranoid aggressiveness. After some experience you will be able to differentiate between them.

RESIDENT: I wonder if anyone has experimented with a paranoid patient by bringing his hated object to him, and having this presumed hating object show obvious signs of affection. What might happen?

DR. TARACHOW: What can sometime be done is the following. In the case of a male patient brutally treated and seduced by a father in childhood the patient was left with a perpetually churning rage and preoccupation and also a hallucinatory type of masochistic surrender to the father. This went on from adolescence into adult life. In real life he had avoided his father for many years. His psychiatrist urged him to visit his father. He did, and found that his father was now old, weak, inoffensive. This was of great help in therapy, though it did not cure the patient. At least to some degree it gave him a certain detachment from his own churning affects about his father, though these hallucinatory churning experiences continued.

In a psychoanalysis the transference is used to carry out almost precisely the experiment you are suggesting. The patient converts the analyst into the hated and hating object, and it is up to the analyst to call the patient's attention to the distortions which the patient is imposing on the figure of the analyst. The patient will see the analyst as mean, cold, and disinterested. Even in a neurotic there may be a certain degree of paranoid distortion of the analyst in the transference. As mentioned earlier, this could represent a plea for the analyst's love, but a plea carrying a high charge of anticipated defeat. It is like saying, "You don't really love me. You hate me."

We can think of the following progression of symptoms. Obsessional symptoms serve to deny any affectionate interest. Masochistic attitudes do express the plea for love, but via the complaint, "I'm so unhappy. I ought to be loved." The paranoiac is quite defeated. He says, "I'm sure you don't love me. You hate me." These are progressions in discouragement. In terms of love the paranoiac has met the greatest defeat. At one end of the scale, the obsessive denies that it matters. At the other end, the paranoiac admits it matters, but expresses no hope.

Chapter 19

Paranoia and Homicide

I shall continue today with an example of a paranoid patient and the related problem of a homicidal impulse.

A patient told me about two dreams, the first of which he had had three days before the session to be described and the second the night immediately preceding the session.

In the second dream, I, the analyst, was sitting around drinking with several men. I was at the stage of being cheerful, a bit too talkative, in the overexpansive stage of mild drunkenness. One of the other men then wrote fragments of words in chalk on my back: none of the words was completed. They all consisted of several letters but no complete words. In the earlier dream, three days before, he had been going for treatment to a different analyst.

The patient first talked about the dream of going to the other analyst, a real person. He compared me with this other man and came to the conclusion that he really did not want to go to the other analyst. He really wanted me. As the patient was talking, he heard me moving about in my chair; this threw him off into another chain of associations. This man had been in treatment with me intermittently for many years. He began at some length to express his fears that I might be getting bored with him, that I was losing interest, that I might want to get rid of him, and much as he was tired of the extremely long treatment, he did not want me to get tired of him. He did not want me to lose interest in him. He thought perhaps I was not even listening to him. While he was talking, an association occurred to me about the second dream, the one in which I was sitting around drinking with several men one of whom wrote fragments of words in chalk on my back. I found myself thinking of the old movie *M* in which Peter Lorre starred as the murderer. The murderer in the movie was trapped by someone chalking the letter "M" on his back.

RESIDENT: The marked man.

DR. TARACHOW: That's right. That's how they marked him for death. Well, while the patient was talking about his fear that I would lose interest in him, I had my association to the dream in which the murderer in the Peter Lorre movie is marked with chalked "M" and finally brought to justice and death. In the patient's dream my back was being marked with chalk. I then assumed that I knew what the dream was about. I was the murderer being marked for death.

I at once interrupted his train of associations and told the patient I would give him my associations. I intended simply to mention the movie *M*, the Peter Lorre movie. As I described the way in which Peter Lorre in the movie had been marked with the chalked "M," the patient recalled a movie he had seen in which a Quisling had been marked for death by having a "Q" chalked on his back. The man marked with a "Q" had been brought to justice and executed.

I then pointed out the connection between his fear of my losing interest in him and the theme of the villain being marked for punishment. I said that since he feared I had lost interest and did not love him any more, he was so furious that he would kill me. To my astonishment he readily agreed, and said that if he really thought I had lost interest in him he would kill me.

After a certain preoccupation with this, he began to worry whether I was now frightened by this impulse to kill me, and now in fear of him would really want to get rid of him. I then pointed out to the patient that just as patients react to analysts, so do analysts react to patients; that it would be absurd for me to deny that his intention to kill me did not stir some fear in me. I added that with a desire to help him and with presumed maturity, I would be able to set the fear aside and to continue to help him without wanting to get rid of him. He did not want me to be afraid of him.

There are two sides to this. The patient does not want you to be afraid of him. That makes him uncomfortable. But, also, patients like to have the feeling that they *do* affect you and that they do influence you, that they do have a real impact on you and that you react. One of the most frustrating aspects of the analytic situation is that the analyst regards the patient's behavior as transference phenomena, he interprets them and is not upset by them. This is annoying to many patients. When they scold the analyst they want him to feel scolded and not be able to say, "This is some transference phenomenon." They feel reduced to childish impotence because the analyst can so brush off their assaults.

I then interpreted his first dream to him without any further associations, namely, his decision in the first dream to go to another analyst. I pointed out to him that he had the dream of going to another analyst, not because he was disappointed in me, but because he was too troubled by his murderous impulses to me and had to get away from me because of the fear of the intensity of this problem.

The patient wondered whether he would ever be cured. I pointed out to him that if he were not afraid to bring up any matter in the treatment, his problems could be solved. At the end of the session when he got up he stood up and told me that he had a new suit, and he wanted to know what I thought of it. He wanted me to admire his new suit. How would you handle the situation with a man who just a few minutes before had been telling you that if he really thought you had lost interest he would kill you.

RESIDENT: Tell him the suit was nice.

DR. TARACHOW: That's exactly what I did. I told him it was a very nice suit. I figured enough was enough.

RESIDENT: Wouldn't the patient be in his own dream somewhere?

DR. TARACHOW: Well, the patient was in the dream. He was all the characters marking me up with chalk. The dreamer is in every dream, and the dreamer's ambivalent feelings are also in every dream. Often the dreamer is in the dream in a number of positions, or as a number of characters, all representing facets of the patient.

This man is attached to me and extremely jealous. For example, this man has enormous difficulty giving Christmas presents to his own children. When he has to give Christmas presents to his own children he goes into a furious rage and depression.

I had one patient who was an extremely demanding man. He wanted me to play many roles in his life. He wanted me to do everything previous figures had failed to do for him. A situation arose in which he thought I should have done something for him in his actual life. He went into a frantic rage in my office. He could not sit. He could not lie. He just paced about my office. He would get up and sit down again. I took a heavy glass ash tray that was near the couch at the time, and while he was pacing around, took it to the side of my office to dump it into a silent butler. Then instead of returning the ash tray back to its position near the couch, I left it on a book shelf. He reproached me for it months later. He said, "You were afraid of me. You took that ash tray and put it out of my reach. You were afraid I'd throw it at you." He was correct. I was afraid. I should have had the insight and courage to regard it as transference. I should not have done that. In an analysis the analyst must treat everything as transference, particularly emotional outbursts at him. What saves the analyst's composure is his grasp of the fact that the outburst is a transference phenomenon. The moment he gets involved in reality the way the patient does, his therapeutic potential as an analyst is ruined. The patient hates you and you start hating him and that is the end of therapy. This is the analytic base line. But, as we have previously discussed, this need not be the conditions of therapy in psychotherapy.

What saves the therapeutic situation is the therapist's knowledge of and self-confidence in the transference. If you show that confidence, the patient will realize it too, and he too will then begin to treat his rages as rage at someone else.

The *New Yorker* once carried a cartoon dealing with the analyst's reaction to a patient's hostility. It showed a patient telling an analyst he hates him. In successive boxes the analyst says, "He doesn't mean me, he means his father, his uncle, etc." Finally in the last box the patient hits the analyst over the head with an ash tray. The analyst says, "Maybe he did mean me." But the joke is incorrect. The patient did not mean the analyst.

I will mention another example. A patient told me one day of his plans for murdering a fellow worker; he told me just how he was going to do it and why. The fellow worker was a fascist and all fascists should be killed. He had it all coolly calculated, and he had the day picked. It was all set up. He knew just exactly when he and this fellow worker would be alone in a certain locker room, and how he could kill this man. This patient did not have too reliable ego controls. I cast about quickly for a point at which to seize the situation, particularly for the provocation for this impulse to murder. I could not think of anything until I reminded myself of the best working rule in psychotherapy or in psychoanalysis. Where should one look if anything arises that one does not understand?

RESIDENT: To the transference.

DR. TARACHOW: Exactly. I began to sweat, since if the rule is true, I was the one he wanted to kill. He was bigger than I was. I thought back to the previous session. I was not able to pinpoint anything; but if the rule is valid, I had to find that the answer had some reference to me. Not quite knowing the answer, but feeling certain of the direction, I said to him, "You know, I don't think you want to kill this fellow. I think you want to kill me." This remark turned his thoughts in my direction, and took us back to the previous session. Then it immediately became quite simple; it turned out that there had been a provocation in the previous session.

In the previous session I had asked him to set up our appointments for next week. Since he did not yet know his work schedule, I suggested that when he learned his work schedule for the next week he should drop me a post card indicating his free time. I would then make arrangements to suit his time and we would work out some appointments for the following week.

He never sent the post card. I think he called me the following week and we set an appointment. What was the problem? What had been provoked by my suggestion to him?

RESIDENT: Perhaps a homosexual fantasy.

DR. TARACHOW: Yes, the underlying problem was essentially a homosexual fantasy, but closer to the surface what was it? I had asked him to report on every minute that he had next week. I had reduced him to utter surrender and utter submission. Send me a card and tell me what you are doing every day of the week! This provoked such a problem of passive homosexuality that I became a persecutor. My simple suggestion to send me the time became to him an extremely aggressive thing. He reacted to it as though it were such; in that action I became a persecutor against whom he had to turn. I was destroying his masculinity and he had to turn around and kill me for it.

I had other paranoid patients who reacted to me with open accusations. "You're trying to destroy my masculinity." This reaction of course will come only from patients so disposed by virtue of tremendous unresolved homosexuality. I mention this to give you an insight into the possible paranoid complications of activity on your part when you are working with a patient whose extreme passivity disposes him to paranoid reactions.

RESIDENT: How do you handle that situation?

DR. TARACHOW: Oh, once we got at the provocation and he expressed his feelings of rage at me over having ordered him around, over having pushed him around to make every hour of the next week subject to my wishes, the impulse to murder his colleague vanished.

RESIDENT: Isn't that why he felt this—he called this man a fascist.

DR. TARACHOW: I was the fascist who had to be killed. One of the clues was that he did not send the card. He had immediately developed too much hatred. It provoked his passivity too much and he developed too much hatred as a defense against it. His fear of me as well as his need to appease me prevented him from turning the rage against me. So he turned it against someone else.

RESIDENT: Was this unconscious or conscious? I mean, not sending you the card because he was so angry at you.

DR. TARACHOW: That's hard to tell. All I know is that he didn't. But once we started to talk about it, his rage about it appeared immediately. But left to his own devices, he probably would not have become aware of it and simply would have remained preoccupied with his need to murder someone else.

RESIDENT: What struck me is the seeming contradiction between the passivity in which he saw himself in the solitary fantasy and the activity which you had to display to bring out this interpretation and make him see what he was angry about. The active interpretive effort which was apparently taken was helpful to the patient, in spite of the intolerance he had of the unconscious fantasy in which he saw himself passively.

DR. TARACHOW: I think what you are saying is that even in the resolution of the problem he maintained his passive relationship to me. You are quite right. I had to be quite active in working it out while he remained quite passive, even though his passivity was precisely the irritant which started the difficulty. I had to do a lot of work in setting up the link between the impulse to kill a fellow worker and to get back to me. I had to do about three fourths of the talking to establish the chain of events: first, because I was more frightened than he was, and second, because it was a dangerous situation and I had to think fast and work fast in breaking it down. Also, perhaps in my activity, I gratified his passivity in a way which he could tolerate.

I once had a patient walk into my office, not even sit down, come up to me, and say threateningly, "You're making me impotent." Well, you've got to think mighty fast. So I offered him a cigarette. He took it. The provoking situation here, too, turned out to be one in which I had played an aggressive role to the patient. You have to seize control of the situation. You've got to be as aggressive as your most aggressive patient. You must never be overwhelmed by your patient.

I would like to mention another clinical instance of a closely related kind. A male patient described a pleasant evening he had spent with an older man. The older man had been kind, considerate, and laudatory of the younger man. During the course of the evening the patient had a sudden thought, "It would be very easy to kill this old man." What developed during the therapeutic session was the tremendous emotional impact of the older man's kindness on the younger one. It stimulated in the latter his latent feelings of love for the older man. This, of course, had to be denied, and his masculinity and independence had to be forcibly restated. The eventual defense against the emergence of the homosexual feeling was the obsessional thought, though not quite an impulse, of murdering the older man. The patient was readily able to associate this incident with innumerable instances earlier in life in which he fought, was disagreeable and destructive as a defense against any affectionate and latently homosexual attachments.

We can now see how either an affectionate or an aggressive posture toward a patient can stimulate homosexual or paranoid reactions in a patient so disposed. Either type of overture is regarded as a homosexual assault, often provoking paranoid defenses. It is precisely this issue which makes the problem of introducing either discipline or kindness into a psychotherapeutic relationship such a difficult one. The transference of the potentially paranoid patient is extremely sensitive and responds to *any* act on the part of the therapist. This response contains the Anlage of potentially homicidal impulses.

Part III

Supervisors' Conferences

The reader should bear in mind that the next three supervisors' conferences represent terminal conferences held with Hillside supervisors over a period of a number of months. The following conferences represent essentially a *summary* of the thinking and discussions that preceded. The earlier conferences were largely involved with discussions of specific problems between supervisors and residents. Other than enumerating a list of the various problems discussed no further detail could be presented here. It would not be fair to the residents under discussion to be spread on the pages of this book. The author trusts that these summary discussions will prove useful, nevertheless.

Chapter 20

Supervision Outline

Let us begin with what I term the basic rule of supervision, and then proceed to the varying degrees of deviation from this basic rule. The basic rule is that *the teaching of the resident should be instruction in terms of the problems and needs of the patient, as expressed in the specific clinical phenomena of the patient. The supervisor is an instructor and not a psychotherapist.* The last point must be emphasized because there is an important difference in teaching psychiatric residents as opposed to teaching residents in other specialties. In other specialties, the resident has to learn only about the disease. In psychiatry, the resident, his personality and the psychological interaction between patient and doctor all become part of the therapeutic effort. This is quite a complicated situation; since the resident's personality is a factor, the temptation to convert supervision into psychotherapy is great.

To return to the problem of the basic rule, you will recall that I had no sooner expressed this basic rule of supervision than you forced me to consider deviations and variations of the rule. You at once submitted experiences indicating that the basic rule required either elasticity or deviations.

It must be emphasized that the supervisor must regard himself as a teacher and not as a psychotherapist. In this role he will find a wide range of activity and interest which can be specified and conceptualized. This range reaches from problems of the patient on one hand to problems of the resident on the other. The basic rule of supervision demands that interest in the problems of the resident must fall short of psychotherapy. It may, however, approach dangerously close. We will begin with a statement of the various legitimate areas in the range of the supervisors' interest. Our roles as supervisors encompass the following six areas:

The first two areas are clearly educational and didactic functions:

I. Problems of the *specific* clinical phenomena and specific pathology of the neurosis or psychosis of the specific patient, and the specific psychodynamics of the individual case. (We shall not be further concerned with these matters in our supervisors' seminars: I am dealing with this in separate seminars with the residents.)

II. *General* problems of patients especially involving indoctrination of residents with concepts of relationship and treatment. The several subdivisions of this are:
   A. Theory of the personal therapeutic relationship.
   B. Theory of hospital treatment. The latter encompasses:
      1) removal of the patient from a difficult reality;
      2) reconstitution of the problem in the hospital;
      3) indoctrination of the resident in observation, recognition, and tolerance of
         regression,
         decompensation,
         acting out,
         ego splitting, or role playing, and
         transference splitting, dilution;
      4) ego-building aspects of hospital treatment;
      5) insight aspect—its timing;
      6) return of the patient to a difficult reality;

7) the family—its reaction to the progress or return of the patient.

The next two areas concern functions moving in the direction of interest in the resident.

III. Problems of *residents in general.* This can be considered under two heads:
   A. Countertransference as a general theoretical problem.
   B. Lines of authority and complications of administration in hospital treatment.

IV. Problems of the *specific resident* in terms of his clinical results and/or behavior of his patient load, or problems of the resident's relations to other services or personnel in the hospital.

The last two functions concern special measures.

V. Personality profile of the resident.

VI. Utilization of the transference possibilities to the supervisor.

You will note a progressive change in direction of interest. We began with the specific patient and ended with the specific resident.

Our general problem is the task of teaching and educating the resident, beginning at one end with the optimal way of doing it, i.e., in terms of the individual patient, and progressively moving to the needs and problems of the therapist.

We broke this down into six headings. The first and theoretically optimal (and realistically impossible) is the education of the resident strictly in terms of the clinical problems of the individual patient. The next area of education might be termed problems of patients in general, with particular emphasis on transference needs, on understanding of behavior, and on the concept of regression especially with reference to the experience and theory of hospitalization.

The third line of educational attack is to teach the resident in terms of general problems of residents. There are two areas of this subject to which the resident could be directed. One would be problems of countertransference in general; and the other would be the problem of authority, the lines of authority and complications of authority in treatment in institutional settings.

We may be pressed by further difficulties in the learning or functioning of the resident. The next step would be to consider the problems of the specific resident. Certain issues have come forward in our discussions of specific residents; I would remind ourselves of some of the problems we have discussed in the past few months, e.g., the resident who:

a) likes or dislikes certain patients, e.g., passive patients or aggressive patients;
b) has problems in his attitudes either to this hospital or to hospitalization;
c) sees only the relationship to the therapist as important, and despises all the ancillary services;
d) is overintellectual, narcissistic, has no warmth, and cannot sense his patients' need for warmth;
e) resents patients who do not get well promptly;
f) is overly empathic and anti-administration;
g) cannot or will not exercise controls and overtly or covertly encourages acting out, or whose own behavior is similar to that of his patients;
h) is sullen and stubborn in supervisory sessions;
i) does not keep good records;
j) is in constant trouble administratively;
k) is disliked by his patients or whose case load shows no improvement;
l) has a case load which behaves or acts out in some uniform fashion;
m) is constantly sinking into masochistic and submissive relations to his patients or supervisor or both;
n) behaves in a godlike, authoritative way to his patients,

or who overestimates the power of his words, expecting them to have prompt, magical, curative powers.

We have moved from the problems of the individual patient and the problems of patients in general, to problems of residents in general, and finally to the problems of specific residents. We are moving closer and closer to the personal problems of the resident.

At this point, we may have to react with special measures. The fifth and sixth areas of thinking about the teaching or training of the resident follow. I regard these as steps taken in face of increasing difficulty or increasing desperation on our parts in working with a resident. The fifth would be the study of his personality profile. You can work one out for yourself or derive it from the literature, or you may adapt one from our discussions.

At this point I would simply raise the question of the timing of any such evaluation, both for your own thinking without a conference with the resident, and also in terms of discussing the resident's profile with him. My own feeling is that this is an open question and would depend on individual cases.

The last heading would be the problem of the use of the resident's transference to you as a supervisor. We talked about this, about the problem of stimulating the transference or simply using it. We talked about the problem of being an example or an ideal *Erzieher* and stimulating the resident in that indirect way. There are two large avenues of approach, either via an empathic seduction or via an intellectual seduction, depending on the needs of the resident and on the route via which the resident can be most effectively reached.

Chapter 21

Teacher or Critic?

Our special measures for the handling of especially difficult residents include two matters. The first is an evaluation of the resident by means of a personality profile set up as simply as possible. I am not at all certain that such a profile should be used routinely or even under exceptional circumstances or whether it should be discussed with the resident at all. Perhaps under certain circumstances, if things are going badly, such a discussion might render a necessary service. At any rate, I can conceive of a situation in which the supervisor and resident discuss the resident's performance in terms of (1) his empathy, (2) his understanding, and (3) his administrative performance.

I am suggesting this most simple outline for the profile. Hyperintellectualism and lack of empathy seem to go hand in hand. The principal problem of the overempathic resident is overidentification with the patient. There is an important distinction between empathy and identification. Empathy facilitates treatment: identification paralyzes it. When there are administrative difficulties I generally suspect paranoid problems, though it need not always be so. Then there are various difficulties in learning or difficulties in the relationship to the supervisor. Some of the problems have been enumerated in the previous seminar.

SUPERVISOR: I am wondering about the necessity or advisability of such a profile. We do form evaluations automatically, almost unconsciously. From time to time, opinions are requested of us by the administration. At such times does not this request automatically orient the supervisor more to the unconscious problems of the resident? That is not really our business as supervisors. Is it not better to unify the two directions, the patient-oriented direction and the resident-oriented direction? You approach a resident primarily by gearing your discussion toward the patient's problems, and slowly a certain interaction between supervisor and resident develops. Secondarily the knowledge of the resident's dynamics will be helpful. But in encouraging yourself to form a profile of the resident as soon as possible, does this not somehow create a distance between you and the resident, and at the same time make you focus too much on the resident's motivation?

Dr. Tarachow: Not necessarily. In the profile I am not at all suggesting any great curiosity about the resident's unconscious. I want a picture of the man's visible capacities, whether he has feelings, whether he is empathic with his patients: I want to know whether he understands, has a grasp of his patients, can formulate a patient's problem. I also want to know about his administrative behavior, his behavior in the wards, with patients, with nurses, with supervisors. Even though this might lead me to suspect that he is paranoid in one instance or obsessive in another, it is still not psychoanalytic interest in your sense; it is an interest in knowing with what instrument I am working. The profile is not a psychoanalytic diagnosis, it is a continuous, working, clinical diagnosis. It is a teacher's impression. We are entitled to have a teacher's impression.

The question I was raising was: should we as supervisors do this as a routine initial formulation or should we do this only when driven to it by severe difficulties, administrative problems, or problems of learning or dealing with his patient load. Should we wait for trouble or do an initial formulation at some early period?

SUPERVISOR: We are really evaluating all the time.

DR. TARACHOW: I am merely advocating some orderly thinking in this area. You should be able to cast your knowledge of the resident into some readily useful mold rather than have many data and an imprecise impression.

SUPERVISOR: There was such an attempt several years ago at another training hospital where it was felt that too many residents were told only at the end of their residency what their teachers and colleagues thought of them. It was the most devastating kind of interview anyone could have. I remember mine clearly. I never knew what these people had been thinking of me and I was not aware of the impression I was making except within the limits of what I could comprehend of my own personality. Later this was altered so that residents in active supervision would be confronted weekly with the problems they were having with patients and with how they were handling these problems. They could then be made aware of their own problems on a current basis.

The resident struggled with the various suggestions. I think the ongoing aspect is important. However, our initial evaluation in this hospital need not be shared with the resident. The impressions may be too far from his own awareness. We would want to point out elements in the context of his work with patients. After about six months he should be ready to be confronted with his major personal difficulties in working with patients.

DR. TARACHOW: I would share your dismay at being confronted too quickly with an evaluation of myself if I were a resident. It could be quite an assault. I would keep such procedures to a minimum, and adopt them only when driven to do so.

SUPERVISOR: A resident who does good work ought to know what his strong points are, too. Why wait until there is trouble?

SUPERVISOR: May I give an example of something in which I was involved? I presented a discussion of a certain resident with whom a number of other staff people and I were having considerable difficulty. I had written an evaluation that was called for, but was quite hesitant about approaching the resident with it. I worried about it a bit, and then put it aside for a while to get some distance. Later I went back to it. I rewrote it with the same ideas, changed the language a bit, and presented it to this resident. Until that point, things had been rather strained between us. Things were not going too well with the resident and his patient, and between us. We were getting along, but it was more of an armed truce than anything else. It was a cold war that threatened to become chronic. The discussion of the evalution was a most remarkable one. He accepted the criticisms. We had a spirited discussion about the various points; he agreed with nine tenths of them. I felt that he was beginning to see why he had been having trouble in the past. Our relationship has changed markedly.

DR. TARACHOW: You got to do this when you were driven to it. That's the impression I have. You were in danger of a long-standing war between the two of you. Do you think you would have been in a position to summarize his personality to him, and do you think his acceptance of it would have been as useful, say, two months after he started his residency?

SUPERVISOR: No, and in any event I wouldn't do it after two months. I need more than two months to be sure of what I am saying about a resident. There are too many things he does not yet know; there are too many things he would be insecure with. It would be unfair.

DR. TARACHOW: The principle I am suggesting, which may not be the best one, though it appeals to me, is that this kind of approach to the resident should be made only after you have waited a long time. It should be done later rather than sooner; should be done only in the face of real difficulties. If the resident is getting along all right, I would not be inclined to bother him with this at all.

SUPERVISOR: Well, maybe we are the products of our culture;

people like to hear that they are doing well or badly. Perhaps residents would prefer a formalized manner of learning about themselves.

Dr. Tarachow: There is no reason why you cannot praise a resident for good work at any time.

Supervisor: I think we do work Dr. Tarachow's way. Some residents do very well; we help them with things they are missing; we talk mostly about the patients; they see it, they go back, they pick up in the indicated areas. It is a pleasure to supervise such people. I would guess that in each class there are maybe one or two who are superior and easy to supervise. Then there are one or two at the bottom who have pathological personality profiles and grave internal problems. They are grossly insensitive and out of contact with their patients, they cannot formulate the patients' problems. Then the supervisor has real difficulty.

Dr. Tarachow: There are even residents who are so imbued with a certain attitude toward their patients that it is impossible to confront them with what they are doing. They play God, and they live out a certain kind of aggressive and omnipotent role; they simply do not want to see themselves at all. The question also arises, under what conditions one should drop a resident altogether. That is a question no hospital administration likes to face.

Supervisor: There is another type of distressing situation, one in which you listen week after week and cannot quite grasp what is going on. Everything is vague; it is presented to you very blandly, and you are never at ease, since you can not be sure of the way the case is going. This is my difficulty with one man right now. Everything is vague and nice, and there are no real problems. Suddenly a crisis comes along. Then you see how much must have been going on all along and had been missed.

There is a large middling group of residents with whom you do get into their personal difficulties. Dr. Tarachow's plan works excellently with the best residents. Unfortunately we are generally dealing with a big middle group of residents who are neither the worst nor the best.

SUPERVISOR: Perhaps the best way to talk is in personal terms, what my own difficulty is, how I feel about myself as a supervisor. I do play some kind of parental figure to the resident. How am I going to help a given resident to become a psychiatrist without participating in a situation of an infantilizing character? This is my major problem: how am I going to avoid interference with the development of the individual, with his growth, and avoid becoming a controlling, criticizing figure?

It seems to me that if I make my attention to the resident's personal difficulties an ongoing process, then the difficulties with a given case can be shown him as the occasions develop. It need not be done formally. It need not be in terms of his psychopathology but in terms of work tendencies or work lapses. Therefore, I can say to a resident at a certain moment, "There is still some kind of tendency inside you to be master of the situation, not to allow anybody to come in."

DR. TARACHOW: I agree. The point of my attitude in supervision is to stay away from the psychotherapeutic position, and to stay away from infantilizing, and to keep to the position of the teacher and not the psychotherapist. This is why you should do even a confronting kind of supervision only as a last resort. You should teach every resident from the beginning as though he had no problems in learning and as though he had no problems in his seeing the material of his patients. Then, as you recognize problems in his dealing with the patients and patient material, you help him first from the patient's side. You go to the side of *his* problems last.

I would like to give an example of how a symptomatic act on the part of the therapist can be used for teaching about the patient and not for psychotherapy of the therapist. I take the position that everything the therapist communicates to me tells me something about his *patient*—even if the therapist makes a slip of the tongue in a supervisory session. I make it clear to the therapist that I consider the slip as revealing some information about the *patient*. For example, one therapist reported that his patient had four siblings, but quickly corrected himself to indicate there were only three. I directed his attention to the slip, not with reference to the psychotherapist's problems, but as indicating some information about the patient. Upon closer scrutiny it developed that a cousin had lived with this patient and had been regarded by the patient as another sibling. This cousin played an important part in the patient's development. The therapist's symptomatic act in supervision communicated data about the *patient*. This is an example of a patient-oriented approach.

All residents will nevertheless show areas of ineffective behavior with one type of patient or another. They will have to be shown where their work with different patients could be improved, and that each resident has his own typical problem which he does not grasp too readily. We are driven to this point with all residents, sooner or later. Nevertheless, the direction of choice is patient first and resident second.

SUPERVISOR: My attitude as a teacher is very much what I expect from any teacher. The teacher knows more and it is up to him to convey that knowledge to the student: the given case is the medium through which this takes place. The teacher's job is to find the best point at which the student is able to receive. My job is to give as much as possible.

DR. TARACHOW: Absolutely. You are not a good teacher unless you have something to give and are willing to give it. The teacher must have a strong maternal feeling, he must be excited and enthused about giving to his students. You should enjoy teaching. You are a teacher first and a psychotherapist only a reluctant second. When you are a teacher you offer yourself as an ideal, not as a critic.

SUPERVISOR: Should not the resident, either by example or

by direct instruction, be brought to develop an idea of what an ideal psychiatrist is expected to be, and what his own goals in the field ought to be? The resident is seeking a role. Is is not the job of the supervisor help him find that role? I would want actively to orient the resident to a particular branch of psychiatry, the one in which he would do best.

DR. TARACHOW: You need not be that directive. The answer will come not through indoctrination but by your example, and, of course, the resident's talents. Your question leads us to our last subject, the use of the transference to the supervisor in teaching.

Chapter 22

The Transference

When I was a resident in a hospital surrounded by people in a ferment of research, of creativity, of studying the literature, of curiosity about what was going on, I did the same. I plunged in along with the rest.

In so far as attitudes to patients were concerned I simply absorbed the attitudes that my attendings had. I do not think one can be directive about this. To the extent that the resident idealizes you, to that extent will he behave like you and absorb the hospital atmosphere. If the entire hospital atmosphere is shoddy, he will have a shoddy attitude. If the hospital attitude is good, if there is intense interest, he will have intense interest.

We turn to special techniques in cases where learning is difficult or where the relationship between the resident and you is strained. The first special technique is the evaluation of the resident in terms of a profile. The other technique is the deliberate use of the transference situation to you, i.e., consciously making use of the transference relationship to you in order to facilitate teaching.

Supervisor: Such transference interaction with the resident is a rather wide use of the term supervision. I would like to underscore my feeling of the importance of the process of identification in the nontransference sense. The ways in which we behave to the resident in extratransference senses will be reflected in their relationship to us and in their ability to learn.

Dr. Tarachow: The problem of distinguishing between transference and nontransference influence upon a resident is an academic one since it is not a *treatment* relationship. If the supervisor avoids psychotherapy, he plays a real role to the resident and influences him in the same way any other real person in his environment does. In another conference I defined transference as the *interpreted* relationship. However, now I am using transference in its widest sense. In simplest terms, we are referring to the relationship the resident brings to his supervisor, burdened by whatever infantile and prior influences. We work with what is presented, call it what you will. A *transference neurosis* is another matter. That is the special state produced in the patient in analysis by the neutral and frustrating position of the analyst. The material and behavior of the patient are then rigidly determined by his fantasies and are *relatively* free of external influences. This is what makes analysis of the transference possible. The analyst can be certain he is dealing with phenomena determined from within the patient, not from without.

Supervisor: There are many residents who look upon us as identification models, especially when they are anxious and do not know what to do. They may form positive or negative feelings toward us which may or may not be strictly on a transference basis. I think the real relationship plays a great role in determining how we go about supervising. One should spend the first few months gathering the profile and using that time to build a relationship before one turns to the resident with any sort of advice or criticism. Later the supervisor can deal with the resident's patterns of behavior and patterns of treatment approach. It is difficult to do so without the support of a real relationship between resident and supervisor.

Dr. Tarachow: You are right. It is difficult to criticize someone before he likes you. I suppose you know this from your work with adolescents and children. It is up to the supervisor to create an optimal atmosphere for supervision, for facilitation of learning and the exposure of residents' problems. Under such optimal conditions the resident will be willing to tell you about his difficulties and countertransference problems more readily. On the other hand, if the supervisor is too reassuring and too friendly, it creates the possibility that the therapist will carry over this reassuring, overfriendly attitude to his patients.

SUPERVISOR: I know of anxious residents who were given reassurance and support with a resultant improvement in their work. But the reverse can also be true. We observed one resident who made an excellent initial impression. His work became progressively worse. Everyone started out liking him but ended up disliking him.

DR. TARACHOW: There are such masochistic characters. They must spoil a good impression, or they must put their worst foot forward. It is a masochistic problem which can yield to analysis. However, we shall avoid discussing specific neuroses in our residents.

SUPERVISOR: Would the sense of this seminar be that the technique of deliberately utilizing the transference should be adopted when all other methods have failed?

DR. TARACHOW: This is the sense in which I am presenting it. I am presenting it in terms of increasing difficulty in teaching, in getting response or improvement. If all other approaches fail, I would deliberately scan the personality and temperament of the resident, and, with the aid of an honest picture of my own personality, try to arrive at how I could best appeal to this resident. How can I, with my particular bent, and with my particular personality and interests, appeal to this person to learn the important things he has to learn? This is the last resort before you say, "You had better be analyzed, because you are not learning anything."

SUPERVISOR: I would like to, in the sense of making an outline, insert as a step prior to the technique you are suggesting, self-analysis on the part of the supervisor in relation to the supervision.

DR. TARACHOW: I do not think we can ask more than that each supervisor have a reasonably honest picture of his own working temperament, not to fool himself about his own implements. I am not suggesting perpetual self-analysis of the supervisor, simply a knowledge of what his own best personality weapons are. Going through a personal analysis is an important and basic element in his training to be a supervisor.

We are pitching to the resident's problem now (we are not setting up profiles of the supervisors). We are setting up profiles of the residents, and we make use of these profiles as best we can.

SUPERVISOR: I am not altogether clear about what specifically you have in mind when you are telling us that we as supervisors should utilize the transference. Do you mean utilizing or fostering?

DR. TARACHOW: I mean utilizing. For example: in an early seminar we discussed a resident who had cold contempt for his patients. In such an instance I would display an intense interest in the emotional reactions of the patient. I would exert myself to do that and would offer myself as a model of passionate interest in the affects of his patients. Sometimes with patients who are isolated, it is you who has to supply the affect. Likewise, you may have to supply the affect for an overintellectualized resident. With an overemotional or overempathic resident you would have to supply the rationality. I would try to be a model of interest and excitement in the area where you believe the resident has to develop. It is in just such areas that you offer yourself as a transference figure for identification.

In another instance where you have an overintellectual resident you might find it most useful to appeal to the intellect directly. Lead the man to what you think he should be led in the best or most accessible fashion that seems possible.

SUPERVISOR: The sense of my question is not to get these details again but rather to question again your use of this behavior on the part of the supervisor as utilizing the transference.

We have already heard and we know that the resident brings a preformed way of looking at you in terms of his attitudes toward authority, etc. His work may be positively or negatively influenced in terms of whatever his past experiences with authority figures have been. When you as a supervisor proceed to make use of the relationship, why do you call this utilizing transference? To the extent that the resident has already proved refractory to teaching, he has already demonstrated to you some measure of negative transference.

DR. TARACHOW: That's true, but the point is you are not analyzing or treating this man. You offer yourself in as real a way as possible, *without interpretation.* Do what you can to overcome his attitudes to you without interpreting them. You use the transference as a real crowbar in the situation. You are *not* interpreting it for your resident, you're *using* it.

SUPERVISOR: Is this not then simply the relationship between two people, one of whom has the role of teacher and the other of whom has the role of student?

DR. TARACHOW: You're right, and as a matter of fact, this goes on unconsciously all the time. What we are talking about are instances where you are up against a difficulty and where you deliberately. . . .

SUPERVISOR: Try to become a better teacher?

DR. TARACHOW: Well, not precisely. This is a step beyond being simply a better teacher. You try to assess your man, then use yourself, consciously.

SUPERVISOR: In this sense of the word, when we say become a better teacher it does not mean we know more but rather we use our total personalities.

DR. TARACHOW: For example, Dr. X. described a situation in which he was driven to the wall and only then tried to do certain things. The suggestion that comes out of our discussion is that if we are a bit more conscious of this entire construction, perhaps he would not have waited so long, perhaps not waited for the moment of desperation. He would have responded with a systematic evaluation of his man and at the proper moment deliberately used himself as a didactic weapon in whatever way he thought would draw out and develop his man best. As it was he waited until he felt antagonistic and frustrated. My suggestion is to be more conscious and more deliberate about what you have been doing. You will end up being speedier.

SUPERVISOR: I think this is the essence of these seminars, to distinguish between the resident as student and as patient. Our efforts have been to improve the quality of our teacher-student relationship. This is a real problem.

DR. TARACHOW: This sense of the use of the transference is as far as I would want you to go in approaching psychotherapy at all; you will notice that I carefully stayed away from specific neuroses in the resident and carefully stayed away from anything resembling interpretation. The ideal is to teach and to be an *Erzieher,* to be a model for identification. It is too bad that we come to a discussion of the model at the very end, at the desperate situation, because we should be a model *Erzieher* from the very beginning. You will notice I have not discussed specific neuroses in the supervisor either.

SUPERVISOR: I think the various factors that I touched on before as ingredients of the relationship were not transference. I thought that you were talking about transference in the specific technical sense.

DR. TARACHOW: Transference in the classical Freudian sense does not come into existence only when a man is in analysis. A *transference neurosis* does depend on the analytic situation, as I mentioned earlier in this seminar.

SUPERVISOR: I think I was using the term technically because I was thinking of a resident who was in analysis and who carried certain transference reactions to his analyst into the relationship with me as his supervisor.

Dr. Tarachow: That would be particularly difficult to deal with in the hospital setting. I do not know how it could be done, except that the resident in one way or another should be made aware of his behavior at least enough so that he is more than likely to bring it up in his analysis and work it out there. But that would make supervision more difficult than usual.

Supervisor: May I present a brief example? I have a resident who tends to be both overdependent and hostile. He is aware of being overdependent. At first I steered clear of this, but it did not work out very well. Now if I understand you correctly, it would be appropriate to let him be overdependent on me if he can tolerate it. This would be utilizing the transference to me. I would do it for the specific purpose of trying to reach him for teaching purposes.

Dr. Tarachow: I would use it in that sense only if he were having trouble, if he were having trouble in his relationship to his patients and to personnel, and in learning. If he were getting along reasonably well, I would neither use it nor abuse it, but if he had some real trouble, I would foster and use it. If he were disinterested in certain kinds of subjects that he ought to be interested in, I would make use of it. I would let him know what my interests were and perhaps even what I thought his interests should be. But I would use it consciously only when the resident has difficulty in functioning.

There may be situations of special difficulty, though, when you do have to plan the best way of offering yourself. We had talked about that and were given several examples of situations in which circumstances forced the supervisor to consider the question. You have to have a profile—a systematic profile—of your man to know how to offer yourself systematically in some special way. There may be special problems, such as having a very competent man who is contemptuous of patients, or an empathic man whose empathy is not under control. You have to offer affects to one man and controls to another. You might have great difficulty offering this when you see your supervisee only once a week. You may have to have a plan of attack or of seduction, if you will. A plan of seduction takes us back to the acceptance of the role of the parent. Our basic role is parental: we indoctrinate our children with our attitudes and our likes and dislikes and our idiosyncrasies and our values; we do it loudly and we do it silently, but we do it. As teachers, we do the same.

SUPERVISOR: I shall mention another matter which I think is fundamental: one supervisor's image of a psychiatrist may differ from another's. How much would this influence the teaching process?

DR. TARACHOW: That is a fact of life. Each one of you is different from the other; furthermore, supervision is done somewhat differently in different hospitals, and in different parts of the country. The resident has to take this into account when he applies to one hospital or another. If anything, this is an advantage; each of the supervisors offers something different.

You may have noticed that in our meetings, we have stayed away entirely from converting this into a group therapy session of ourselves. We have been talking about our students all the time, our residents. If there are any differences among us, it is all to the advantage of the resident. We have kept even *our* discussion of the problems of supervision focused on the resident and away from ourselves. We are assuming we have no problems, an ideal assumption, I must admit.

SUPERVISOR: I want to correct an impression regarding the image of the psychiatrist. I think we all have a very *similar* idea of what a psychiatrist is, but we differ in how to present certain material to people who want to become psychiatrists and under what circumstances they are willing to accept our images of the ideal psychiatrist.

DR. TARACHOW: No. Just as there are differences in parents,

differences in disciplining children, there are differences in attitude toward supervision, and there are differences in the image you have of a psychiatrist. Even here, the idea has been suggested by one of you that when you teach something to a resident, disregard his personal problems entirely; let his anxieties go by the board, and just ram through to him what he has to know about the patient. In other words, disregard the personality of the resident altogether. In one way or another knowledge and grasp will get through to him. On the other hand, there might be great interest in the resident's personality and also in what type of person or psychiatrist he should be. There might be a strong doctrinaire and indoctrinating attitude as to what his ideals should be. This would certainly influence his treatment of patients. He might become just as dictatorial.

My original conception of a psychiatrist, when I was a medical student, was a picture of you here today, sitting around a table; a psychiatrist sits back and smokes cigarettes. It was, as you can note, quite an ideal of passivity. When I got into training and discovered I actually had to work I was quite astonished. Events indoctrinated me. I could not become a psychiatrist simply by smoking cigarettes. The conception of activity, the degree of activity as a conception of a psychiatrist will vary from one of us to another. We all know we have to work, some think more, some less, some in one way, some in another. There must be quite a spread even in this group. Such a spread is normal. There are going to be differences in attitude to acting out and to misbehavior, to suffering, to medication, to insomnia. The resident has a problem of growth and maturation. He may have one supervisor who says, "No pills," but another who says the opposite. When the resident finishes his training he will have to decide for himself.

You may recall that at the beginning of these seminars some of you handed me prepared questions dealing with supervision. It might be worth repeating some of the questions at this point to see to what extent we have come to some useful position about these questions. "What are the supervisor's different concepts of supervision?" We have just been speaking about this. "Can a seminar function as a forum for comparison of modes and opinions concerning the supervisory process?" That is what we have been trying to do. "What methods are appropriate for teaching psychotherapy in this setting?" This was dealt with largely in the seminar dealing with the theory of hospital treatment. "What problems are aroused by the supervisors also having patients in treatment?" Patients have an attitude to the fact that supervisors also carry a case load, as do the residents. It is a competitive problem which might burden some of the more sadistic and competitive residents. It is perhaps an even greater problem for the patients. Patient A feels, "I have a supervisor." Patient B feels, "I have a beginner." However, the patient with the supervisor-therapist might well have ambivalent reactions. "I must be the sickest of the lot."

"What are the different kinds of problems the resident might present from one time to another?" If a resident has a problem, it does not change. Everyone has his own permanent style of neurosis or idiosyncrasy. "What is the influence of the institutional structure?" This was covered with the residents under the heading of administrative problems. "The boundary between supervision and psychotherapy." No further comment needed. "The supervisor's responsibility to the patient." I would differ with the official policy of the hospital which makes the supervisor responsible for the treatment. The resident will learn more when he is responsible. "What are the supervisor's problems with residents of different degrees of clinical experience?" We have dealt with this in our discussion of regression in the hospital. I might add here that the beginner resident might need the assistance of the split between administrative and therapeutic roles. A more seasoned resident could carry the burden of both administration and therapy.

SUPERVISOR: I should like to bring up a question in relation to the Outline. You have presented it to us as steps in the face of increasing difficulty, starting with patient-oriented techniques. Would you consider it an error in supervision to deal with a personal problem a resident brings up early in the contact, something which is his own particular problem? Supposing a resident says, "This patient is just like me, he's got the same problems I have, and I can't treat the patient because I can't solve my own problems."

DR. TARACHOW: First of all I think that would be quite unusual, and his statement of the similarity might even be inaccurate. But if a resident comes to you with such willingness to confront himself this way, like Jacobowsky and the Colonel, it may be either a good or a bad sign. It is a bad sign if the resident is masochistically driven and looking for criticism and ready to open himself up so much so soon. We *do* want some resistance. We do not want to write on water. But it might also be a good sign. If it is a good sign, I think one should first carefully direct him to the appropriate literature dealing with the clinical material of the patient. I would at all costs avoid psychotherapy. If the resident is really in trouble and he is willing to look for help, and if he is not in treatment or analysis, and if his problem is incapacitating, that is another matter. Your question is: we set up a certain progression; supposing the resident jumps the progression, what are we going to do? Well, try not to be too aggressive about your help.

SUPERVISOR: You really have to meet the resident where he is. You cannot take him back to a patient-oriented type of discussion if he is bringing up his own problems. You cannot get him back to the patient if he really wants to discuss his own particular problems in treating a certain patient.

DR. TARACHOW: You should be careful not to be drawn into psychotherapy with such a man. I do not think the average resident will consciously want his supervisor to be his psychotherapist. Unconsciously, though, the resident is hoping that the supervisor will cure his problems via the patient.

SUPERVISOR: Must one maintain the progression, or is it only meant for orientation?

DR. TARACHOW: This outline is not a strait-jacket: it is meant only for orderly thinking and orderly discussion.

SUPERVISOR: But you do place a high value on the first category—patient-oriented approach?

DR. TARACHOW: Absolutely. Deviate only as forced to.

SUPERVISOR: I have the impression that Ekstein and Wallerstein (1958) start at your stage three, with problems between the patient and resident.

DR. TARACHOW: I am not insisting my approach is the only one: it is simply one orderly way of thinking based on a conception of the factors increasing the difficulties in teaching. In fact, the use of the transference, though it is last in my outline, is at work in the first moment of contact with the resident. It belongs at the end of the outline in terms of the progressive context. This is not an outline of behavior: it is an outline of conceptions.

SUPERVISOR: I had just such a resident some years ago. He came to me, stating, "I fear that there is too great a similarity between myself and the patient." He did not want to treat a certain patient. We talked about it, and I felt I had to pitch my remarks to the problems of the patient and not to the resident. I made some comment to the effect, "You should be able to understand him and it might be very good to work with him." After we finished discussing the *patient,* without any further reference to himself, the resident felt quite relieved because he recognized that there *was* a difference between the patient and himself. He felt he could try to work with the patient and understand him. It turned out to be a very successful treatment situation. I never again heard about how similar the two were. But it was an initial reaction of some anxiety, and almost panic.

DR. TARACHOW: Was this a first-year resident?

SUPERVISOR: No, this was a second-year resident. The resident and patient were actually dissimilar. If they had been the same, he would not have been able to work with him.

DR. TARACHOW: This reminds me of what patients will say on occasion, "You look exactly like my father." Really there is no resemblance. It is a transference distortion. Residents have infantile transference distortions not only to their supervisors but also to their patients. This might have been such a transference reaction on the part of your resident toward his patient. When you forcibly led him back to reality, he was led away from his own transferences and was reassured by the reality discussion of the patient.

One of the greatest sources of anxiety is the problem of ego boundaries and ego control, the fear of the primary process. We fear dissolution of the ego boundary. Patients come into the hospital at a point which their controls are shaky and their ego boundaries under partial dissolution; their ego controls are poor. This sets up a reverberating anxiety in the resident. The patient is strange. What is strange to our conscious ego is also feared. Your resident apparently used his patient to project some of his own difficulties. Projection involves a loss of ego boundaries; something in himself was imputed to the patient. What you did was to restore his own ego boundary by emphasizing the circumscribed nature of the patient's problem. You pulled the two apart. You did not have to talk to him about *his* problem, but you separated him from his patient and he felt more comfortable.

SUPERVISOR: This example is interesting from another point of view. The supervisor might not have intended doing psychotherapy, but he did. He offered this anxious resident an image of a supervisor very much in control of the situation; this was a support for the resident and an opportunity for identification. This helped the resident to re-establish his own ego boundaries and feel quite separate from and independent of the patient.

Dr. Tarachow: In a sense it is a variety of psychotherapy. By offering himself as an ideal the supervisor contributed to the stability of the resident, with consequent diminution of anxiety.

At the same time, he was teaching; it was teaching in its best sense, with the emphasis in the right direction. However, please note now that two points have been made: one, the discussion of the patient helped separate the patient from the resident and helped the resident see that he and the patient were *not* alike. The second point was that the supervisor, by his lack of anxiety, can contribute to the stability of the man he is supervising. Both of these processes diminish anxiety for the resident. The first is in the area of teaching, the second is in the area of offering an ego ideal, and is in a way also a psychotherapeutic measure, though also a necessary aspect of clinical teaching. When you have an empathic resident, as he begins to deal with the inner experiences of patients, he may be disturbed to the extent that he recognizes he has certain experiences similar to those of the patient. He becomes anxious and threatened and fears the eruption of his own impulses.

Supervisor: Or, similar problems in himself of an archaic kind.

Dr. Tarachow: You are right, because the uncontrolled id is a terrible thing; the patient is afraid of it, and so are we.

Supervisor: The specific kind of professional armor that one develops, e.g., in regard to such things as feces, is lost after a while. Many residents at first defend themselves against this, not with a fear of loss of ego controls, but sometimes simply with repugnance. The healthy ego unprofessionally steeled will meet these affects and primary-process break-throughs with repugnance.

Supervisor: As you start out supervision, it seems to me the resident comes in, presents his patient's performance and relationships. You would like to keep the discussion at that level. Perhaps with the ideally composed resident this is possible.

We have had extremely bright residents who have done quite well. In fact, at the end of our supervision we felt we had not affected them very much. I would say that this is not the average situation. With the average resident, one sees immediately at the beginning that he is either not relating to the patient or has one or all of the problems we have been presenting in the seminars. There is some limitation in his performance, and this limitation becomes something that is a limitation in supervision; one can not get over to him the reason the patient is reacting to him in a certain way. It is something he just does not see. But you try. You may go along the progression and show him, through patients in general, what their needs are, to get him to increase his awareness of what is happening to this patient as well as to all patients. The average resident does not respond too well to that, and maybe you have to touch on his problems in general. I would think than when you see such a block to learning, you may label this the man's psychopathology. You send him to analysis and hope he gets help.

SUPERVISOR: It can also be labeled a learning problem. This is the choice of Ekstein and Wallerstein. If you are going to regard the difficulty as a learning problem, then you can approach it via the supervision route. Ekstein and Wallerstein have a unique technique of conveying to the resident that he is behaving in the supervisory process similarly to the way in which the patient is behaving to him. We have not found a high correlation of this phenomenon here, although in some cases it is certainly true. Generally we find we are dealing with limitations *within* the residents and consequent learning problems. The supervisor sees more and more areas which are not grasped by the resident. In our sickest residents we are unable to influence this learning problem; they make no progress whether you teach them or attempt a variety of seduction.

But with the average middle group of residents we have some success. Each one has to be managed differently and one does need a profile to map out a method of procedure. After the resident has developed a liking for you and you have built a basis for identification, you could point out the difficulties.

DR. TARACHOW: The resident can be inspired even by the hospital, by identification with the spirit of the hospital. I am inclined to feel that Ekstein and Wallerstein get too close to psychotherapy with their residents. I would be inclined to think that the learning block depends more on the character of the resident's own problem than on his repetition of the patient's problem.

SUPERVISOR: Still, their approach differs from that of a direct psychotherapeutic approach. They point out the resident's behavior and also the patient's behavior. They point out the problem in terms of deficiency in technique of dealing with the patient. The resident's attention is called to what the patient is producing and to the material the former is neglecting. The resident is sent back to the fray, to the task of handling the patient's material. Within such a narrow frame the resident is focused. The resident can then be shown clearly his defects in the management of a specific hour with a patient. He now has new intellectual equipment and can consciously take the suggestions and act differently.

DR. TARACHOW: Ekstein and Wallerstein use the resident's behavior with the supervisor as the model for the understanding of the patient's posture to the resident. I would not regard such an approach as patient oriented. Some time ago a catatonic was presented to me in a conference. The patient had an enormous degree of latent passive homosexuality. The resident could not see this and was obviously afraid of this. Under such circumstances the resident came to the conclusion that he should treat the patient formally and distantly. The patient was slowly getting worse. In the conference several things were done. The *patient's* enormous burden of homosexuality was demonstrated to the resident; the *patient's need* for *some* gratification was indicated; the *patient's feelings of rejection* at the hands of the therapist were made clear; the advantages of a more friendly relationship were indicated. The case was followed up, and we discovered there were good results both for the patient and the resident. This was teaching at a patient-oriented level. The instruction was solely in terms of the needs of the patient. There was no suggestion made of any similarity of problem in the patient and resident.

SUPERVISOR: In other words, be a teacher and not a psychotherapist.

SUPERVISOR: But this brings Ekstein and Wallerstein along to step four in your outline.

DR. TARACHOW: My impression is that they elect to deal with the resident's personality at once.

SUPERVISOR: The point made by Ekstein and Wallerstein is that it is more convincing to use the immediate supervisory situation as the area for demonstration rather than the discussion of the third party, the patient, who is not present in the office. They use the present and the parallel as demonstration.

DR. TARACHOW: In effect, then, they plunge at once into analysis of the transference of the resident to the supervisor. I would rather "use" this transference than "analyze" it.

However, I am struck by the systematic aspect which their method presents. One might differ with their method, but it does have the advantage of a systematic approach. However, it is too close to psychotherapy to suit me. They start with the resident. I start with the patient.

Bibliography

Aichhorn, A. (1935), *Wayward Youth,* New York: Viking Press.

Alexander, F. (1953), Current Views on Psychotherapy, *Psychiatry,* 16:113-122.

———(1954), Psychoanalysis and Psychotherapy, *Journal of the American Psychoanalytic Association,* 2:722-733.

Allen, S. (1956), Reflections on the Wish of the Analyst to "Break" or Change the Basic Rule, *Bulletin of the Menninger Clinic,* 20:192-200.

Bak, R. (1946), Masochism in Paranoia, *Psychoanalytic Quarterly,* 15:285-301.

Balint, M. (1950), Changing Therapeutical Aims and Techniques in Psychoanalysis, *International Journal of Psycho-Analysis,* 31:117-124.

———(1952), *Primary Love, and Psychoanalytic Technique.* London: Hogarth Press.

Benjamin, J. D. (1947), Psychoanalysis and Nonanalytic Psychotherapy, *Psychoanalytic Quarterly,* 16:169-175.

Berliner, B. (1940), Libido and Reality in Masochism, *Psychoanalytic Quarterly,* 9:322-333.

———(1941), Short Psychoanalytic Psychotherapy: Its Possibilities and Its Limitations. *Bulletin of the Menninger Clinic,* 5:204-213.

———(1942), The Concept of Masochism, *Psychoanalytic Review,* 29:386-400.

———(1947), On Some Psychodynamics of Masochism, *Psychoanalytic Quarterly,* 16:459-471.

Berman, L. (1949), Countertransference and Attitudes of the Analyst in the Therapeutic Process. Abstract in: *Bulletin of the American Psychoanalytic Association,* 5:46-48.

Bibring, E. (1954), Psychoanalysis and Dynamic Psychotherapy, Similarities and Differences, *Journal of the American Psychoanalytic Association,* 2:745-770.

Bond, D. (1954), Discussion of paper by Anna Freud, Problems of Technique in Adult Analysis, *Bulletin of the Philadelphia Association for Psychoanalysis,* 4:52-53.

Bychowski, G. (1953), The Problem of Latent Psychosis, *Journal of the American Psychoanalytic Association,* 1:484-503.

Cheney, C. O., ed. (1934), *Outlines for Psychiatric Examinations.* New York State Department of Mental Hygiene, State Hospitals Press.

Colby, K. M. (1951), *A Primer for Psychotherapists,* New York: Ronald Press.

Coleman, J. V. (1949), The Initial Phase of Psychotherapy, *Bulletin of the Menninger Clinic,* 13:189-197.

Deutsch, F. & Murphy, W. F. (1955), *The Clinical Interview, Vol. 1: Diagnosis; A Method of Teaching Associative Exploration,* New York: International Universities Press.

Deutsch, H. (1933), Motherhood and Sexuality, *Psychoanalytic Quarterly,* 2:476-488.

———(1934), Uber einen Typus der Pseudoaffektivität (als ob), *Int. Zeitschrift f. Psychoanalyse,* 20:323-335.

———(1942), Some Forms of Emotional Disturbance and Their Relationship to Schizophrenia. *Psychoanalytic Quarterly,* 11:301-321.

Eissler, K. R. (1953), The Effect of the Structure of the Ego on Psychoanalytic Technique, *Journal of the American Psychoanalytic Association,* 1:104-143.

Ekstein, R. & Wallerstein, R. S. (1958), *The Teaching and Learning of Psychotherapy,* New York: Basic Books.

Ferenczi, S. (1926), The Problem of Acceptance of Unpleasant Ideas—Advances in Knowledge of the Sense of Reality, *Further Contributions to the Theory and Technique of Psychoanalysis,* London: Hogarth Press, 1950, pp. 366-379.

Fisher, C. (1954), Dreams and Perception. The Role of Preconscious and Primary Modes of Perception in Dream Formation, *Journal of the American Psychoanalytic Association,* 2:389-445.

Fleming, J. & Hamburg, D. (1958), Analysis of Methods of Teaching Psychotherapy with Description of a New Approach, *A.M.A. Archives of Neurology and Psychiatry,* 79:179-200.

Freud, A. (1950), Probleme der Lehranalyse, In: *Max Eitingon in Memoriam,* Jerusalem: Israel Psychoanalytic Society, pp. 80-94.

———(1954a), Problems of Technique in Adult Analysis, *Bulletin of the Philadelphia Association for Psychoanalysis,* 4:44-69.

———(1954b), The Widening Scope of Indications for Psychoanalysis, *Journal of the American Psychoanalytic Association,* 2:607-620.

Freud, S. (1909), Notes upon a Case of Obsessional Neurosis. *Standard Edition,* 10:153-318. London: Hogarth Press, 1955.

———(1923), *The Ego and the Id,* London: Hogarth Press, 1942.

———(1937), Analysis Terminable and Interminable, *International Journal of Psycho-Analysis,* 18:373-405.

Friedlander, K. (1942), Children's Books and Their Function in Latency and Prepuberty, *American Imago,* 3:129-150.

Fromm-Reichmann, F. (1950), *Principles of Intensive Psychotherapy,* Chicago: University of Chicago Press.

———(1954), Psychoanalytic and General Dynamic Conceptions of Theory and Therapy, *Journal of the American Psychoanalytic Association,* 2:711-721.

Frosch, J. (1945), Some Reactions Seen after Electric Shock Treatment, *American Journal of Psychiatry,* 102:311-315.

———(1961), The Psychotic Character. Abstract in: *Psychoanalytic Quarterly,* 30:314-316.

———& Impastato, D. (1948), The Effects of Shock Treatment on the Ego, *Psychoanalytic Quarterly,* 17:226-239.

Garner, M. H. (1961), Passivity and Activity in Psychotherapy, *Archives of General Psychiatry,* 5:411-417.

Geisel, J. E. (1951), Discipline Viewed As a Developmental Need of the Child, *Nervous Child,* 9:115-121.

Gill, M. M. (1954), Psychoanalysis and Exploratory Psychotherapy, *Journal of the American Psychoanalytic Association,* 2:771-797.

———Newman, R., Redlich, F. C., & Sommers, M. (1954), *The Initial Interview in Psychiatric Practice,* New York: International Universities Press.

Glover, E. (1928), *The Technique of Psycho-Analysis* [Supplement No. 3 to *The International Journal of Psycho-Analysis*]. London: Baillière, Tindall and Cox.

———(1931), The Therapeutic Effect of Inexact Interpretation: A Contribution to the Theory of Suggestion, *International Journal of Psycho-Analysis,* 12:397-411.

———(1955), *The Technique of Psychoanalysis,* New York: International Universities Press.

———(1960), Psychoanalysis and Psychotherapy, *British Journal of Medical Psychology,* 33:73-82.

Glynn, E. (1957), The Therapeutic Use of Seclusion in an Adolescent Pavilion. *Journal of the Hillside Hospital,* 6:156-159.

Greenacre, P. (1959), Certain Technical Problems in the Transference Relationship. *Journal of the American Psychoanalytic Association,* 7:484-502.

Greenson, R. R. (1950), The Mother Tongue and the Mother, *International Journal of Psycho-Analysis,* 31:18-23.

Grotjahn, M. (1953), Training the Third Ear: Report of an Attempt at Teaching Conjecture in Psychotherapy. In: *Explorations in Psychoanalysis,* ed. R. Lindner, New York: Julian Press.

Group for the Advancement of Psychiatry (1961), *Reports in Psychotherapy: Initial Interview,* Report No. 49, New York.

Jensen, V. W. & Petty, T. A. (1958), The Fantasy of Being Rescued in Suicide, *Psychoanalytic Quarterly,* 27:327-339.

Johnson, A. M. & Szurek, S. A. (1952), The Genesis of Antisocial Acting Out in Children and Adults, *Psychoanalytic Quarterly,* 21:323-343.

Kanzer, M. (1958), Image Formation during Free Association, *Psychoanalytic Quarterly,* 27:465-484.

Kardos, E. & Peto, A. (1956), Contributions to the Theory of Play, *British Journal of Medical Psychology,* 29:100-112.

Kempe, C. H., Silverman, F. N., Steele, B. F., Droegmueller, W. & Silver, H. K. (1962), The Battered Child Syndrome, *Journal of the American Medical Association,* 181:17-24.

Kirby, G. H. (1921), *Guides for History Taking and Clinical*

Examination of Psychiatric Cases, Utica, N.Y.: State Hospitals Press.

Knight, R. P. (1952), An Evaluation of Psychotherapeutic Techniques, *Bulletin of the Menninger Clinic,* 16:113-124.

Lewin, B. D. (1946), Countertransference in the Technique of Medical Practice, *Psychosomatic Medicine,* 8:195-199.

Lewis, N. D. C. (1943), *Outline of Psychiatric Examinations,* 3rd ed. Utica, N.Y.: State Hospitals Press.

Macalpine, I. & Hunter R. A. (1956), *Daniel Paul Schreber: Memoirs of My Nervous Illness* [translated and edited, with notes, introduction and discussion]. London: William Dawson and Sons.

Margolin, S. (1953), Discussion in Panel: The Essentials of Psychotherapy As Viewed by the Psychoanalyst, *Journal of the American Psychoanalytic Association,* 1:550-561.

Menaker, E. (1942), The Masochistic Factor in the Psychoanalytic Situation, *Psychoanalytic Quarterly,* 11:171-186.

Miller, E. (1950), Treatment of Obsessive Neuroses, *Proceedings of the Royal Society of Medicine,* 43:999-1001.

Mowrer, O. H. (1950), Pain, Punishment, Guilt and Anxiety. In: *Anxiety,* ed. P. H. Hoch and J. Zubin, New York: Grune & Stratton.

Niederland, W. G. (1960), Schreber's Father, *Journal of the American Psychoanalytic Association,* 8:492-499.

Nunberg, H. (1951), Transference and Reality. *International Journal of Psycho-Analysis,* 32:1-9.

———(1953), Discussion in Panel: Problems of Identification, *Journal of the American Psychoanalytic Association,* 1:547.

Orens, M. H. (1958), The Genesis of Environment, *Journal of the Hillside Hospital,* 7:162-177.

Panel (1953), The Essentials of Psychotherapy As Viewed by the Psychoanalyst, *Journal of the American Psychoanalytic Association,* 1:550-561.

———(1954), Psychoanalysis and Dynamic Psychotherapy—Similarities and Differences, *Journal of the American Psychoanalytic Association,* 2:152-166.

———(1955), Psychoanalysis and Psychotherapy, *Journal of the American Psychoanalytic Association,* 3:528-533.

Pious, W. L. (1950), Obsessive-Compulsive Symptoms in an Incipient Schizophrenic, *Psychoanalytic Quarterly,* 19: 327-351.

Preu, P. W. (1943), *Outline of Psychiatric Case Study,* 2nd ed. New York: Hoeber.

Rangell, L. (1952), Macroscopic Transmission and the Macroscopic Point of View, *Journal of the Hillside Hospital,* 1:228-233.

———(1954), Psychoanalysis and Dynamic Psychotherapy—Similarities and Differences, *Journal of the American Psychoanalytic Association,* 2:734-744.

Reider, N. (1952), Clinical Notes on the Defense Structure in Psychotherapy, *Samiksa,* 6:70-118.

———(1953), A Type of Transference to Institutions, *Journal of the Hillside Hospital,* 2:23-29.

———(1955), Psychotherapy Based on Psychoanalytic Principles. In: *Six Approaches to Psychotherapy,* ed. J. L. McCary, New York: Dryden Press.

Rosen, J. N. (1947), The Treatment of Schizophrenic Psychosis by Direct Analytic Therapy, *Psychiatric Quarterly,* 21:3-37.

———(1953), *Direct Analysis.* New York: Grune & Stratton.

Rosen, V. H. (1958), The Initial Psychiatric Interview and the Principles of Psychotherapy; Some Recent Contributions, *Journal of the American Psychoanalytic Association,* 6:154-167.

Saul, L. J. (1957), The Psychoanalytic Diagnostic Interview, *Psychoanalytic Quarterly,* 26:76-90.

Savitt, R. A. (1954), Extramural Psychoanalytic Treatment of a Case of Narcotic Addiction, *Journal of the American Psychoanalytic Association,* 2:494-502.

Schmideberg, M. (1953), Some Clinical Implications of the Sense of Bodily Reality, *Journal of the Hillside Hospital,* 2:207-212.

Simmel, E. (1946), Anti-Semitism and Mass Psychopathology, Chapter III in *Anti-Semitism: A Social Disease,* New York: International Universities Press, pp. 33-84.

Sperling, M. (1951), Psychoanalytic Aspects of Discipline, *Nervous Child,* 9:174-186.

Stephen, K. (1950), Discussion on the Treatment of Obsessional Neuroses, *Proceedings of the Royal Society of Medicine,* 43:1002-1007.

Sterba, R. (1934), The Fate of the Ego in Psychoanalytic Therapy, *International Journal of Psycho-Analysis,* 15:117-126.

———(1944), The Formative Activity of the Analyst, *International Journal of Psycho-Analysis,* 25:146-150.

———(1960), Therapeutic Goal and Present-Day Reality, *Journal of the Hillside Hospital,* 9:195-217.

Stone, L. (1951), Psychoanalysis and Brief Psychotherapy, *Psychoanalytic Quarterly,* 20:215-236.

———(1954), The Widening Scope of Psychoanalysis, *Journal of the American Psychoanalytic Association,* 2:567-594.

———(1961), *The Psychoanalytic Situation,* New York: International Universities Press.

Szurek, S. A. (1958), *The Roots of Psychoanalysis and Psychotherapy,* Springfield, Ill.: Thomas.

Tarachow, S. (1945), A Short Contribution to the Problem of Simulation of Insanity, *International Journal of Psycho-Analysis,* 26:168-169.

———(1954), Contribution to a Symposium on the Place of Values in Psychotherapy, *Journal of the Hillside Hospital,* 3:19-24.

———(1956), Concerning Homicidal Impulses toward the Psychoanalyst, *Journal of the Hillside Hospital,* 5:416-418.

———(1962a), Supervisors' Conference. The Problem of Reality and the Therapeutic Task, *Journal of the Hillside Hospital,* 11:21-28.

———(1962b), Initial Interview Conference, *Journal of the Hillside Hospital,* 11:127-153.

———(1962c), Reality and Interpretation in Psychotherapy, *International Journal of Psycho-Analysis,* 43:377-387.

———& Fink, M. (1953), Absence of a Parent As a Specific Factor Determining Choice of Neurosis, *Journal of the Hillside Hospital,* 2:67-71.

Winnicott, D. W. (1958), The Capacity to Be Alone, *International Journal of Psycho-Analysis,* 39:416-420.

Wolberg, L. R. (1954), *The Technique of Psychotherapy,* New York: Grune & Stratton.

Bibliographical Note

Chapter 2: The Theory of the Therapeutic Relationship

In addition to being presented to both residents and supervisors, this material under the title of "The Problem of Reality and the Therapeutic Task" was read at meetings of the Psychoanalytic Association of New York on May 15, 1961 and the American Psychoanalytic Association on May 5, 1961. It was published under the title "Supervisors' Conference: The Problem of Reality and the Therapeutic Task" in *Journal of the Hillside Hospital,* 11:21-28, 1962.

Chapter 4: Types of Psychotherapy

In addition to being presented to both supervisors and residents, much of the material of this chapter was incorporated into a paper entitled "Definitions of Psychotherapy" and read at a meeting of the Psychoanalytic Association of New York on March 19, 1962. This material has also been incorporated into another paper entitled "Reality and Interpretation in Psychotherapy" in the *International Journal of Psycho-Analysis,* 43:377-387, 1962.

Chapter 5: The Theory of Hospital Treatment

The material of this chapter was presented at seminars for supervisors as well as residents. In order to retain the continuity of material of the chapters in this part, which is directed to residents, the remarks of the supervisors have been assimilated partly into the remarks of the residents and partly with those of the author.

Chapter 11: Education and Reality

In addition to being presented to the residents, some of this material was presented as part of a panel discussion on "Borderline States" in the course "Psychoanalysis in Psychiatric Practice," in San Francisco on January 12, 1958.

Chapter 12: Values in Psychotherapy

This material was originally read as a contribution to a symposium on "The Place of Values in Psychotherapy" at a meeting of the Schilder Society on March 27, 1952, in New York City. It was subsequently published under the same title in the *Journal of the Hillside Hospital,* 3:19-24, 1954.

Chapter 13: The Initial Interview

This conference is a composite of several conferences devoted to the initial interview conducted separately for first-year residents at Hillside Hospital, Glen Oaks, N.Y., and on the psychiatric service at Kings County Hospital, Brooklyn, N.Y.

This conference was published separately in the *Journal of the Hillside Hospital,* 11:127-153, 1962.

Chapter 16: Acting Out and Psychopathy

In addition to being presented to the residents, this material, in varying forms, was presented to the Psychiatric Section of the Puerto Rican Medical Association on April, 22, 1957, to a clinical meeting of the Asociacion Psicoanalitica Mexicana in Mexico City on August 8, 1958, and a small part was presented as a discussion of a lecture on "Acting Out" by Ralph R. Greenson in the course "Psychoanalysis in Psychiatric Practice" in San Francisco, January 12, 1958.

Chapter 19: Paranoia and Homicide

In addition to being presented to the residents, part of the material of this chapter was published as "Concerning Homicidal Impulses Toward the Psychoanalyst," *Journal of the Hillside Hospital,* 5:416-418, 1956.

Author Index

Aichhorn, A., 90, 333
Alexander, F., 6, 42, 333
Allen, S., 5, 333

Bak, R., 283, 333
Balint, M., 8, 145, 174, 333
Balzac, H., 222
Benjamin, J. D., 3, 333
Berliner, B., 47, 278, 333
Berman, L. 96, 333
Bibring, E., 6, 42, 333
Bond, D., 76, 334
Breuer, J., 99
Bychowski, G., 141, 334

Cheney, C. O., 154, 334
Colby, K. M., 5, 70, 154, 334
Coleman, J. V., 42, 174, 334
Coward, N., 177

Deutsch, F., 155, 334
Deutsch, H., 9, 222, 334
Droegmueller, W., 336

Eissler, K. R., 5, 334
Ekstein, R., 3, 327, 330, 331, 332, 334

Federn, P., 143
Ferenczi, S., 12, 334
Fink, M., 202, 339
Fisher, C., 154, 334
Fleming, J., 3, 334
Freud, A., 4, 5, 76, 79, 335
Freud, S., 12, 99, 143, 179, 208, 217, 266, 286, 335
Friedlander, K., 91, 335
Fromm-Reichmann, F., 6, 335
Frosch, J., 141, 272, 335

Garner, M. H., 19, 20, 335
Geisel, J. E., 90, 146, 335
Gill, M. M., 6, 17, 42, 153, 335
Glover, E., 6, 14, 18, 40, 44, 45, 86, 96, 248, 336
Glynn, E., 88, 336
Greenacre, P., 17, 336
Greenson, R. R., 258, 336
Grotjahn, M., 336

Hamburg, D., 3, 334
Hoch, P. H., 337
Hunter, R. A., 283, 337

Impasto, D., 272, 335

Jensen, V. W., 281, 336
Johnson, A. M., 249, 336

Kanzer, M., 261, 336
Kardos, E., 17, 336
Kempe, C. H., 264, 336
Kirby, G. H., 154, 336
Knight, R. P., 6, 42, 337

Lewin, B. D., 120, 337

Macalpine, I., 283, 337
Margolin, S., 12, 337
McCary, J. L., 338
Menaker, E., 13, 337
Miller, E., 233, 337
Mowrer, O. H., 144, 145, 148, 337
Murphy, W. F., 156, 334

Newman, R., 335
Niederland, W. G., 190, 337
Nunberg, H., 5, 21, 22, 43, 337

Orens, M. H., 197, 337

Peto, A., 17, 336
Petty, T. A., 281, 336
Pious, W. L., 233, 338
Preu, P. W., 154, 338

Rangell, L., 6, 41, 175, 190, 338
Redlich, F. C., 335
Reider, N., 47, 338
Rickman, J., 145
Róheim, G., 65
Rosen, J. N., 23, 111, 338
Rosen, V. H., 6, 338

Saul, L. J., 156, 338
Savitt, R. A., 251, 338
Schmideberg, M., 16, 338
Silver, H. K., 336
Silverman, F. N., 336
Simmel, E., 148, 338
Sommers, M., 335
Sperling, M., 90, 145, 146, 338
Steele, B. F., 336
Stephen, K., 233, 338
Sterba, R., 17, 66, 75, 339
Stone, L., 5, 6, 8, 42, 156, 339
Szurek, S. A., 49, 50, 249, 339

Tarachow, S., 202, 214, 215, 228, 282, 336, 339

Urbach, H. J., 255

Wallerstein, R. S., 3, 327, 330, 331, 332, 334
Winnicott, D. W., 11, 339
Wolberg, L. R., 6, 339

Zilboorg, G., 267
Zubin, J., 337

Subject Index

Abandonment, as symbolized by therapist's leaving room, 92
Absence from sessions, *see* Sessions missed
Absolute therapeutic barrier, 26
"Acting in," 237-238
Acting out
  absence of real object relations in, 246
  aggressive, 90
  and depression, 239
  and psychodrama, 141
  and psychopathy, 236-263
  as reaction to therapist's impending vacation, 119
  built-in, 236-237
  characteristics of delusion formation in, 246
  childhood deprivation and, 240
  definition of, 236
  depression underlying, 240
  fantasy as, 11
  foreign language used as, 227, 255-263
  imagery as, 261
  in adolescence, 72
  in psychoanalytic relationship, 72
  in resistance, 72
  interference with, 253-256
  interpretation as interference with, 10, 13, 242
  in treatment: 236-239; hospital, 70-72; office, 236-263
  lateness of patient as, 127
  love in treatment of, 90, 242
  magical aspect of, 240-241
  mutual, 9, 10
  neurotic vs. patient, 241
  object directedness and, 282
  obscenity as, 263
  of transference, 79
  oral aspect of, 240-241
  pathological lying, 240-241
  patient vs. neurotic, 241
  permissiveness in handling aggressive, 90
  reality in treatment of, 243
  requests as, 125
  slang as, 263
  stealing, 240-241
  symptomatic, 241
  symptoms of, 236
  teaching resident about, 304
  tendency to find accomplice in, 248
  transference in treatment of, 242-243
  vs. action, 245-246
  vulgarity as, 263
  see also Adolescence, Role playing
Acting-out patients
  admission of deprivation by, 249
  communication with, 243, 259-261
  goals of treatment of, 83
  illusions of, 243, 245
  reality confrontation in treatment of, 253-255
  self-responsibility in treatment of, 244
  testing by, 242
  therapist as real object to, 243, 245
Acting-out psychopaths
  and money, 132
  following termination of treatment, 132
  therapist as real object to, 10
  therapist's envy of, 250
Action vs. acting out, 72, 245-246
Activity, in prognosis, 174
Administration, hospital, *see* Hospital administration

Administrative vs. therapeutic considerations, 33-34, 58, 108-117, 325-326
Adolescence, acting out in, 72
Affect
 function of therapist to supply to obsessive-compulsive neurotic, 223
 isolation: 205, 224-225; foreign language as means of, 227; principal defense of obsessive-compulsive neurosis, 206, 224
Affection
 homosexual reactions to, 298-299
 in object relationship, 103
 paranoid reactions to, 298-299
Age of patient as factor in therapy, 41
Aggression
 and masochism, 277, 280, 283, 285
 and oedipal problems, 287
 and reassurance, 100-101
 and religion, 148
 as a therapeutic technique, 110
 as aspect of ambivalence, 110
 as central problem: 53; of suicidal patient, 264
 as characteristic of obsessive-compulsive neurosis, 205, 233
 avenues for, in psychoanalysis, 148
 capacity for, 103
 difficulty in expressing, 103
 factors in, 67
 homosexual reactions to, 97, 298-299
 in children, 90
 in depressive, 265-273, 275
 in paranoia, 282
 in regression, 67
 judgments about one's own, 147
 paranoid reactions to, 298-299
 sacrifice of, by Western man, 148
 toward father, 284
Aggressive characters, passive, in supplying displacements, 40
Aggressive drives, impulses, 54-55
Aggressive needs, 148-149
Aggressiveness
 erotic, 136
 of the psychoanalyst, 19
 of the therapist, 298
 on resumption of treatment following vacation, 120
 real vs. paranoid, 288-289
Alcoholics
 office treatment of, 251
 retarded ejaculation of, 174
Alzheimer's disease, 61, 160
Ambivalence
 aggression and, 110
 homosexuality and, 110
 in depressives, 268-269, 272, 275
 in dreams, 294
 in masochism, 280, 285
 in object relations, 109-110
 in obsessive-compulsive neurosis, 205, 209, 230
 in regression, 67
 loss of parent and, 203
 masochism and, 110
 normal, 221-222
 of parents about children, 138
 to a single object, 110
 to therapist, 34, 110
 toleration of, 78
Anal preoccupations, 105
Anal sadism, in obsessional neurosis, 40
Anality
 as neglected aspect of psychotherapeutic technique, 52
 in obsessional neurosis, 40
Anatomy
 as symbolism, 184
 concern with, as symptom, 184
 discussion of, with patients, 138
 dreams concerned with, 184
Anger
 as a sign of therapist's concern for patient, 38
 as cause of patient's lateness, 127
 of patient at appointment setting, 130
 of therapist at patient, 74, 99, 233-234
 see also Hatred, Hostility, Rage
Anxiety
 conversion of character disorder into, for treatment, 253
 in initial interview, 154, 172
 in new resident, 59
 in therapeutic relationship, 43
 patients with severe, 28
 release of phobic, 93

Anxiety (cont.)
risk of psychotic, in patient, 40
sexual difficulty of working through, 169
Appointments
breaking of, 118
days of, 118, 130
keeping of, 118
overtime, 125-126
patient's lateness for, 126-127
setting, 130
therapist's lateness for, 126
time of, 118
see also Initial interview, Sessions
Archaic behavior, self-acceptance of, 180-181
Archaic thinking in obsessive-compulsive neurosis, 205
Archaic wishes and drives, expression of, 39
Assessment by therapist, initial, 40-41
Association
in ego functioning, 181-182
in psychotherapy, 29
of manics, 182
of schizophrenics, 181-182
to previous sessions, 128
see also Free association
"Associative anamnesis" (Deutsch and Murphy), 156
Authoritative position of therapist in treating depressives, 269-270, 275
Authority
in hospital treatment, 305-306
patient's response to, 89

Barrier, 24-25
therapeutic, *see* Therapeutic barrier
Behavior
archaic, self-acceptance of, 180-181
explaining to patient, 134-136
hospital pattern of, 79
infantile, self-acceptance of, 180-181
judgments about one's own, 147
neurotic, impact on other people, 140
observable, in hospital treatment, 70-71
patient's total, in hospital treatment, 73
sadistic, explanation of to patient, 135-136
Behavior disorders, permissiveness in treatment of, 146
Behavior pattern, importance of patients', 91
Biogenetic factors, in initial interview, 182
Biological needs, 8
Biological orientation in psychoanalysis, 145
Birth, as a reality in therapy, 30
Bisexuality and paranoia, 283
Blushing as symptom, 174
Body-ego fears and passivity, 55
Body-image difficulty in decompensation, 59
Borderline patient
education of, 141-143
payment by, following termination of treatment, 132
reality, in treatment of, 95, 141-143
tension-releasing drives in treatment of, 143
therapeutic approach to, 142-143
transference with, 95, 142
Breast, fantasy of sucking, 56

Cannibalism
as problem in depression, 273
dreams of, 179
Cannibalistic love-murder, as factor in depression, 40
Castration anxiety, 55
in passive patient, 53
Catatonic patient, female, and male therapist, 97-98
Character disorder
acting out, 146
conversion into anxiety and depression to treat, 253
Character formation, 146
Childhood deprivation, of acting-out patients, 240
Childhood experiences, 11, 12
as life pattern, 199, 201-204
homosexual, 177-178
Childhood stories, memories of, 237

Childhood transference, re-created in treatment of obsessive-compulsive neurosis, 234
Childhood wishes, in pathological lying, 245
Children
aggression in, 90
and residents, 65-66
compulsive thoughts of, 87-88
dealing with healthy and psychotic, 66
development of self-discipline in, 146
discipline in rearing, 146
hospitalized, therapist's treatment of regressed, 64
importance of large families to, 165
institutional treatment of disturbed, 90
level of expectation in treatment of, 65
parents' fear of impulses in, 146
permissiveness in treatment of, 65
regression in, 65
transmission of superego defects from mothers to, 249-250
treatment of, as compared with adults, 64
values in rearing of, 146
with fantasies of being an orphan, 105
Circumlocution as obsessive-compulsive defense, 228-230
Communication
continuity of, in treatment, 263
interference in, as resistance, 261
in treatment vs. ordinary life, 260
regressive, in therapist, 261
use of, in hospital treatment, 71
with acting-out patients, 259-261
see also Language, Speech
Compulsive behavior, *see* Obsessive-compulsive neurosis
Compulsive character, 232-233
Conflicts
defenses against, 54
infantile intrapsychic, 41
in theoretical ideal of treatment, 35
symptoms in psychopath, 83
unconscious, 4, 42
Confrontation
in the therapeutic process, 5, 69-70
susceptibility to, 40
Conscience, in neurosis, 144
Coprophagia, in obsessional neurotics, 171
Countertransference
as problem for residents, 305-306, 318
as source of danger, 99
patient's ability to tolerate, 124
therapist's ability to tolerate, 124
vs. object need, 10
Crises, as cause of treatment, 159
Criticism
interpretation felt as, by patient, 147
of therapist, by patient, 36-38
Cruelty, in therapeutic relationship, 123; *see also* Sadism
Crying, as guide to suicidal risk with depressives, 274
Cultural values in psychoanalysis, 145
Culture, patient's identification with, 144

Daydreams as focal area of regression, 63
Death as a reality, in therapy, 30, 34-35
Decompensation, 28, 59-62, 110, 304
Defenses
ability of ego to form new, 40
against forming object relationship, 102
against infantile wishes, 54
balance of, 40
brittle, preventing psychotherapy becoming psychoanalysis, 50
depressive, 273
education as strengthener of, 46
free associations as demand on, 19
generalization as, 226-228
in decompensation, 59
in initial interview, 153-154, 156
in schizophrenia, 60
interpretation of, 137
in therapeutic ego dissociation, 17
magnitude of, 40
manic, 103

Defenses (cont.)
necessity of, as treatment guide, 53-54
obsessive-compulsive, *see* Obsessive-compulsive defenses
patient's guarding of, 101
primitivization of, 59-60
psychoanalysis vs. psychotherapy, 41, 44
regressed quality of, 40
regression of, 59
reinforcing, 44
stability as support of, 46
style of patient's, 252
taking at face value in psychotherapy, 50-51
understanding, 87
Delusion
formation, 246
in displacement, 45
paranoid, 190
Dependency
as aspect of psychotherapy technique, 52
reactions, avoidance of, in exploratory psychotherapy, 42
relationships, pathological, 46
Depression
aggression in, 265-273, 275
and acting out, 239, 240-243
and paranoia, 272
and suicidal risks, 264-276
as symptom, 26, 188
cannibalism as problem in, 40, 273
compulsive rumination in, 273
danger of, in psychotherapy, 48
ego in, 273
from hatred, 269
homicide, as problem in, 264, 268-269
involutional melancholia, 272
mania as defense against, 239
mild, in therapy, 20
mother, aggression against, as problem in, 273
neurotic vs. psychotic, 273-274
object internalization in, 268
object relationships in, 165
oral demands in, 273-275
pathological lying and, 245
psychotic, 173-174
rigidity in, 274
superego in, 271, 275
treatment of, authoritative position of therapist in, 268-272, 275
vs. psychopathy, 249
see also Depressives
Depressives
ambivalence in, 269, 272, 275
crying, as guide to suicidal risks with, 274
electroshock, in treating, 272
externalization vs. projection, in treating, 272-273
grief in, 264, 268-269
guilt in, 267-270
hatred in, 265-266
hostility of, 265, 267-268, 271-272, 275
insight, in treatment of, 266, 271-272
isolation and, 273
masochism of, 270-271
mourning in, 264
need for love in, 272, 275
need for punishment in, 269
object loss in, 268-269
obsessive defenses and, 273
projection as problem in, 272-273
sadism in, 267, 275
suicidal risks, 264-276
superego, pathological, 271
therapist as object to, 276
therapist's narcissism in treatment of, 266
transference in treatment of, 266
Deprivation
admission of, in acting out patients, 249
and interpretation, 101
and masochism, 277-278
imposed on patient by therapist, 25
in hospital situation, 28
in therapy, 18
of patient in transference, 109
of therapist, self-imposed, 25
tolerance of, 98
vs. gratification, 87-101
Diagnosis, in initial interview, 159-164

Dirtiness, extreme, as a symptom, 180-181
Disappointment, 13, 112
Discipline
by therapist, 28, 100, 113
in character development, 146
in child rearing, 146
in treatment, 146
need for, in children, 90
role of resident in, in hospital, 108
Disorderliness, ego structure as barrier to, 40
Displacement, 45-46
as obsessive-compulsive defense, 206
offering of, examples of, 49-51
supplying, as psychotherapeutic principle, 43-44
types of, 45-46
unanalyzed transference and, 46
Doctor-patient relationship, *see* Therapeutic relationship
Dreams
ambivalence in, 294
anatomy in, 184
as sign of ego development, 179-181
defensive structure of patient as key to, 252
dreamer in his own, 294
latent and manifest content of, 180
of cannibalism, 179
of homicidal patient, 291-294
of homosexuality, 179
of incest, 179
transference attitude as reflected in, 52
two in one night, 218
use of in psychotherapy, 46, 51-52
Drives, archaic, 39
Drug addiction, treatment of, office vs. hospital, 251
Drug medication, informing patient of planned, 166

Education
and reality in treatment, 134-143
as block to fantasy expression, 46
as principle in psychotherapy, 43
as restrictive in terms of unconscious, 46
as strengthener of resistances, 46
in sexual facts, 134
in treatment of borderline states, 141-143
of obsessional neurotics, 140-141
vs. free association, 139
see also Teaching therapy
Ego
and values, 148
approval of symptoms, 40
as barrier, 40
associations in functioning, 181-182
controls, 17
defect, 24
defense formation by, 40
deformities, psychotherapy vs. psychoanalysis, 50
development, dreams as sign of, 179-180
differentiation, 12
disturbances of, 59-60
expansion of patient's, 139
factors, 5
fear of passivity, 55
formation, 44
hospital as symbol of, 69
in initial interview, 179-181
in psychotic depression, 273
in regression, 67
in schizophrenic patient, 60
in treatment of neurosis, 144-145
modification of, 147-149
play and, 17
psychology, 5
regression, 60, 74
in psychopath, 147-148
structures, in psychotherapy design, 40
therapeutic dissociation of the patient's, 17
weak, 46-47
Ego boundaries
as source of anxiety, 329
between patient and therapist, 12
in therapy, 15-17
of schizophrenics, 16, 163
Ego building
as psychotherapeutic principle, 43
aspect of hospital treatment, 75, 77, 304
to supply stability, 48

Ego control
as source of anxiety, 329
loss of, in projection, 328
Ego ideal, and values, 148
Ego splitting
and loneliness, 18
and transference neurosis, 21
examples of, 63
in therapy, 17
of patient, 6
teaching resident about, 304
varieties of, 62
Ego structure
as barrier, 39-40
in therapeutic interview, 74
primitivization of, 59
Ego support
as source of stability, 46
education as means of, 46
vs. free association, 139
Ego-syntonic feelings, buttressed in psychotherapy, 54
Ego-syntonic personality elements, 40
Ejaculation, 174
Electroshock, in treating depressives, 272
Emergencies, patient's, *see sub* Patients
Empathy vs. identification, 308
Enuresis, 184
Envy by therapist, 74
Erotic aggressiveness, 136
Erotic suppression, 205
Exhibitionism, 176
Experiments, psychological, patients in, 154
Exploratory psychotherapy, 42
Expression
barriers to, 39
regressed patients with difficulty in, 37
see also Communication
Externalization vs. projection, 272-273

Family
early relations as life pattern, 199, 201-204
history in initial interview, 182-184
incidence of psychosis in, 158
informing of patient's suicidal risks, 274-275
large, importance of, to children, 165
patient's, 41
provocation of regression, 79
responsibilities to patients, 32
teaching residents to deal with patient's, 305
toleration of problems by, 158
Fantasy(ies)
about therapist, 99
and masturbation, 171
and reality, 252
dangers of, in psychotherapy, 48
education as block to expression of, 46
heterosexual implications of, 55-56
homosexual, in homicidal patients, 296
in depression, 40
interpretation of, 13, 42
in transference relationship, 11
Medusa, 219
of aggression toward father, 284, 286
of being an orphan, 105
of sucking the breast, 56
permissiveness for, as value judgment, 146
pregenital implications of, 55-56
reality created to suit, 197, 199
schizophrenia and, 162-163
unconscious, 10, 43
vs. reality, 109
Father
aggression toward, 284, 286
and homosexuality, 283, 287
difficulties dealing with, 54
identification with, 283-284
in formation of masochism, 283, 285-286
in formation of paranoia, 184, 283
son's attachment to, 54
therapist as, 23
Fear
of emerging material as cause of lateness, 127
of impulses in children and parents, 146
of penetration, 55

Fear (cont.)
of punishment, 36
therapist's, of patient, 293-294
Fees, 123-124
missed sessions, 121-122
owed, after termination, 131-132
patient's cheating in, 132-133
therapist's mistakes in, 129-130
Fellatio
as symptom of homosexuality, 286-287
fantasies, 56
Female
and male therapist, 97-98
attire of, as diagnostic factor, 176
exhibitionism, 176
history of masturbation, 169-171
homosexuality, 54-55
recognition of castration, 176
sexual expectations of, 136
therapist, and male patient, 97-98
Feminine identification, 54, 175-179
Fetishism as example of ego splitting 63
Financial status of patient as factor in therapy, 41
Free association
analyst's demand for, 19
in place of education and ego support, 139
unconscious fantasy in, 10
see also Association
Frequency of treatment, 139-140; *see also* Appointments
Friendliness between therapist and patient, 153, 255
Functioning, neurotic barriers to, 40
Fusion in object relations, 12, 16, 18

Genital level in regression, 67
Gifts from patient, 142
Grandparents, 138
Gratification
balance of, 101
degree of, 98
hospital as source of, 87
in therapy, 18
of patients, 13, 109
regression through, 87
therapist as source of, 87
through hearing therapist's voice, 91
transference and, 98
treatment relationship as, 87
vs. deprivation, 87-101
Grief
as normal problem, 30, 34-35
as problem with suicidal patient, 264, 268-269
see also Mourning
Group therapy, 226-227
Group values, in psychoanalysis, 145
Guilt
as a result of therapist's kindness, 122-123
in depressives, 267-270
in masochists, 277, 286
lessening of, 36
mechanisms of psychotic patients, 82
vs. shame, 171

Hatred
and aggressive needs, 148
and paranoia, 289
as defense against passivity, 297
in dependency relationships, 46
in depressives, 265-266, 269
in object relationships, 103
in therapeutic relationship, 13
internalized by patient, 90
see also Aggression, Anger, Hostility, Rage
Happiness, neurotic barriers to, 40
Heterosexuality, emphasis on, in treatment of homosexuality, 55-56
History taking
illustration of, 187-204
in hospital treatment, 78
in initial interview, 154-156
in terms of romance and story, 185-186
neglect in, by resident, 61
patient's object relations in, 164-165
psychosis vs. neurosis in, 158
style of, 185-186
symptoms in, 158
undirected, 155
Homicidal patient
homosexual fantasies of, 296

Homicidal patient (cont.)
interpretation in treatment of, 296
passivity and, 297-298
rage in, 294-295, 297
transference in treatment of, 294-296
Homicide
and paranoia, 291-299
as problem in depression, 264, 268-269, 271
evaluating risks of, 266
Homoerotic strivings, 282-283
Homosexual attachment to therapist, unconscious, 111
Homosexual fastasies
dangers of, in psychotherapy, 48
heterosexual implications of, 55-56
in homicidal patients, 296
Homosexual reaction
and aggression, 97, 298-299
and reassurance, 96-97
and supportive treatment, 97
in male patient, 15
in paranoia, 298-299
interpretation of, 97
latent, as material to work with, 111
on resumption of treatment following vacation, 120
to affection, 298-299
Homosexual transference love, unconscious, 99
Homosexual wish of paranoid schizophrenic patient, 37
Homosexuality
and castration problems, 55
as aspect of ambivalence, 110
as source of paranoid trends, 272
as suggested by passivity to therapist, 54
blushing as a symptom of, 174
dreams of, 179
element of in every person, 178
experience(s) of, in childhood, 177-178
father and, 283, 287
feeding problems as symptom of, 183-184
fellatio as symptom of, 286-287
heterosexuality in treatment of, 55-56
history of, as factor in diagnosis, 177-178
in men, social permission of, 55
in prognosis, 177-178
in treatment of obsessive-compulsive neurosis, 208-209
in women, 54-55
latent, 48, 50-51, 110, 288
mother and, 56, 287
normal incorporation of, 178
normal sublimation of, 178
oedipal problems and, 286-287
paranoia and, 283, 286-287
passive, 254, 287
pregenital aspects of, 56, 286-287
reality and, 287
treatment of, 247, 251
Hospital
as ego-building function, 75
aspects of transference, 109
as source of gratification, 87
consistency of punishment in, 115
psychiatrist in, 58
re-creation of neurosis and psychosis in, 68
role of therapist in, 108-117
stress in, as compared with outpatient department, 64
symbolism of, 68-69
therapeutic process in, 69
toleration of aggression in, 76
Hospital administration
and resident, 305, 325-326
and therapist, 33-34, 108-117
as messenger of bad news, 112
punishment as responsibility of, 33-34
separation of functions in, 108-109
Hospital patients
aggression in, 63
assignment of therapeutic task to, 24
decompensation of, 61
deprivation imposed by therapist on, 25
discipline needs of, 58
fighting of therapist by, 25
initial interview with, 155
interest of therapist in, 61-62
motivation of, in treatment, 24

Hospital patients (cont.)
object need, technique of frustrating, 24
object relations of, 78
observed behavior of, 57
reality and, 23
reality of therapist to, 61
real life of, in psychotherapy, 23-31
regression of, 61, 67, 75
role of therapist with, 58
setting reality limits for, 24
supervision needs of, 58
task imposed on, 25
total behavior of, 73
visiting of, by therapist, 35
Hospital therapy
acting out in, 70-72
application of observed data in, 57
ego building aspect of, 77
ego building function of therapist in, 75
history taking in, 78
insight aspect of, 77
neutrality in, 116-117
occupational therapy in, 71
outline of, 57
personal therapeutic process in, 69
reconstruction of patient's problems in, 57
regression in, 67, 76-77
regressive transference in, 73
removal of the patient from external problems in, 57
splitting of transference in, 68
superego reinforcement in, 88
supportive, 61
teaching theory of, 304. *See also* Teaching therapy.
theory of, 57-80
therapeutic barrier in, 67
therapeutic task in, 75
total behavior of patient in, 73
transference in, 67
ward assignment in, 88
Hostility
analyst's reaction to patient's, 294-295
and religion, 148
expressed as sexual impotence, 84
in depression, 265, 267-268, 271-272, 275
in obsessive-compulsive neurosis, 206, 209, 217, 229-230, 234
in patients, 34, 113
in therapeutic relationship, 248-249
negativism as, 90
of therapist to obsessive-compulsive neurotics, 233-235
see also Aggression, Anger, Hatred, Rage
Husband
and wife, relation between, 31
as intermediate object, 103
explaining the psychology of, to wife, 136
Hypnosis, 45
Hysteria
and loss of parent, 203
and obsessional neurosis, 83
as barrier to incestuous sexual wishes, 40
as symbolic gratification of incestuous sexual wishes, 40
vs. acting out, 236
vs. obsessional neurosis, 24

Id
disturbances of, 59
hospital as symbol, 68
in schizophrenic patient, 60
in treatment of neurosis, 144
resistances, preventing psychotherapy from becoming psychoanalysis, 50
uncontrolled, as source of fear, 329
Identification
and symbiotic feelings, 12, 16
ascertaining sexual, 287-288
development of self-discipline through, 146
feminine, 54, 175-179
in supervision, 316-317, 319, 331
in therapeutic relationship, 18
of therapists with children, 64
vs. empathy, 308
with culture, 144
with father, 283-284
with mother, 54
with society, 144

Illusions, of acting out patients, 243, 245; *see also* Delusion
Imagery, as acting out, 261
Impatience, ego structure as barrier to, 40
Impotence, sexual, in men, 84
Impulse life, patient's self-view of, in prognosis, 174
Incest barrier, 25
  dreams of, 179
Incestuous sexual wishes
  in hysteria, 40
  of women patients, 120
Independence, feelings of, 49
"Inexact interpretation" (Glover), and the unconscious, 46
  as opposed to incomplete interpretation, 44
  examples of, 49-51
  purpose of, 45
Infantile behavior, self-acceptance of, 180-181
Infantile intrapsychic conflicts in psychoanalytic treatment, 41
Infantile mental life, 4
Infantile object(s), supplying in reality, as principle of psychotherapy, 43
Infantile object relations, 104-105
Infantile projections, 8
Infantile transference, re-created in treatment of obsessive-compulsive neurosis, 234
Infantile valuations, 149
Infantile wishes
  defenses against, 54
  expression of, 39
  patient's guarding of, 101
Information as means of ego support, 46
Initial interviews, 153-186
  anxiety in, 154, 172
  associations, in ego functioning, as factor in, 181-182
  "associative anamnesis" (Deutsch and Murphy) in, 156
  beginning therapy in, 153
  biogenetic factors, 182-184
  closed office, 161-163
  curiosity as factor in, 174-175
  defenses, disturbance of, 153-154
  diagnosis in, 159-164
  diagnostic direction in, 157
  ego structure, disorganization of, as indicated in, 179-181
  family history, 182-184
  history taking in, 154-156, 185-186
  masturbation, history of, as prognostic factor, 169-171
  neurosis vs. psychosis, 157-158
  obligations of therapist in, 153-155
  passivity of therapist in, with psychotic patients, 155
  patient's awareness of unconscious, 174-175
  patient's defenses, 156
  patient's object relations, in prognosis, 164-175
  prognosis in, 164-175
  psychogenetic factors, 182-184
  psychosis vs. neurosis, 157-158
  regression as factor in, 179
  sexual history of patient, 175-179
  speech patterns in, 173
  symptoms, history of, 183-184
  therapeutic relationship in, 168
  therapist in, obligations of, 153-155
  transference complications of, 154
  treatment plan, discussion of with patient, 166-167
  unconscious wishes of patient in, 154
  undirected, 155
  see also Appointments, Sessions
Insanity, simulated, 228
Insight
  as aspect of hospital treatment, 77
  as treatment tool, 137
  by therapist, 153
  in new resident, 59
  in treatment of depressives, 266, 271-272
  in treatment of schizophrenics, 271
  offered to patient, 147
  teaching residents about, 304
  tolerance to, 40
  used as justification for not changing, 137
Instinct theory, 145, 150
Instincts

Instincts (cont.)
in therapeutic ego dissociation, 17
realistic view of, in psychoanalysis, 150
Intellectualization as obsessive-compulsive defense, 206
Interest, in object relationships, 103
Interpersonal relationships in treatment, 134
Interpretation
accuracy of, 85
and ego dissociation, 17
and working through, 86
as frustration to patient, 147
as interference, 10
as rationalization 100
as treatment technique, 255
as values, 148-149
cruelty in, 123
degree of, in psychotherapy, 49
deprivation and, 98, 101
dual nature of, 19
experienced as criticism, 147
first, 14
in brief therapy, 85
in exploratory psychotherapy, 42
in first session, 85
in psychoanalysis, 43
in psychotherapy, 9, 13
in supervision, 320
in therapy as real situation, 24
in treatment: of acting out patients, 242, 262-263; of homicidal patients, 297; of obsessive-compulsive neurosis, 208-209, 223, 230
inexact, 85-86
need for a second, 21
of defensive mechanisms, 137
of homosexual reactions, 97
of patient's lateness, 127
of substitutive mechanisms, 137
of symbolic mechanisms, 137
of the unexpected, 91
of transference gratification, 98
painful aspects of, 270
principal consequences of, 20
susceptibility to, 40
to help patient understand regression, 87
to patient, 134-137
Interpretive attitude of therapist, 70
Intervention, areas of, 40
Interview, initial, *see* Initial interview
Intrapsychic change, assessment of possibilities of, 40
Intrapsychic conflicts, 41, 45
Introjection
as displacement, 45
of mother, 11
Involutional melancholia, 272
Isolation
and schizophrenia, 212-213
as defense in depressive, 273
in obsessive-compulsive neurosis, 205-206
in schizophrenia, 107

Kindness, in therapy, 48, 122-123

Language
as an obsessive-compulsive defense, 226
foreign, in treatment sessions, 255-263
see also Communication, Speech
Latent homosexuality, 48, 50-51, 110, 288
Latent psychosis, 141
Law, as societal institution, 149-150
Lesbianism, 54-55
Libidinal impulses of psychotic patients, 82
Libidinal level, symptoms as clue to, 183
Libidinal suppression as characteristic of obsessive-compulsive neurosis, 205
Loneliness
analyst's capacity for, 11, 13
in therapeutic relationship, 18
psychotherapy vs. psychoanalysis, 43
therapist's capacity for, 13
Love
as symbolized by the therapist's entering room, 92
capacity for, 103
difficulty in expressing, 103
grief from, in depressives, 268-269
in handling aggressive acting out, 90

Love (cont.)
in object relationship, 103
in obsessive-compulsive neurotics, 234-235
in therapeutic relationship, 13
in treatment of acting-out patients, 242
internalized by patient, 90
need for: in depression, 272, 275; in masochism, 277-280, 282-283, 285; in paranoia, 281
of therapist by patient, 49
scolding as symbol of, 150
transference, 99
Love-making
as focal area of regression, 62-63
as object relation, 16
isolated, in obsessive-compulsive neurosis, 218-220
subway, 218-219
Love-murder, cannibalistic, 40
Lying, 133; *see also* Pathological lying

Magical aspect of acting out, 240-241
Magical thinking
in masochism, 285
in obsessive-compulsive neurosis, 205
in regression, 67
Male
blushing in, 174
feminine identification in, 175-176
history of masturbation, 169-171
patient, and female therapist, 97-98
problems of, on resumption of treatment, 119-120
therapist, and female patient, 97-98
Mania, as defense against depression, 239
Manics
and reality, 102-103
associations of, 182
defenses, 103
Marasmus, 282
Marriage
as factor in therapy, 41, 176-177
as reality in therapy, 30
Masculine identifications, 175-179
Masculinity, as compensation, 288
Masochism
aggression and, 277, 280, 283, 285
ambivalence and, 110, 280, 285
and paranoia, 277-290
as pressure for support, 239
clinical orientation toward, 283
deprivation, statements of, as technique of, 278
father and, 283, 285-286
guilt in, 277, 286
homoerotic strivings and, 282-283
indirectness as technique of, 278
love, need for, and, 277-280, 282-283, 285
magical thinking in, 285
moral, 279
narcissism in, 280-281
object directedness in, 281
object relations in, 280-283
oedipal situation in formation of, 284, 286
of depressives, 271
of patients, 112-113, 123, 270
paranoia and, 277-290
passive techniques of, 283
psychotic vs. neurotic, 270
sadism and, 278, 280
selfishness and, 279
social, 279
vs. obsession, 289-290
vs. paranoia, 281-283, 289-290
worry and, 48
Masochistic aspects of treatment relationship, 13
Masochistic fantasies, dangers of, in psychotherapy, 48
Masochistic object relations, 164
Masochistic perversions, incidence of, 279-280
Masochistic psychotic patients, 82
Masochistic reactions
and reassurance, 97
as material to work with, 111
by patients, 15
Masochistic symptoms, on resumption of treatment after vacations, 120
Masturbation
and schizophrenia, 169
discussion of, with patient, 138

Masturbation (cont.)
  history of, as prognostic factor, 169-171
Medusa fantasy, 219
Melancholia, involutional, 272
Memories, isolation of, in obsessive-compulsive neurosis, 217-218
Menstruation
  discussion of with patient, 138
  relationship to onset of psychopathy, 249
Mental life, infantile, 4
Moral masochism, 279
Mother
  aggression against, as problem in depression, 273
  analyst in role of, 14
  and homosexuality, 56, 287
  daughter's attachment to, 54
  hospital as symbol of, 68
  identification with, 54
  in obsessive-compulsive neurosis, 216-217, 220
  obesity and patient's relationship with, 184
  passivity to, 54
  split view of, in obsessive-compulsive neurosis, 220
  symbiotic tie with, 12, 14
  therapist as, 23-25, 32, 37
  transmission of superego defects to child, 249-250
Motivation, in choosing technique, 24
Mourning
  as normal task of patient, 29-30, 34-35
  as problem with suicidal patient, 264
  as termination problem, 14
  see also Grief
Murder, *see* Homicide
Murderous impulses, patient with, 93

Narcissism
  and transference, 10-11
  in masochism, 280-281
  in masturbation, 170-171
  therapist's, 49, 266
Narcissistic object relationships, 12
Narcissistic satisfaction, given by psychotherapy, 47
Negative transference, 11, 112
Negativism, 90
Neurosis
  and speech of patient, 15
  approach through ego, 145
  approach through object relations, 145
  approach through superego, 144-145
  as barrier to expression, 39
  ego in treatment of, 144
  id in treatment of, 144
  loss of parent as factor in choice of, 202-203
  obsessive-compulsive, *see* Obsessive-compulsive neurosis
  onset of, 157-158
  re-creation of, in hospital, 68
  superego in, 144
  transference, *see* Transference neurosis
  vs. psychosis, 157-158
Neurotic
  decompensated, 59
  identification of therapist with own conscience, 144
  in payment difficulties, 132
  modification of ego and superego in, 147-148
  obsessional, retarded ejaculation by, 174
  office treatment of, 241
  paranoid distortion in transference, 289
  treatment of the, 44-45
  vs. acting-out patient, 241
  vs. psychotic, 215-216
  vs. real difficulties, 38
Neurotic balance, syndrome of, 60
Neurotic barriers, 40
Neurotic behavior, impact of other people on, 140
Neurotic depression vs. psychotic depression, 273-274
Neurotic illness, frontal assault on, 70
Neurotic masochism vs. psychotic masochism, 270
Neurotic patients
  reality of transference relationships, 95

Neurotic patients (cont.)
therapeutic goals in treatment of, 81
Neurotic problem, conversion into real problem, 37
Neurotic reality, in patients fighting therapist, 25
Neurotic symptom(s)
as barrier, 40
concern with anatomy as, 184
Neurotic worry, 20, 48
Neurotically prepared attitudes of patients, 27
Neutrality
degree of by therapist, 114-115
in hospital therapy, 116-117
in psychoanalysis, 116
of therapist, 38, 101, 113-114

Obesity and relationship to mother, 184
Object, infantile, therapist and patient as, 43
Object choice, split, 110, 220-222
Object directedness
and acting out, 282
in masochists, 281
in paranoiacs, 281
in schizophrenics, 281-282
in suicides, 281-282, 284-285
Object hunger, 17
Object loss, 20-21
in depressives, 268-269
Object needs
as problem in therapy, 7-8
of analyst, 11-12, 24
of patient, 24, 48
of therapist, 13, 24
primary, 11
technique of frustrating patient's, 24
Object relations
affection in, 103
ambivalence in, 110
anaclitic, 12
as basis of transference, 164-165
as prognostic sign, 102
as sign of adjustment to reality, 16
between patient and therapist, 8-22, 106
compulsive, 105
criteria for, 103
defense against forming, 102
differentiated, 104
estimating patient's, 102
fusion in, 18
hatred, 103
importance of establishment of, in treatment, 20
in paranoia, 281
in problems of depression, 165
in psychoanalysis, 20, 23, 145
interference in regression, 67
internalization of, by depressives, 268
kind desired by patient, 122
loving, 103
narcissistic, 12
neurotic, approach to, 145
of homicidal patients, as guide to risk, 265-266
of hospital patients, 78
of infantile kind, 104-105
of masochists, 164, 280-283
of schizophrenics, 102, 106
of suicidal patients, 264-266
orientations, in psychoanalysis, 145
origins, 12
patient's, as factor in prognosis, in initial interview, 164-165
psychotherapy vs. psychoanalysis, 43
real, absence of, in acting out, 246
regression in, 16
root of, 12
sadistic, 164
split in, 109
therapeutic, sadomasochistic, 19-20
transference as, 105-106
with one object, 104
withdrawal from, 18
Obscenity, as acting out, 263
Obsessional neurotics
decompensated, 59
detachment of, 141
education of, 140-141
explanation of others' actions to, 140
impact on others, 140
retarded ejaculation of, 174
see also Obsessive-compulsive defenses *and* neurosis

Obsessional symptoms
  vs. masochistic symptoms, 289
  vs. paranoid symptoms, 289-290
Obsessional thought vs. acting out, 236
Obsessive-compulsive defenses, 205-235, 273
  affect isolation, 206, 224
  agreement as, 231
  ambivalence, 205, 209
  circumlocution, 228-230
  displacement, 206
  doing and undoing, 206
  generalization as, 226-228
  homosexual problem in treatment of, 208-209
  ingratitude, 210-211
  insanity, simulated, 228
  intellectualization, 206
  isolation, 205-206, 208-220
  language as, 226
  procrastination, 229
  reaction formation, 206
  rumination, 206
  simultaneous trains of thought, 230
Obsessive-compulsive neurosis, 205-235
  affective isolation in, 205
  and anal sadism, 39-40
  and archaic anality, 39-40
  characteristics of, 205
  coprophagia in, 171
  defenses in, *see* Obsessive-compulsive defenses
  education and, 135
  goals of treatment, 83
  homosexual problem in treatment of, 208-209
  interpretation in treatment of, 208-209, 223, 230
  isolation in, 205-206, 208-220, 230
  loss of parent and, 203
  love in, 234-235
  masturbation in, 171
  mother and, 216-217
  nose picking in, 171
  re-creation of infantile transference in treatment of, 234
  split object choice in, 220-222
  subway love-making, 218-219
  superego in, 148
  therapist's control of annoyance, importance of, 233-235
  therapist's function in treatment of, 223-224, 233-235
  vs. compulsive character, 232-233
  vs. hysteria, 24
Occupational status of patient as factor in therapy, 41
Occupational therapy in hospital treatment, 71
Oedipal period, sons in the, 284
Oedipal problems
  and homosexuality, 287
  in masochism formation, 284, 286
  patient's solution of, 175
Oedipus complex, reverse, as source of homosexuality, 286-287
Oral aggression, 148, 273
Oral aspect of acting out, 240-241
Oral demands in depression, 273-275
Oral level in regression, 67
Orality, as aspect of psychotherapeutic technique, 52
Organic brain damage, decompensation as a result of, 61
Organic disorders, as diagnostic consideration, 160-162
Outpatient department vs. hospital, stress in, 64
Outpatient vs. inpatient, 58

Paranoia
  aggression in, 282
  aggressiveness in, 288-289
  and bisexuality, archaic, 283
  and depression, 272
  and hatred, 289
  and homicide, 291-299
  and masochism, 277-290
  benign psychotherapeutic, 45
  characteristics of, in men, 54
  clinical orientation toward, 283
  father in formation of, 283
  foreign languages in, 259-260
  homoerotic strivings and, 282-283
  homosexual problems as source of, 272
  homosexuality and, 283, 286-288, 296-299

Paranoia (cont.)
need for love in, 281
object directedness in, 281
object relations in, 281
passivity and, 282, 296-298
sadism in, 282
therapist as object, 289
transference in treatment of, 289, 294-296, 299
vs. masochism, 281-283, 289-290
vs. obsession, 289-290
Paranoid accusations, 37
Paranoid aggressiveness vs. Real aggressiveness, 288-289
Paranoid delusions as distorted repetition of real events, 190
Paranoid feelings on resumption of treatment after vacations, 120
Paranoid patient, criticism by, 37-38
Paranoid psychosis
of overt homosexuals, 55
precipitated by therapist's interpretation, 56
precipitated by uninterpreted transference relationship, 56
Paranoid reactions
and reassurance, 97
in treatment, 298-299
to affection, 298-299
to aggression, 298-299
Paranoid symptomatology and patient's relation with father, 184
Parent
analyst as, 150
fear of impulses by, 146
loss of, as factor in choice of neurosis, 202-203
supervisor as, 323
therapist as, 150
see also Father, Mother
Paresis, 160
Passive dependence and homosexuality, 55
Passive drives, pathological, 54
Passivity
and paranoia, 282
anxieties about, 55
as defense vs. central problem, 53
as masochistic technique, 282
as suggestion of homosexuality, 54
hatred as defense against, 297
in prognosis, 173-174
in weekly therapy, 56
masculinity as compensation for, 288
of analyst, 19
of homicidal patient, 297-298
of therapist in initial interview, 155
patients with problems of, 48
to mother, 54
to therapist, 54
Pathological dependency, treatment of in psychotherapy, 51
Pathological lying
as acting out, 240-241
basic problem in, 241
childhood wishes in, 245
denial of depression in, 239
depression underlying, 245
treatment of, 241-247
Pathological stealing, 240-241, 247
Patients
ability to tolerate transference, 124
acting out, *see* Acting out
age of, 41
and therapeutic barrier, 9-10
and therapeutic task, 9-10
answering questions of, 131
approach to, 79
as infantile object, 43
as object to analyst, 14, 43
as object to therapist, 11-13, 29, 43
as pacesetter for sessions, 129
associations of, to previous sessions, 128
battle between therapist and, 101
behavior in hospital, as diagnosis, 79
borderline, *see* Borderline patient
cheating, 132-133
criticism of therapist by, 36-38
danger of seduction by, 99
decompensated, *see* Decompensation
dependence need of, 92-93
disappointment, 112
doing favors for, 123
drives of, 79
ego boundaries, *see* Ego boundaries
ego dissociation, 17

Patients (cont.)
emergencies, 251-252
explanation of behavior to, 134-136
explanation of missed appointments to, 125
family responsibilities to, 32
feelings of independence, 49
financial status of, 41
friendly relationship with therapist, 255
gratifications of, *see* Gratification
homosexual reactions of, *see* Homosexuality
hospital, *see* Hospital patients
impact of therapist on, 109
importance of behavior patterns of, 91
in need of superego reinforcement, 88
in psychological experiments, 154
in therapeutic relationship, 5-10, 13
inability to face complete truth, 45
informing of bad news, 30-32
initial defenses of, 156
insight offered to, 147
interpretation to, 134-137
kind of regression sought by, 77
knowledge of therapist, psychoanalysis vs. psychotherapy, 92
lateness of, 126-127
lying, 133
marital status of, 41
motivation, 18
need for analysis, 84
need for prolonged psychotherapy, 84
need to convert doctor to real object, 24
neurotically prepared attitudes of, 27
object need of, 7-10, 17, 48
occupation of, 41
paranoid schizophrenic, 37
passive position of, 100
provocation of analyst by, 150
psychodynamic balance of, 84
question asking by, 90-92
rage, 113-114
reality issues of, 42
reality of, 18, 35-36
reality of therapist to, 33
reality of transference to, 96
regressive pattern of, 68; *see also* Regression
relationship between resident and, 68
response to authority, 89
right to reject treatment, 154
role of, in supervision, 303-304
sadism, *see* Sadism
sadomasochism, *see* Sadomasochism
schizophrenia, *see* Schizophrenia
self-interest of, 137
sex of, 41
sexual identification of, 175-179
social class of, in therapy, 66
speech of, *see* Speech
supervisor's responsibility to, 325
talents of, 41
therapist: as messenger of bad news to, 113; as real object to, 28, 150; as real person to, 94; entry into real life of, 31; fear of, 293; telephoning, 35
tolerance of, for analysis vs. therapy, 41
toleration of ambivalence in, 78
unconscious wishes of, in initial interview, 154
understanding of defenses, 87
unhappiness of, as sadistic symptom, 26
view of interpretation, 147
wish for anger on part of therapist, in, 38
wish for role of helpless child in, 38
with aggressive impulses, 93
with phobic impulses, 93
with problems of passivity, 48
with severe anxieties, 28
Patriotism, as example of ego splitting, 63
Payment, *see* Fees
Peace, 149
Penetration, fear of, 55
Permissiveness
by therapist, 100
in handling aggressive acting out, 90
in treatment of behavior disorders, 146

Personality
as barrier to expression, 39
as conglomeration of drive and defense, 39
ego-syntonic elements of, 40
Personality profile of residents, 305, 307-312, 316
Perversions
as example of ego splitting, 63
masochistic, incidence of, 279-280
Phallic level in regression, 67
Phobia, 233
benevolent, 45
Phobic patients, 93
Physician, therapist as, 35
Play, as focal area of regression, 63
Positive indications for psychotherapy, *see sub* Psychotherapy
Positive remarks by therapist, 100
Positive transference, 85, 108, 112
Pregenital implications of homosexual fantasies, 55-56
Pregnancy as acting out, 238
Prejudice, 148-149
"Primal transference" (Stone), 8
Primitivization of defenses, 59
Procrastination as obsessive-compulsive defense, 229
Prognosis
activity in, 174
and compulsive character, 232-233
associations in, 181-182
biogenetic factors in, 182-184
dreams as factor in, 179-181
ego, degree of disorganization of, in, 179-181
family history in, 182-184
homosexuality in initial, 178
impulse life, patient's view of his, in, 174
in initial interview, 164-175
informing patient of, in initial interview, 166-168
masturbation as factor in, 169-171
passivity in, 173-174
patient's object relations as factor in, 164-165
psychogenetic factors in, 182-184
speech patterns of patient as tool in, 173
verbs, patient's use of, as tool in, 173
Projection
as displacement, 45
in depression, 272-273
infantile, 8, 11
in transference neurosis, 10
loss of ego boundaries in, 328
risk of, in treating depressives, 272
vs. externalization, 272-273
Psychiatrist
concurrent treatment with two, 214-215
degree of activity of, 324
informal classification of, 173
in hospital situation, 58
resident's image of, 323-324
seduction of, by patients, 99
self-image of, 323-324
values of, in therapeutic situation, 66
see also Psychoanalyst, Psychotherapist
Psychiatry, clinical, 4
Psychoanalysis
acting out in, *see* Acting out
as basic model for therapeutic relationship, 8-9
as institution, 149-150
as valuation, 147
avenues for aggression in, 148
biological orientation to, 145
brittle defenses and, 50
classic, 4, 19, 20, 23
coincidences as indicators in, 192
conceptualization of, 39
condition of, 18
definition of, 41
disappointment in, 13
ego boundaries in, 16, 17
ego modifications in, 149
exposure of residents to, 3
id resistances in, 50
incomplete interpretation as step in, 44
incomplete treatment as resistance, 86
infantile valuations in, 149
initial interview, *see* Initial interview

Psychoanalysis (cont.)
instinct development, theory of, 145
interpretation in, 13, 14, 43, 147; *see also* Interpretation
loneliness in, 43
love in, 13
main theme of treatment in, 128
need for prolonged, 83
neutrality in, 166
of psychoneurotic patient, 112
patient's values in, 148
patterns as indicators in, 192
payment for, 121-124; *see also* Fees
realistic view, 150
reality assistance in, 15
reality in, *see* Reality
residents in, 321-322
reverse goal of, 49
scolding in, 150
similarities between religion and, 147
social orientation, 145
spontaneous acts in, 13
superego modifications in, 149
techniques, 4, 9-10, 23, 44
thinking, joint, in, 16
tolerance of patient for, 41
transference and transference neurosis in, 10-11, 41, 294-295
unconscious conflicts in, 42
vs. psychotherapy, 4-6, 8-9, 13-14, 43-44, 49-50, 86
working through in, 17
Psychoanalyst
aggressions of, 19
as administrative authority in hospital, 33
as messenger of bad news to patient, 30-32
as parent, 150
as physician, 35
as real object to patient, 28, 43, 150
dedication of, 96
demands by, 19
denial of patient as real object by, 14
detachment of, 11-12, 19
ego splitting by, 17
in role of mother, 14
involvement in reality, 294-295
knowledge of, 5
loneliness tolerance of, 11
passivity of, 19
patient as real object to, 27
reaction to patient's hostility, 294-295
reality of, 18
resistance of ordinary helpful impulses by, 26
roles of, as compared with therapist, 13-14
scolding by, 150
self-observation of, 35
speech of, 15
spontaneous acts by, 13
therapeutic task of, 26-27
training of, 4
values of, in treatment, 147
vs. psychotherapists, 13-14
Psychoanalytic psychotherapy, *see sub* Psychotherapy
Psychodrama, acting out method of, 141
Psychogenetic factors
in initial interview, 182-184
in treatment of depressives, 268, 271-272
Psychoneurotic patients, personal psychoanalysis of, 112
Psychopath
acting out, 10
acting out, in relation to money owed, 132
modification of ego and superego in, 147-148
transference in treatment of, 253
Psychopathy vs. depression, 249
Psychosis
diagnosis of, in initial interview, 162-163
family history of, 158, 182-184
latent, 141
onset of, 157-158
reality in treatment of, 10
re-creation of, in hospital, 68
vs. neurosis, 157-158
see also Psychotics
Psychotherapist
acceptance of regressed patient by, 64

Psychotherapist (cont.)
acting out and, *see* Acting out
activity of, 19
aggressiveness of, 19, 298
and patient's conscience, 144
and therapeutic barrier, 9
and therapeutic task, 9
anger of, 74
answering patient's questions, 131
as accomplice of acting out patient, 248
as administrator of authority in hospital, 28, 33-34, 110, 113
as father, 23-24
as infantile object, 43
as messenger of bad news for patient, 30-32, 112
as mother, 14, 23-25, 32, 37
as object to depressive, 276
as object to paranoiac, 289
as parent, 150
as physician, 35
as real object to patient, 14, 28, 39, 43, 61, 94, 243, 245
as route to reality, 98
as source of discipline, 108-109
as source of gratification, 87
as superego figure to children, 90
as supervisor, *see* Supervisor
as teacher, *see* Teacher
authoritative position of, in treating depressives, 269-270, 275
battle between patient and, 101
connection with relationship between patient and spouse, 31
control of anger by, 233-235, 240
criticism of, by patient, 36
dedication of, 96
degree of control of, 114-115
denial of patient as real object by, 14-15
detachment of, 19
development of particular theme by, 128
ego boundaries between patient and, 12
ego splitting by, 17
entry into patient's real life by, 31
envy on part of, 74, 250
explanation of missed appointment by, to patient, 125
fear of patient, 293
friendly relationship of, with patient, 153, 255
functions of, in treating obsessive-compulsive neurosis, 223-224
hatred of acting-out psychopaths by, 250
hostile relationship with patient, 248-249
identification with regressed hospitalized children, 64
impact upon patient, awareness of, 109
informing patient of impending vacation of, 119
in hospital setting, *see* Hospital
insight of, 153
interest in hospitalized patients, 61
interpretive attitude of, 70
in therapeutic relationship, 5-9
involvement in reality, 295
isolation of obsessive-compulsive patient from, 208-212
knowledge of, 5
lateness of, for appointment, 126
mistakes in charges by, 129-130
narcissism in, 49
neutrality of, 38, 101, 113-114
object hunger of, 17
object needs in, 7-8, 13
obligations of, in initial interview, 153-155
passivity of, 19, 155
passivity to, 54
patient as real object to, 27, 35-36, 43
patient's fighting, 25
patient's knowledge of, 92
positive remarks by, 100
possession by patient, 122
preparation for each session, 127
reaction to patient's fantasies, 99
reality of, to patient, 18, 33, 35, 96
recognition of patient's re-creation of psychosis by, 68
relation with psychotic, 213
remembrance of preceding session by, 129
resentment of, by patient, 37

Psychotherapist (cont.)
resistance of ordinary helpful impulses by, 26
responsibility of, to set reality limits, 24
role of, with hospitalized patient, 58
sadism of, 270
sadomasochistic reactions of, 99-100
sadomasochistic relationship with patient, 62, 248-249
self-confidence of, 153
self-imposed deprivation of, 25
self-observation of, 35
social class of, in therapy, 66
speech of, 15
spontaneous acts by, 13
support of hospitalized patient by, 62
sympathy: from, 37; restraint of, by, 29
telephoning of patient by, 62
theoretical bias of, 19
therapeutic task of, 13, 26-27
tolerance of loneliness in, 13
tolerance of regression by, 66-67, 74
treatment: of depressives, 269-270, 275; of regressed hospitalized children, 64; plan of, 41
value judgments of, 146-147
values of, in therapeutic situations, 66
view of patient as real object, 27, 35-36
visiting of patient by, 35
voice of, patient's gratification through hearing, 91
vs. psychoanalysts, 13-14
see also Psychoanalyst, Resident
Psychotherapy
acceptance of regression in, 67
acting out and, *see* Acting out
and relation between husband and wife, 31
anger in, *see* Anger
association in, *see* Association
bad, 42
behavior patterns in, 70
brief, 83, 85
brittle defenses and, 50
closing phase of, 5
coincidences as indicators in, 192
conceptions underlying, 42
conceptualization of, 39
confrontation in, 5
conditional, 82
cure, premature mention of, in, 92
current, 6
danger of: depression in, 48; masochistic fantasies in, 48; paranoid ideas in, 48
defenses in, *see* Defenses
definition of, 41
degree of interpretation in, 49
dependency in technique of, 52
deprivation in, 18
depth of working out in, 269
design of treatment in, 40
disappointment in, 13
discharge, premature mention of, 92
dreams, *see* Dreams
education as principle in, 43
ego boundaries in, 16-17
ego building as principle in, 43
ego-syntonic feelings buttressed in, 54
entering room, significance of, in, 92
exploratory, 42
exposure of residents to, 3
goals of, 39-40
gratification in, *see* Gratification
group, 226-227
hatred in, *see* Hatred
hostility in, *see* Hostility
id resistances in, 50
importance of structure in, 116-117
initial interview, *see* Initial interview
interpretation in, *see* Interpretation
intrapsychic change, possibilities of, in, 40-41
joint thinking in, 16
leaving room, significance of, in, 92
life pattern in, 70
limiting interpretation scope as technique of, 52-53
loneliness in, 18, 43
love in, *see* Love
major issues of treatment, 128
masochism in, *see* Masochism

Psychotherapy (cont.)
material for, 29
middle phase of, 5
narcissism in, *see* Narcissism
need for prolonged, 84
neurotic worry in, 48
new symptoms, as principle in, 43, 48
object hunger in, 17
object need in, *see* Object need
object relations, *see* Object relations
on the side of defense, 45
opening phase of, 5
orality, as aspect of technique, 52
patterns as indicators in, 192
payment for, *see* Fees
place of patient's real life in, 23-31
positive indicators for, 4, 8-22
premature mention of cure in, 168
principles of, 43-47
problems of, 6
punishment and, 23, 33
question-asking patients in, 90-91
real, 23
real needs of hospital patients in, 61
reality and, *see* Reality
regressive communication in, 261
reward in, 23
schizophrenia, *see* Schizophrenia
selection of treatment theme in, 128
social class of patients and, 66
spontaneous, 42
spontaneous acts in, 13
stability supplying, in, 43, 46
supplying displacement, as principle of, 43-44
supplying infantile objects in reality, as principle of, 43
supportive, 42
sympathy in, 37
taking at face value in, 50-51
teaching of, *see* Teaching therapy
techniques of, 43-47
temptation to fusion, 13
therapeutic barrier, *see* Therapeutic barrier
therapeutic relationship, *see* Therapeutic relationship
tolerance of patient for, 41
unconscious homosexual attachment in, 111
unintended, 42
values in: 144-150; of therapist, 66
vs. psychoanalysis, 4-6, 8-9, 13-14, 43-44, 49-50, 86
when to treat patient as real object in, 29
working through in, 86
see also Hospital therapy, Psychoanalysis, Treatment
Psychotics
conditional discharge of, 82
dealing with, 66
giving to, 28
guilt mechanisms of, 82
libidinal impulses of, 82
masochistic, 82
object relationship between therapist and, 106
office treatment of, 241
reality of transference relationship to, 95
regressed, treatment of, 23
relationship with therapist, 213
response to reality, 89
sadistic, 82
suicidal, 82
symptomatology in treatment of, 81
therapeutic goals of treatment of, 81-83
vs. neurotic, 215-216
Psychotic anxieties, risk of, in patient, 40
Psychotic balance, syndrome of, 60
Psychotic character, 142
Psychotic children, dealing with, 66
Psychotic depression, 273-274
Psychotic masochism vs. neurotic masochism, 270
Psychotic reality, in patient's fighting therapist, 25
Psychotic symptomatology, concern with anatomy in, 184
Psychotic wishes, 21
Punishment
by therapist, 100
consistency of, in hospitals, 115
fear of, 36
in therapy, 23

Punishment (cont.)
need for, in depressives, 269
responsibility for in hospital administration, 33

Question(s), answering patient's, 131
Question-asking by patients, 90-92

Rage
expressed as sexual impotence in men, 84
of the patient, 113-114
see also Aggression, Anger, Hatred, Hostility
Reaction formation, as obsessive-compulsive defense, 206
Readiness for transference, 21
Real aggressiveness vs. paranoid, 288-289
Real difficulties vs. neurotic, 38
Real needs of hospital patient in psychotherapy, 61
Real object
need for, 39
patient as, 27, 29
therapist as, 28, 39, 61, 94, 150, 243, 245
Real problem, conversion of neurotic problem into, 37
Real relationship, need for, of hospital patient, 57-58
Reality
adjustment to, 16
analyst's involvement in, 294-295
and education in treatment, 134-143
and homosexuality, 287
and inner fantasy, 252
and manics, 102-103
and masochism, 28
and paranoia, 281
and therapeutic task, 23-31
and transference, 21
as dictated by childhood experience, 197, 199, 201-204
as principle in psychotherapy, 43
confronting acting-out patients with, 253-255
created to suit inner fantasy, 197, 199
dealing with, in exploratory psychotherapy, 42
degree of, 98
education of borderline patients to, 142-143
helping patient to understand, 134
hospitalization as new, 58
in borderline patients, 95
in hospital psychotherapy, 57, 67
in neurotic patients, 95
in psychotic patients, 95
in therapeutic relationship, 13, 18, 37-38
in therapy, 19, 30, 34-35
in treatment: of acting out patients, 243; of borderline patients, 41-43
issues of, 42
limits, responsibility of psychotherapist to set, 24
neurotic, in patient's fighting therapist, 25
of patient to therapist, 35-36
of therapist to patient, 33, 35, 49, 61
of transference, 96, 142
orientation of treatment with borderline states, 142-143
outside treatment sessions, therapist's attitude toward, 128
possibilities of, 40
preparation for, 109
psychoanalysis vs. psychotherapy, 42
psychotic, in patient's fighting therapist, 25
psychotic patient's response to, 89
realistic view of, in psychoanalysis, 150
removal of patient from difficult, 304
resistance to, 12
sense of, 12, 67
supplying infantile objects in, as principle of psychotherapy, 43
symptoms as, 43
therapeutic barrier in terms of, 28
therapist as route to, 98
therapist's involvement in, 295
vs. fantasy, 109
Reality testing in treatment of regression, 67
Reassurance
and homosexual reactions, 96-97

Reassurance (cont.)
- and sadomasochistic treatment relationship, 20
- as aggression, 100-101
- complications of, 96
- in psychotherapy, 48
- of hospital patients, 62
- masochistic reactions and, 97
- paranoid reactions and, 97
- with patient of the opposite sex, 97

Regressed patients, acceptance of, 64

Regressed psychotic, treatment of, 23

Regressed quality of defenses, 40

Regression
- aggression in, 67
- ambivalence in, 67
- anal, 67, 205
- and free association technique, 87
- as diagnostic factor in initial interview, 179
- as example of decompensation, 59
- daydreams as focal area of, 63
- difficulty in expression in, 37
- ego in, 67
- focal areas of, 62-63
- genital level in, 67
- in children, 65
- in decompensation, 62
- in hospital treatment, 28, 57-58, 67, 75-77
- in inpatients, 58
- in object relations, 16, 67
- in outpatients, 58
- in sectors, 62
- in transference relationship, 62
- interpretation to help patient understand, 87
- kind sought by patient, 77
- love-making as focal area of, 62-63
- magical thinking in, 67
- of defenses, 59
- of ego, 60
- of superego, 89
- oral level in, 67
- overcoming, 58
- play as focal area of, 63
- provocation of, by family, 79
- reality testing in treatment of, 69
- religious feeling as focal area of, 63
- reversal of, 75
- self-destructive, 76
- sense of reality in, 67
- sleep as focal area of, 63
- teaching resident about, 304
- therapist's demands and, 17
- through gratification, 87
- toleration of: by hospital, 76; by residents, 58-59; by therapist, 61, 74; children vs. adults, 66-67; dilution and, 78-79
- use of foreign language in, 259

Regressive action of adults vs. children, 65

Regressive aspects of observed behavior of hospital patients, 57

Regressive communication of therapist, 261

Regressive pattern of patients, 68

Regressive transference, in hospital treatment, 73

Reinforcement of superego, 88

Rejection, feelings of, as reaction to therapist's vacation, 118-119

Relationship between patient and resident, 68

Relationship between patient and therapist, *see* Therapeutic relationship

Relationship of patient and spouse, therapist's connection with, 31

Religion
- aggression and, 148
- as societal institution, 149-150
- similarities between psychoanalysis and, 147

Religious feelings
- as example of ego splitting, 63
- as focal area of regression, 63
- as object relation, 16

Repression, 4, 41

Resentment of therapist by patient, 37

Resident
- acceptance of, by patient, 64, 67
- administrative performance of, 308
- and authority, in hospital treatment, 305-306
- and child patients, 65-66
- anxiety in new, 59
- as arm of hospital administration, 117

Resident (cont.)
as seen by patient, 57
beginning, difficulties of, 59
ego boundaries of, as source of anxiety, 328
ego control of, as source of anxiety, 328
empathy of, 308
evaluation of, 308-315
exposure to psychoanalysis and psychotherapy, 3
general problems of, 305-306
hospital administration and, 305, 325-326
hospital structure and, 115
hyperintellectualism in, 306, 308
identification with supervisor, 316-317, 319, 331
image of psychiatrist held by, 323-324
in analysis, 321-322
insight in the new, 59
learning problems of, 330-331
limitations of, 329-330
masochistic, 318
neglect in history taking by, 61
personality profile of, 303, 307-312, 316
possible roles of, in hospital administration, 108
problems of specific, 305-307, 326-327
psychiatric vs. other kinds, 303
psychopathology of, 330
real relationship between supervisor and, 317-318
role of, in hospital, 108-117
teaching, 6, 303-307, 320-321; *see also* Teaching therapy
transference between supervisor and, 305-307, 316-322
transference distortions of, 328
Resistance
acting out in, 72
communication interference as form of, 261
education as strengthener of, 46
id, preventing psychotherapy from becoming psychoanalysis, 50
importance of resident's understanding, 4
in exploratory psychotherapy, 42
in psychoanalysis, 41, 86
in psychotherapy, 41
new, as principle in psychotherapy, 43
psychoanalysis vs. psychotherapy, 44
to dilution of transference, 77
to reality, 12
to transference, 21-22, 49
transference as, 22
Reward in therapy, 23
Rigidity in depression, 274
Role playing
by patient, 243
in psychotherapy, 48
teaching resident about, 304
see also Acting out
Role reversal, as a means of understanding, 136
Rumination
as obsessive-compulsive defense, 206
compulsive, in depression, 273

Sadism
anal, as factor in obsessional neurosis, 40
and masochism, 278, 280
and paranoia, 282
as characteristic of obsessive-compulsive neurosis, 205, 234-235
depression as symptom of, 26
in depressives, 267, 275
of therapist, 270
unhappiness of patient as symptom of, 26
worry as flight from, 48
Sadistic behavior, explanation of, to patient, 135-136
Sadistic impulses of psychotic patients, 82
Sadistic object relations, 164
Sadomasochistic aspects of masochism, 280
Sadomasochistic therapeutic relationships, 19-20, 48, 62, 99, 248-249
Schizophrenia
and fantasy, 162-163
diagnosis of, in initial interview, 162-163
generalization as defense in, 226-228

Schizophrenia (cont.)
homosexuality and, 37
insight in treatment of, 271
isolation and, 107, 212-213
male desire for equality in therapy, in, 38
masturbation and, 169
object directedness in, 281-282
reality in treatment of, 10
therapeutic relationship in treatment of, 106
Schizophrenics
autistic nature of associations of, 182
defenses in, 60
ego boundaries of, 16, 163
ego in, 60
id in, 60
lack of privacy felt by, 163
loose associations of, 181-182
misconceptions of treatment held by, 139
object relationships of, 102, 106
reality testing by, 162, 181
superego in, 60
therapeutic relationship with, 148
thought disorder of, 181-182
Scolding, as symbol of love, 150
Seduction of therapist by patient, danger of, 99
Self-confidence of therapist, 153
Self-discipline, *see* Discipline
Self-observation of therapist, 35
Self-pity in treatment, 136
Sessions
charges for, 121-122
daily, 130
first, *see* Initial interview
missed, charges for, 121-122
pace of, 129
payment for, 121-124
spaced, 130
see also Appointments, Initial interview
Sex of patient as factor in therapy, 41
Sexual acting out as reaction to therapist's impending vacation, 119
Sexual anxieties, difficulty of working through, 169
Sexual expectations of female, 136
Sexual facts, education in, 134
Sexual history of patient and initial interview, 175-179
Sexual identification of patient, 175-179
ascertaining, 287-288
Sexual impotence in men, 84
Sexual intercourse
as object relation, 16
discussion of, with patients, 138
Sexual interest in psychotic depression, 174
Sexual reaction to reassurance, in patient of opposite sex, 97
Sexual wishes, incestuous, 40, 120
Sexuality, judgment about one's own, 147
Shame vs. guilt, 171
Slang, as acting out, 263
Sleep, as focal area of regression, 63
Social stability and the gravity of pathology, 54-55
Social masochism, 279
Social orientation, in psychoanalysis, 145
Society
patient's identification with, 144
problems of peace, in, 149
Somatic symptoms in displacement, 45
Speech
patterns of patients, in prognosis, 173
of patient, 15
see also Communication, Language
Stability, supplying, in psychotherapy, 43, 46, 48
Stealing, pathological, 240-241, 247
Sublimation of homosexual feelings, normal, 178
Substitute mechanisms, interpretation of, 137
Subway love-maker, 218-219
Suggestion
as therapeutic measure, 49
as transferred obsessional symptom, 45
Suicidal patients
aggression in, 264-267
and depression, 264-276
grief as problem with, 264

Suicidal patients (cont.)
mourning as problem with, 264
object directedness in, 281-282, 284-285
object relations of, 264
psychotic, 82
risks, evaluating, 265-266, 274-275
sadism in, 281
Suicide
depression and risks of, 264-276
visiting attempted, 35
Superego
amelioration, 79
and values, 148
approval of symptoms, 40
building as principle in psychotherapy, 43
concept of primitive, 89
defects, transmission of, from mother to child, 249-250
development of, 144
disturbances of, 59
formation of, 146
hospital as symbol, 68
in depression, 271, 274-275
in making therapist real to patient, 150
in neurosis, 144
in obsessional neurotic, 148
in schizophrenic patient, 60
mediation between id and, 48
modification of: in neurotic, 147-148; in psychoanalysis, 149; in psychopath, 147-148
neurosis, approach to, 144-145
of therapist, 65
regression of, 89
reinforcement in hospital treatment, 88
strengthening to supply stability, 48
support, 46
tensions, over sadistic drives, 48
Supervision, 303-332
basic rule of, 303
general problems of patients, 304-305
identification in, 316-317, 319
interpretation in, 320
outline of, 303-307
problems of specific resident in, 305-307
specific clinical problems in, 304-305
transference in, 305, 307, 316-332
Supervisor
areas of interest of, 304-305
as ego ideal, 328-329
as parent, 323
as teacher vs. therapist, 3, 6, 303-315, 320-321, 326-327, 329, 332
evaluation of residents by, 308-315
functions of the, 303-307
identification of resident with, 316-317, 319, 331
real relationship between resident and, 317-318
responsibility to patient, 325
transference between resident and, 305, 307, 316-332
Support
in psychotherapy, 49
of hospital patient, 62
superego, 46
verbal, explicit, in psychotherapy, 49
Supportive appointment setting, 130
Supportive psychotherapies, as classification, 42
Supportive treatment and homosexual reactions, 97
Symbiotic feelings, 12, 14, 16
Symbolic mechanisms, interpretation of, 137
Sympathy
in therapy, 37
restraint of, by therapist, 29
Symptoms
acting out, 236, 241
and family history, 183-184
as clue to patient's libidinal level, 183
as reality, 43
blushing in men as, 174
character of, in prognosis, 180-181
concern with anatomy as, 184
defensive structure as key to, 252
derived from infantile intrapsychic conflicts, 41
ego approval of, 40
ego-dystonic, 241

Symptoms (cont.)
formation of new, 45
gastric, 233
in history taking, 158
in theoretical ideal of treatment, 35
of patient, understanding, 87
onset of, 158
premature vs. retarded ejaculation as, 174
new, as principle in psychotherapy, 43, 48
relapse, 46
somatic, in displacement, 45
superego approval of, 40
unhappiness of patient as sadistic, 26
Symptomatic pattern of patient, 68
Symptomatology
clinical, in hospital treatment, 69
in treatment of neurotic and psychotic patients, 81

Talents of patient as factor in therapy, 41
Teacher, therapist as, 3, 4, 303-315, 320-321, 323, 326-327, 329, 332; *see also* Supervisor
Teaching therapy, 3, 4, 303-315, 320-321, 323, 326-327, 329, 332; *see also sub* Resident
Techniques
degree of therapeutic task in sound, 27
ego defects in choosing, 24
nonanalytic, 45
psychotherapeutic, 43-47
therapeutic barrier in establishing, 25
Telephone
as tension reliever in treating borderline patients, 143
calling of patients by therapist, 35
Termination of treatment, 84, 86, 131
in summer, 121
mourning as problem in, 14
planning with reference to vacations, 120
premature mention of, 92
with patient owing money, 131-132
Therapeutic alliance, 8, 17
Therapeutic approach to borderline patients, 142-143
Therapeutic assessment, 40-41
Therapeutic barrier, 8-10, 13, 15-16, 24
absolute, 26
against patient's view of the therapist as real object, 28
degree of, 9-10
human reactions in, 30
in establishing techniques, 25
in hospital psychotherapy, 67
in terms of realities, 28
Therapeutic function in hospitals, 108-117
Therapeutic goals in treatment of,
borderline patients, 143
neurotic patients, 81
psychotic patients, 81-83
Therapeutic intention, 39-41
Therapeutic interview, ego structure in, 74
Therapeutic position, calculated risk in, 265
Therapeutic process
confrontation in, 69-70
personal, in hospital treatment, 69
Therapeutic relationship
anxieties in, 43
dual nature of, 8-19
equality of roles in, 38
ideal, 18
in initial interview, 168; *see also* Initial interview
loneliness in, 18
masochistic aspects of, 13
object need as problem in, 7-8
psychoanalysis as model for, 8
reality in, 15, 18, 23-31, 37
romantic tensions in, 98-99
sadomasochism in, 19-20, 99
secrecy of communication in, with acting-out patients, 243
status and function of, 42-43
teaching residents about, 304; *see also* Teaching therapy
technique in, 24
theory of, 8-22
therapeutic alliance in, 8
therapeutic barrier in, 8-9

Therapeutic relationship (cont.)
therapist's plan for, 41
therapist's viewing as real, 35-36
warmth in, 148
Therapeutic task, 9, 13-16, 18, 255
and degree of barrier, 25
and reality, 23-31
assignment to patient, 24
degree of, 9, 10, 27, 29
examples of, 29
human reactions in, 30
imposed on patient, 25-26, 36
imposed on therapist, 26, 36
in hospital treatment, 75
lessening of, 36-37
overburdening with, 27
reminding patient of, 131
when not imposed, 30
Therapeutic vs. administrative considerations, 108-117
Therapist, *see* Psychoanalyst, Psychotherapist, Resident
Therapy, *see* Hospital therapy, Psychoanalysis, Psychotherapy, Treatment
Thinking
archaic, 205
joint, in therapy, 16
Thought, simultaneous trains of, in obsessive-compulsive neurosis, 230
Thumb sucking as symptom, 180
Transference, 4, 10, 11, 13-15, 17-18, 20
acting out of, 79
and reality, 21
as a resistance, 22
as affected by frequency of treatment, 140
as annoyance to patient, 293
as an object relationship, 105-106
as motivation for change in patient, 147
as weapon in hospital psychotherapy, 67-68
between resident and supervisor, 305, 307, 316-332
complications of, in initial interview, 154
conditions for, 10
distortions of residents, 328
displacement onto, 45
establishment of, 11, 21
gratification, degree of, 98
hostile aspects of, 109
in exploratory psychotherapy, 42
in overcoming infantile valuations, 149
in personal therapeutic process, 69
in planning therapy, 41
in treatment: of acting out patients, 242; of depressives, 266; of homicidal patients, 294-296; of neurotic patients, 95; of paranoia, 289, 294-296, 299; of psychopaths, 253
negative, 11
outside of treatment, 321
pain of, 18
patient's object relationships as basis of, 164-165
positive, 85, 108
"primal" (Stone), *see* "Primal transference"
prototypes for, 165
psychoanalysis vs. psychotherapy, 43-44, 294-295
readiness for, 21
reality and, 96, 142, 266
reconciliation of mixed feelings in, 110
re-creation of infantile and childhood, in treatment, 234
regression in, 62
regressive, 63, 73
resistance to, 21-22, 49
resistance to dissolution of, 77
split, 77-78
splitting of, in hospital treatment, 68
testing, by acting-out patients, 242-243
unanalyzed, 39, 43, 46
vs. identification, in supervision, 316-317
vs. transference neurosis, 10-11, 317
Transference attitude
as reflected in dreams, 52
derived from latent homosexuality, 50
Transference cure, 85
Transference deprivation, 19
Transference distortions, 18

Transference love, 99
Transference neurosis, 10-12, 17-18, 21-22
conditions for, 10
in planning therapy, 41
vs. transference, 10-11, 317
Transference splitting, teaching resident about, 304
Treatment
acting out in, 236-239
adults vs. children, 64
as a continuous process, 128
character of termination, 49
choice, 41
commitment of patient to, 85
conditional, 82
crisis as cause of, 159
design, 40
discipline in, 146
duration of, 81-83
education in, 134
effect of family history of psychosis on, 182-183
explanation of, to patient, 139-140
failure of, 22
frequency of, 83, 139-140
goals, 39-40, 81-86
incomplete, 86
insight as tool of, 137
long term, 81
material for, 29
misconceptions about, of schizophrenics, 139
of acting-out patients, 83, 240, 242, 250, 253-255
of alcoholics, 251
of borderline states, 141-143
of children, 65, 90
of depressives, 249, 266, 268-273, 275-276
of drug addiction, 251
of homicidal patient, 100
of homosexuality, 55-56, 208-209, 247, 251
of neurotic, 144-145, 215-216
of obsessive-compulsive neurotics, 83, 205, 208-209, 223-224, 233-235
of paranoia, 289
of psychopaths, 249, 253
of psychotic vs. neurotic depression, 273-274
of regressed psychopaths, 23
of schizophrenics, 271
office, of depression, 268
pathological liars, 241
patient's right to reject, 154
plan, discussion of, with patient, 166-167
principles of psychotherapeutic, 42
process, theory of, 39
psychoanalytic, *see* Psychoanalysis
psychotic vs. neurotic masochism in, 270
reality in, 154; *see also* Reality
relationship, *see* Therapeutic relationship
self-pity in, 136
situation, symbols of, in dreams, 52
stealing, 241
superego of therapist in, 65
task, 39
teaching concepts of, to residents, 304
termination of, *see* Termination of treatment
theoretical ideal of, 35
therapist's narcissism in, 266
therapist's reactions to events outside of, 128
with two psychiatrists concurrently, 214-215
see also Hospital therapy, Psychoanalysis, Psychotherapy

Unanalyzed transference, as principle of psychotherapy, 43
Unconscious conflict, 4
Unconscious content in exploratory psychotherapy, 42
Unconscious fantasy, 10
Unconscious homosexual attachment, 111
Unconscious orality, 52
Unconscious truth about self, 44-45
Unconscious wishes of patient in initial interview, 154
Undirected history taking in initial interviews, 155
Undoing, 206
Urethral problems, 184

Vacation
in treatment planning, 120
informing patient of impending, 118
planning discharge with reference to, 120-121
problems on resumption of treatment following, 119
reactions to announcement of impending, 118, 120
Valuation, analysis as a, 147
Value judgments of therapist, 146-147
Values
and ego, 148
and superego, 148
and inner discipline, 146
as superego support, 46-47
cultural, in psychoanalysis, 145
in child rearing, 146
in psychotherapy, 144-150
interpretation as, 148-149
of analyst, as factor in therapy, 147
of patient and values of analysis, 148
Verbs, use of, in prognosis, 173
Visiting of patient, by therapist, 35
Voodoo, as form of magical thinking, 285
Vulgarity as acting out, 263

Wife
as intermediate object, 103
and husband, relation between, in therapy, 31
explaining psychology of, to husband, 136
Wishes
by patient, 38
incestuous, sexual, in hysteria, 40
infantile, expression of, 39
unconscious, in initial interview, 154
Wishful thinking, psychotic, 134
Withdrawal from object relationship, 18
Women, *see* Female
Working through, 17, 86, 108, 119
Worry
as masochistic defense against sadistic object relationship, 48
as masochistic flight from extreme sadistic preoccupations, 48
neurotic, *see* Neurotic worry